ACCOUNTABILITY

Why We Need to Count Social and Environmental Cost for A Livable Future

ALSO BY DAVID A BAINBRIDGE

*Game Changer: World War 2, Radar, the Atomic Bomb,
and the Life of Kenneth Tompkins Bainbridge*

The Raven Chronicles

*Tenacity: Remarkable People of the Fur War—Heroes,
Oligarchs, Psychopaths, Survivors, Scoundrels, Observers*

*Fur War: The Political, Economic, Cultural and Ecological
Impacts of the Western Fur Trade 1765–1840*

*Gardening with Less Water: Low-Tech, Low-Cost
Techniques; Use up to 90% Less Water in Your Garden*

*A Guide for Desert and Dryland Restoration: New Hope for Arid
Lands (The Science and Practice of Ecological Restoration Series)*

ACCOUNTABILITY

Why We Need to Count Social and
Environmental Cost for A Livable Future

David A. Bainbridge

ACCOUNTABILITY
Why We Need to Count Social and Environmental Cost for A Livable Future

Copyright © 2023 by David A. Bainbridge

ISBN 979-8-9872619-2-7 (paperback)
ISBN 979-8-9872619-3-4 (eBook)

Layout and text design: David A. Bainbridge and AuthorImprints. Illustration credits at back of book.

Rio Redondo Press Mission: Advancing sustainability accounting and reporting, increasing sustainable management of resources and people, and protecting future generations.

Manufactured in the United States of America First Edition ©2023

CONTENTS

Definition of ACCOUNTABILITY, Merriam Webster:
a willingness to accept responsibility
and account for one's actions.

THE CHALLENGES WE FACE

Throughout my fifty-year career as an environmental scientist, I have always worked to make the future less dangerous and more sustainable. My research has included reducing the adverse health and environmental impacts of buildings, energy, water use, agriculture, and manufacturing. I have seen remarkable progress in some areas, but enormous challenges remain.

This book addresses what I have long felt is the heart of the problem: flawed economics. I was trained as an environmental scientist, but have always been interested in economics because it plays such an important role in families' lives, communities, resource management, and business. I have always tried to understand the economic pressures that shape how we treat the environment and each other. This has helped refine my approach to many of these challenges as well as the nature of my recommendations for change.

I have often been alone in this. In the 1970s, I attended meetings over energy policy as one voice alongside two or three underpaid or unpaid renewable energy experts among thirty or forty utility lawyers and executives protecting their profits and ignoring health and environmental damage. You can imagine who won those debates.

We have also made mistakes in our educational system, which has ignored the economics of sustainability until very recently. Environmental science classes first became common in the 1970s, but were often marginalized. When I first started teaching in San Diego, it made our university president visibly uncomfortable to even hear the word "sustainable." Although more environmental science and ecology programs today offer environmental economics classes, few ecologists have been trained in economics[1] or sociology. Business schools are getting on board. But fewer economists and lawyers have been exposed to the science of ecology or the problems of health, inequity, and history. The narrow focus and specialization inherent to our current system has enabled many of our problems to metastasize. Recommendations from academic and applied studies and reports from communities and NGOs have been on the right track, but haven't been able to persuade Congress, the courts, or politicians to take action.

As a result, we consider only a small part of the exchanges we make and the impacts of our actions. Everything we do has consequences. Climate change gases (CCG) have received more attention in recent years, but emissions have continued to rise. Emissions from human activity have become so great that they are changing the planet's climate. But climate change is just one of many problems we face. Harmful pollution is found around the world, even in remote areas of the Arctic. Species are dying out at a rate so fast it is being called the Sixth Mass Extinction, predicted to be the most devastating extinction event since the asteroid impact that wiped out the dinosaurs. This time around, the cataclysm is us.

One of the greatest risks for the future is least often discussed. This is the potential for unexpected tipping points, where something we thought we understood suddenly spirals out of control. This can happen when a feedback loop develops where each step reinforces the previous step.

My broader view was shaped in the 1970s when I was able to attend the University of California–Davis in an innovative interdisciplinary program called the EcoGrad Group. Interdisciplinary programs are becoming more common today, and they enable students to combine classes from many disciplines. But we still have problems in estimating costs and risks because most scholars engage in highly specialized programs of study and research.

The Chinese describe the problem as 井底之蛙 or *jing di zhi wa*, "the frog in the well." The frog at the bottom of a well thinks he understands the world, but he does not. This has been a particularly serious problem for economics. The late Milton Friedman and his disciples, including Alan Greenspan and many others, simply ignored environmental limits, Nature's Services, Natural Capital, and ecosystem stability. Special interest groups have spent millions of dollars to further confuse these issues when concerns are raised. Millions of dollars are spent every year to protect profits made by ignoring social and environmental impacts and disasters that lead to costly public spending.

Incomplete accounting has also facilitated the unequal treatment of women and people of color. Women still do most of the household work, but this is not counted in economic analyses because they are not paid. Women working outside the home make 84 percent as much as men in the same job in the US, and even less in many European countries.

Many people, families, businesses, and politicians simply don't realize that we all depend on natural systems for the air we breathe, food we eat, water we drink, and materials we use to build. Modern conveniences mask the critical connections we have to natural and managed ecosystems. Water comes from a faucet or in a plastic single-use bottle; food comes prepared, packaged, and free of dirt (but not of pesticides, plastic bits, and plasticizers); energy flows through a wall socket from a distant and unseen polluting power plant; and wastes are simply flushed away or picked up by the garbage truck. Out of sight, out of mind—but there really is no "away."

Our ignorance and the "science denial" efforts of conservative think tanks have made it easy for many people to ignore the often staggering "external" costs of our everyday activities. It's as if they don't matter. The pundits and purported experts who have led the United States (and the world) into its current predicament have closed their eyes to the problems they cause. But no more!

My goal with this book is to help everyone better understand their impact on the planet, what it costs, and how it can be changed while improving our quality of life. The wealthier the person and the nation, the greater the impact—but also the easier it is to afford the changes we need to make. Counting the true cost will change behavior and where we make investments. It will encourage local self-reliance and discourage overseas production that chases the lowest price at any cost. Coupled with improved policies and education, it may be enough to reduce damage and make for a more livable future.

David A. Bainbridge
San Diego

CHAPTER 1

TRUE COSTS

T
he way we live is causing enormous damage to ecosystems and communities around the world. The environmental and social impacts will be increasingly severe, costly, and tragic unless we make considerable lifestyle changes. Climate change is perhaps the most widely publicized issue, but there are many other serious problems, all of them driven in part by incomplete cost accounting. True cost accounting that considers most (if not all) impacts can help us make wiser decisions that add true value.

Many of the largest costs of our actions are currently ignored, uncounted, or incorrectly attributed. In the past, this has led us to treat symptoms rather than causes. As a result, global markets perform very poorly on any measure of sustainability. Social and environmental costs are ignored by governments and businesses, and are dismissed as "externalities" by economists. These externalities are left out of the pricing of goods and services but include the very

Energy utility caused Paradise Fire cost 85 lives and 16.5 billion dollars. *Photo by Andrew McCall, Direct Action*

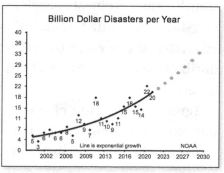

The true cost of climate change—increases in billion dollar disasters

large social costs related to pollution, disease, death, human suffering, lost productivity and community breakdown.

External costs also include damage to vital ecosystem services, depletion of nonrenewable resources, and other harm to Nature's Services and Natural Capital.[2] Nature's Services include water and oxygen. Natural Capital includes natural resources, such as the standing stock of trees and groundwater on land and fisheries in the ocean. Many privately generated costs are passed on to workers, the public at large, and future generations. The burden falls hardest on the poor, people of color, and the powerless. Growth that ignores these social and natural costs is unsustainable. Our current embrace of unsustainable growth will punish the future generations who will pay the price.

There's been plenty of talk and international statements of accord on the need to control climate change gas emissions, but they continue to rise. The root cause of this failure is rarely addressed. As the Dutch say, "No sense mopping the floor until you turn off the water." We need to "turn off the water" with market reforms that address most if not all of the social and environmental costs of our current choices. Only then will the market function properly and sustainable solutions be embraced for a more secure and prosperous future.

We also need to improve how we consider the value of assets currently missing from most accounting systems. These include people's health, skills, intelligence, and initiative. The vitality of communities and cultural cohesion are rarely valued. And we must also consider the contributions of Nature's Services through healthy ecosystems; the value of renewable and nonrenewable resources, antibiotic effectiveness, and other critical but vulnerable biological assets.

Ignoring the value of these assets has contributed to many of our worst problems. Much better accounting is needed to develop more sustainable management practices at all levels, from the individual to the family, neighborhood, community, sector of the economy, piece of land, watershed, water body, company, forest, farm, and nation. Monitoring and reporting asset values over time often reveals that operations thought to be profitable today are not so, either now or in the long run. The true asset values are commonly declining or collapsing.

A popular bumper sticker in the mining communities of the West reads "If it isn't farmed, it's mined." Unfortunately, most potentially sustainable resources are being mined as well. If a harvest exceeds its rate of regrowth or recovery, then Natural Capital is being mined. Forestry, fisheries, ground water, soils, and farmland are being mined, and they are not likely to be managed better until asset values are tracked and reported.

Assets that have historically been ignored by economists are a crucial part of the value equation. Considering only money and property while ignoring Natural and Social Capital as well as Nature's Services provides an incomplete and dangerous view of the world. More complete asset value considerations encourage a more complex, time-linked view from the past to the future.[3] Life cycle costs and benefits are important and stewardship should be measured in decades or generations, not months, quarters, and years.

When facilities, products, and equipment are cared for and properly maintained, they will last for decades or longer and reduce the impact on climate change. Irv Gordons's 1966 Volvo P1800 passed the three-million-mile mark with the original engine block and transmission. My 1923 Singer sewing machine is still working well as it nears 100 years of service.[4] Good design and good maintenance reduce environmental impacts.

Few companies today are concerned about longevity or social equity. Too often the goal is short-term profit with "the lowest price at any cost." Companies also face stakeholders' expectations for ever-increasing size (like a cancer) and profit. Moving production to the lowest cost country with the cheapest labor and few (if any) environmental and social rules fits Chicago School economist Milton Friedman's 1970 argument that, "... there is one and only one social responsibility of business—to use its resources and engage in

activities designed to increase its profits." In this view, only money
matters.

The Changing Tide

Friedman's philosophy has been the dominant vision, but it has lost
ground and modest progress has been made in improving corporate
responsibility. The Global Reporting Initiative (GRI) was launched
in 1997 to encourage sustainability reporting from companies and
organizations. There is still much to be done to strengthen the economic sections of these reports. Most external costs are neglected,
even fewer are monetized, and the financial risks of climate change
may not be covered.

The 2021 UN climate change Conference of the Parties, COP26,
provided little except more words, but governments are taking action. Larger Swedish and British firms now have to report climate
impact. In the UK, firms and organizations will have to begin making "climate-related financial disclosures."[5] The US Securities and
Exchange Commission is exploring options for reporting external
impacts, but has not advocated true cost reporting yet. The Supreme Court's decision (2022) to gut the Environmental Protection
Agency is likely to further delay the American response. The European Union requires some types of reporting and has also taken
steps to improve oversight and review. These efforts have focused
on big companies and the financial industry.

Progress is being made and thousands of companies have completed Global Reporting Initiative (GRI) reports. The staff at GRI has
worked hard with stakeholders to improve the value of this kind of
reporting. International accounting groups are also working hard to
improve true cost reporting.[6] Corporations need to rise to the challenge because governments clearly cannot do it all by themselves.
The nonprofit B Lab has provided a framework for more than 4,000
certified B-corporations in more than 70 countries and over 150 industries that now balance profit and purpose for a sustainable future (https://bcorporation.net/about-b-corps). These organizations
are in many ways the opposite of Milton Friedman's "for profit only"

corporation. They meet high standards for verified social and environmental performance, public transparency, and legal accountability—but they don't yet count true costs.

Some companies have gone further and prepared true cost estimates. Bulmers Cider was one of the first, with an excellent report by David Bent at the Forum for the Future. Bulmers followed up with changes in their operations and with a study of the true cost of their cider orchards. Others have followed, and an emerging group of true cost accountants is taking up the challenge. The results are often surprising, with external costs greater than profits.

One day we will be able to see true costs at the store. The first True Price store opened in Amsterdam in 2021. This market includes the true cost of products alongside the typical retail value. A chocolate bar that would otherwise sell for $3.12 has a true price of $4.11. A pair of jeans that would sell for $50 has a true cost of $90. Consumers are encouraged to pay the true cost, the added income from which goes toward supporting education and research to count environmental and social impacts. The largest share of the cost increase has been to reduce labor exploitation.

The consulting firm Deloitte's Amsterdam office, known as "the Edge," has set up a true price coffee bar. Will employees and office visitors be inclined to pay the actual price (including environmental and social costs) or adjust their consumption behavior?

Challenges to Transition

Our dependence on natural systems would not be a problem if we did not take more from the earth than we give back and did not dump more waste than nature can absorb and detoxify. By any measure, this imbalance is creating global climate change, extensive and often severe health problems (particularly for the poor), healthcare costs (20 percent of US GDP), societal crises, environmental refugees, destruction of ecosystems, the collapse of important fisheries, and species extinction.

High external social costs arise from this race to the bottom. Companies following Friedman felt justified in moving production offshore to havens where labor exploitation was allowed and the adverse physical and mental health impacts of manufacturing— exposure to toxins, chemicals, and pesticides; reduced lifespan; prejudice and discrimination; and destruction of once stable communities—could be ignored. Even in the US and other wealthy nations, these very real costs are ignored, uncounted, or incorrectly attributed.

Many of these privately generated costs are passed on to the public and to future generations. One exploration of the long-term impacts of climate change suggested that the true cost of a ton of carbon might be more than $10,000 and perhaps as high as $750,000.[7] However, the US currently considers that cost to be $50; Sweden, $137.50. The transfer of costs to "others" has helped many companies and individuals to get rich. Some use their wealth to address global problems, but many others use this power to defend their willful neglect of social and environmental costs.

The Problem with Subsidies

Powerful interests develop and defend their cash subsidies, the perverse effects of which are well known. They were first described by Adam Smith in 1776 when he wryly quipped, "It has, I am afraid, been too common for vessels to fit out for the sole purpose of catching, not the fish, but the bounty." Subsidies increase revenue flow to special interests that reap the benefits in return for large political contributions. In this way, subsidies are used to maintain political power and suppress dissent.

Subsidies for environmentally friendly technology are increasingly touted as a necessary policy improvement—but the government has not proven to be a wise investor. In California I saw fake windmills that were built to take advantage of early subsidies for renewable energy. Solar cell company Solyndra went bust, despite the subsidized government loan of $570 million. Abound Solar lost another $401 million. The battery company Ener1 blew $118 million in federal subsidies and also went broke. The solar power towers in the desert cost hundreds of millions of dollars and were flawed from the beginning. Many other government "investments" have been equally flawed.

The choices for more sustainable options are best offered by a free market with true cost accounting. Rather than subsidizing clean energy, we should end the direct and external cost subsidies for fossil fuels—which far exceed those for clean energy and which globally amount to more than $500 billion every year. Agricultural sector subsidies in the US can reach $20 billion a year and result in enormous adverse health and environmental impacts we can ill afford.

These subsidies come in many forms, including direct payments, low-cost loans, below-cost services, tax credits and exemptions, indirect payments (e.g., market protection, below-cost money, allowed environmental damage), free access to land or resources, insurance against predictable risks, and protection from liability for direct and external costs. These subsidies hide market signals and protect industries from liability for damages to the global climate, public health, communities, and the environment. They encourage inertia and waste while stifling innovation. Subsidies also tend to have very high transaction costs. Rather than working for the public good, they too often create public illth.[8]

Rather than charging for lost resources and future risks, the government currently rewards those who deplete resources—still providing tax subsidies to the oil and gas industries that are worth billions of dollars, year after year. In 1926, Congress approved the "depletion allowance," which let oil producers deduct more than a quarter of their gross revenues. Texas senator Tom Connally, who sponsored the break, admitted, "We could have taken a 5 or 10 percent figure, but we grabbed 27.5 percent because we were not only hogs but the odd figure made it appear as though it was scientifically arrived at." In 2002, this mine and fossil fuel depletion deduction cost the government nearly $10 billion in lost revenue.

Independent oil and gas (and other mineral fuel) operations can still deduct 15 percent of their gross income from production, rather than simply writing off the actual cost. The Depletion

Deduction allows fossil fuel companies and mine operators to deduct an amount equal to the reduction in value of their assets as the mineral is extracted and sold. This costs the government about one billion dollars each year. The Intangible Drilling Costs Deduction allows companies to deduct a majority of the costs incurred from drilling new wells domestically—this also costs us about one billion dollars each year. The Clean Coal program also garners a $1B per year subsidy. The timber industry gets a smaller but equally foolish depletion allowance; theirs is subtracted from the timber sale proceeds to compute the taxable gain or loss. Get paid for destroying resources!

Global Climate Change as an Example

Global climate change is a clear case of failed accounting. It illustrates many of the challenges and potential benefits of true cost accounting. CCGs (climate change gases) include carbon dioxide, methane, nitrous oxide, and fluorinated gases. Carbon dioxide is considered the base global warming gas and assigned a global warming potential of 1. Methane's global warming potential is 28-36 times greater, nitrous oxide is 265-298 time more potent, and the fluorinated gases are thousands or tens of thousands of times worse.

The impact of CCGs is related to their residence time in the atmosphere. When chlorofluorocarbons (CFC) contain hydrogen in place of one or more chlorines, they are called hydrochlorofluorocarbons, or HCFCs. Some of these gases will remain in the atmosphere for 50,000 years. Sulfur dioxide is regarded as an indirect greenhouse gas because when coupled with elemental carbon, it forms global warming aerosols that can come down as acid rain. A growing number of people are aware of climate change risks, and programs and news reports appear almost daily. But little progress has been made in reducing these emissions because the key factor of cost has been ignored.

Reporting of carbon impacts has improved, but the critical step of true cost accounting has not been addressed. Only this can ensure that climate change can be minimized and that there will be more efficient, comfortable, and safe housing, healthful foods, clean drinking water, adequate medical care, and security. Reform will not be easy. The current set of subsidies, incentives, and regulations has created powerful special interest groups that are very effective at protecting themselves from considering the external costs of climate change. The fossil fuel industry spends millions of dollars every year to confuse the issue and avoid responsibility. In 1968, Exxon's profit was $1.2 billion—just a bit less than the tax revenue for the state of California. Power not to the people.

More than fifty years ago, Elmer Robinson and R. C. Robbins at the Stanford Research Institute prepared a report for the American Petroleum Institute that noted the rise of global warming gases and discussed the cause: "... none seems to fit the presently observed situation as well as the fossil fuel emanation theory." The paper warned that continued warming could melt ice caps, increase sea levels, change fish distributions, and increase plant photosynthesis. Forty years ago, Roger Cohen, then director of the Theoretical and Mathematical Sciences Laboratory at Exxon, stated:

> The consensus is that a doubling of atmospheric CO_2 from its pre-Industrial Revolution value would result in an average global temperature rise of 5.4 ±1.7 °F. There is unanimous agreement in the scientific community that a temperature increase of this magnitude would bring about significant changes in the earth's climate, including rainfall distribution and alterations in the biosphere.

Exxon chose to deny their own research. In 1998, the American Petroleum Institute organized a $5 million plan to challenge the science of climate change. Following the success of Big Tobacco in denying the health risks of smoking, Exxon, Peabody Coal, the Western Fuels Association, and many others contributed tens of millions to debunk climate science. They even hired the same public relations firms that had protected the death merchants at the tobacco companies. Exxon would continue funding climate contrarian "research" until 2015, and perhaps even under cover today.

Conservative "think tanks" have written articles and books, developed social media campaigns, and given talks on the "junk science" that was discovering the adverse effects already being seen and felt as well as the future risks of climate change. Of 141 books critical of climate science published up to 2005, 92 percent were from conservative think tanks. These have cast the scientists and sustainability supporters as evil threats to Western civilization. They not only attack the science, but the individual scientists as well, much like the McCarthy era attacks on liberals. The American Academy for the Advancement of Science has reported that US scientists have received many threats and abusive emails. Conservative lawmakers and activist groups have sought detailed disclosure of records from climate researchers, asking their universities to turn over thousands of emails and documents. Virginia attorney general Ken Cuccinelli, a climate change skeptic, demanded many of the same documents in the hope of showing that a scientist had somehow defrauded taxpayers in obtaining research grants. NASA was sued to disclose records detailing climate scientist James Hansen's compliance with federal ethics and disclosure rules. In Australia, top climate scientists have been targeted by an unrelenting email campaign that has resulted in police investigation of death threats. This is like a homeowner suing the fire department for trying to put out the flames as their house burns down.

All of this disinformation has paid off. In 2020, only 55 percent of right-leaning respondents said that they believe warming will hurt them at least a moderate amount. In a 2019 survey, a remarkable number of Americans—15 percent—felt the climate was not changing or was unaffected by human activity. A surprising number of respondents in another survey said they expect global warming will *help* them personally. The expenditures supporting denial have helped build a growing share of people who don't believe scientists on any issue, which has made dealing with the COVID-19 pandemic more difficult and has led to many avoidable deaths. One of the great challenges in the years ahead will be reaching out to the denial community. They have children, grandchildren, and hopes for the future, but unless denial can be overcome, that future may be grim indeed.

Two states have launched fraud investigations of Exxon's public disinformation campaign about climate risks in denial of their own early science studies. New York lost, but the case in Massachusetts is still in play. Nine cities and counties, from New York to San Francisco, have sued major fossil fuel companies, seeking compensation for climate change damages. The victims of Hurricane Ida could probably make a case for their losses. Developing countries hit hard by climate change could sue the US and EU members for damages.

Young people are filing lawsuits around the world, claiming their governments have an obligation to safeguard the environment. The Supreme Court of the Philippines agreed that these cases have standing. However, these strategies are unlikely to succeed with conservative courts that are selected and supported by the most powerful people with the dirtiest hands. Still, there may be surprises. In a groundbreaking judgment delivered on May 26, 2021, the Hague District Court ordered Royal Dutch Shell to reduce its worldwide CO_2 emissions by 45 percent by 2030.

Opportunity and Challenge

With true cost accounting, we can find better ways to meet basic human needs that protect the environment, families, and communities, as well as future generations. Access to resources and opportunities must be more equitable. Society needs to favor the industrious, kind, creative, frugal, and compassionate—not the greediest. We need policy that conserves resources and future options. We need to revoke subsidies and legal protections that enable individuals, governments, and corporations to avoid responsibility for climate change emissions and health and environmental damage.

It is important to better understand the magnitude of the risks we face. Despite considerable investment and research, the global impacts of climate change remain only partially understood. The rapid intensification of Hurricane Ida from a Category 1 to Category 4 storm is a good example. It caught everyone by surprise. The US Hurricane Center's definition of rapid intensification is at least a 35 mph increase in wind speed in 24 hours, but Ida strengthened that much in just six hours! Climate change may require two new categories of hurricane strength. A Category 6 hurricane would start with winds of 180 mph. A Category 7 hurricane would have winds of at least 210 mph. Hurricane Dorian in 2019 would have rated as a Category 6. Hurricane Patricia in 2019 would have been a Category 7 with its sustained winds of 215 mph.

The size category of a hurricane doesn't give full credit to the problems hurricanes cause. Ida came ashore as a Category 4 in August 2021 and caused tremendous damage. Human suffering and loss of life was intense. At the peak, 1.1 million people were without power during the steaming hot summer days. Ten days after the hurricane hit, the governor reported 271,000 people were still without power. In 2008, the Natural Resources Defense Council suggested that climate change would lead to hurricane damage of $43 billion in 2050 and $142 billion in 2075. They were far too conservative. The damage from Hurricane Ida in 2021 approached $100 billion—36 years before that level of impact was expected!

Tipping Points

A tipping point is reached when a small change has unexpected impacts that lead to a sudden cascade of events. For example, research suggests that the rapid melting of the Greenland ice sheet may be slowing the Atlantic Meridional Overturning Circulation Current. This important Atlantic Ocean current transports heat from the southern to the northern hemisphere and affects rainfall around the planet. Decay or collapse of the current could dramatically increase winter cold temperatures in Europe and disrupt the monsoon rains critical to food production for 1.5 billion people. It will likely be impossible to restart the current if it fails.

True cost accounting is a critical step in combatting climate change, encouraging more sustainable resource management and reducing the risk of unanticipated tipping points. A year after Jim Hansen's testimony to Congress on climate change in 1987, the United Nations World Commission on Environment and Development report titled "Our Common Future" defined sustainability as "... development that meets the needs of the present generation without compromising the ability of future generations to meet their own needs." The report highlighted the necessity of addressing poverty and inequity in preventing continued environmental deterioration.

We can use true cost accounting to create an economic system that is sustainable and improves the environment and the quality of people's lives around the world. The market will have to be reshaped to include consideration of life cycle costs and benefits, asset values, and clear cost estimates of current and future impacts on the environment and social systems, both globally and locally. This will require a better educated citizenry and a culture of sustainability. The younger generations are already getting there.

Awareness of the serious problems with global climate change, local and global ecosystem stability, resource availability, and sustainability is increasing in the scientific and business communities. Consumers are also getting the message. In Germany, for instance, the share of the population "very concerned" about the personal ramifications of global warming has increased 19 percent since 2015 (from 18% to 37%).[9] In Canada, about 34 percent of the public are truly "alarmed" by climate change. In Sweden, two-thirds of eighteen to twenty-nine-year-olds are at least somewhat concerned about the personal impacts of climate change in their lifetime, compared with just 25 percent of those 65 and older. Seventy-five percent of respondents in the Philippines and 74 percent in Vietnam said they thought climate change would have "a great deal of impact" on their lifestyles, while 19 percent from both countries said they thought it would have "a fair amount of impact." Similarly, 94 percent of respondents from Thailand felt climate change would have a "great deal" or "fair amount" of impact on their lifestyles.

A recent Boston Consulting Group (BCG) survey[10] of more than 3,000 people across eight countries found the pandemic has led people to be more concerned about addressing environmental challenges and to be more committed to changing their own behavior to advance sustainability. Some 70 percent of survey respondents said they are more aware now that human activity threatens the climate and that degradation of the environment, in turn, threatens humans. The survey also found that people want to see aggressive action on the environmental front. More than two-thirds of respondents thought that economic recovery plans should make environmental issues a priority. The BCG study also showed that crisis is driving change at the individual level, with 40 percent reporting their intent to adopt more sustainable behaviors. The PwC consulting firm global survey in 2021 found that half of the consumers surveyed globally said they have become more eco-friendly in the past six months. In 2019, a PwC study found that almost half of the Canadians were willing to pay a premium for organic food items.[11] Two-thirds of the Canadians cared first and foremost about buying local products and were willing to pay a premium for them.

In the US, only 27 percent of the respondents were "very concerned," about climate change, but most liberals were willing to make changes to reduce climate change impacts—far fewer conservatives would do the same. Younger people are rightfully more concerned. In a 2021 Pew survey, two-thirds of Gen Zers in the US as well as 61 percent of millennials said they had talked with friends or family about the need for action on climate change in the past few weeks.

The tide is turning. Now is the time to bring true cost accounting into wide use. Accountants need to be more involved. The American Institute for Certified Public Accountants (AICPA) is getting involved. Andrew Harding (fellow of the Chartered Institute of Management Accountants, a chartered global management accountant, and the association's chief executive for management accounting) noted the change in 2021:

We believe that we will see profound changes in the next few years in the work of management accounting and public accounting to embed new practices and standards relating to sustainability. The Association will continue to provide education and guidance to all areas of the profession, ensuring that it is ahead of this transformation.

The following chapters help show how this can be done by improving analysis and reporting. We can save the future with true cost accounting. It is time for you to get involved!

CHAPTER 2

COMPLETING THE MARKET

The economist Arthur C. Pigou was far ahead of his colleagues in 1920 when he pointed out that the "market" would fail unless it included all costs. Sadly, his message went unheeded, and most markets and economic calculations remain incomplete and imperfect. One hundred years later, it has become clear that incomplete accounting is a primary contributor to climate change and many of the other environmental and social problems we face. Profits are concentrated in the hands of a few, while most costs are uncounted and spread across society and future generations. These costs fall disproportionately on the poor. The task ahead is to count the true cost and include it in the market.

Pigou's discussion of external (or uncounted) costs included the damage caused by wildfires started by sparks from locomotives. Today, utility company equipment failures cause wildfires that lead to catastrophic destruction. In 2018, for example, Pacific Gas and

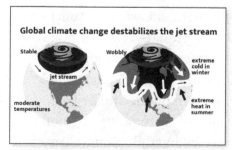

Adding the uncounted costs of social and environmental damage. Global climate change will produce more and more extreme weather.

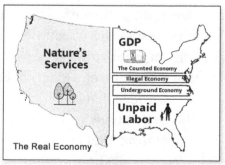

Considering the full economy—not just Gross Domestic Product. Unpaid labor and nature's services can't be ignored any longer.

Electric equipment is believed to have started the Camp Fire that destroyed the town of Paradise, claimed eighty-five lives, and led to $17 billion in damage. In 2021, the Dixie Fire was also linked to PG&E equipment. It burned across the Sierra mountain range from west to east and consumed close to a million acres, with lives lost, towns wiped out, and firefighting costs alone approaching $300 million. About 1,300 structures burned, and one town was wiped out entirely. There was also costly damage to infrastructure, property, forests, and ecosystems. PG&E is likely responsible for more than $20 billion in "external costs." These may be external—but they are very real, and someone does pay them. If PG&E customers had to pay the true cost, each account would owe almost $4,000.

Most other external social and environmental costs are missing from the market and ignored by economists. Instead, most transactions consider only a small subset of the total cost (and value). Neoclassical economists are not troubled by these limitations and rarely acknowledge their existence in pages after pages of calculations, equations, and functions describing how the economy theoretically should work. This work often falls into the category that my mentor, agricultural engineer Tod Neubauer, called "precisely wrong." Although their work is very precise, it is environmentally ignorant and socially bankrupt. Economists should be required to take basic ecology and sociology courses. I also argue that ecologists should have to take economics.[12]

True costs include *internal costs*—the currently counted costs (production, transport, marketing, overhead, sales, profit)—and *external costs*—the uncounted costs of climate change, pollution, health impacts, adverse social impacts, loss of biodiversity, resource depletion, etc. External costs can be significant at the local, regional, and global levels and can be both public and private.

The large public external costs related to smoking, alcohol use, transportation, and air pollution have been studied more carefully in recent years. The enormous external costs of smoking have led to policy changes. We can expect the same type of change as the rapidly rising external costs of climate change become clearer. These include the damage and loss of life from increasingly severe hurricanes and storms, floods, droughts, and wildfires.

The external public costs of catastrophic losses in the asset value of water supplies, overdrafts of ground water, deaths of forests, declines in agricultural production, collapsing fish stocks, loss of function of antibiotics, diminished biodiversity, social unrest, environmental refugees, and increased pest populations are also important. These are even less frequently discussed and calculated. They include the loss of valuable ecosystem services like flood control and water supplies. They also represent a decline in the value of natural capital as valuable fisheries fail and fish populations are lost.

There are many more local, private external costs that are transferred to neighbors who live downstream or downwind. A good example is the loss of water from thousands of individually owned and community water wells in the San Joaquin Valley. Nut growers and farmers have sucked these aquifers dry by drilling ever deeper and more expensive wells. This growing catastrophe led to California's landmark Sustainable Groundwater Management Act, which requires consideration of the sustainability of water use in individual groundwater basins. In many cases, groundwater resources are not renewable and cannot be restored once they are depleted. The plans submitted in 2020 estimated that 1.7 million acre-feet of water are currently being used beyond what is sustainable. To bring water use into balance with sustainable supplies will likely require removing half a million acres from production. The value of this land (if it had water) might be $10,000 an acre, so the change in value will be several billion dollars. The lack of water from the long-term drought that is driving high ground water use is related to climate change.

If external costs are included in the market (however imperfectly), many of our problems will become clear. Better knowledge about cost would help reshape the market—but it is a tool, not a panacea. Making needed changes will not be easy because embedded subsidies are tightly held by powerful people, companies, and organizations. Calculating external costs will also take work. Some costs are relatively easy to determine and could be added to the transaction cost quickly; others are more difficult to value in dollar terms. Some are difficult because of their nature, but most are challenging because we have a limited understanding of the world around us. What costs will Europe face if the Atlantic Meridional Overturning Circulation Current collapses? What is the dollar value of biodiversity? We may not know until we lose it.

Other costs are difficult to calculate because they are related to our preferences and beliefs. What is a safe and secure future for our grandchildren worth? What is the value of a beautiful view? We can ask people what they would pay—but this is difficult to do for future generations. Who has their proxy vote?

The Supreme Court of the Philippines recognized future generations' standing as "legal persons" in a case on timber licenses. Many lawsuits by young people are pending around the world, filed in an effort to slow global warming and protect their future. In 2007, Hungary established an Ombudsman for Future Generations. We should always be very careful to apply the precautionary principle when our understanding is limited. When resources are mismanaged, their loss can be very costly, extending for generations.

Ecosystem goods and services need to be examined carefully to establish benefits as well as costs. Street trees, for example, may provide sound control, air cleaning, health benefits, reduced air conditioning costs, reduced heating costs, and carbon sequestration that far outweigh the costs of sidewalk damage, falling branches, and maintenance. Sustainably managed farms and forests provide many public benefits—oxygen, flood control, water collection, water purification, and carbon sequestration—yet these values are never counted in the profit and loss of a farm, company, or government. They are also missing from economic monitoring and traditional economic assessments like the flawed but widely used concept of Gross National Product.

The city of New York considered the environmental services that nature can provide in developing their future water supplies.[13] A new filtration plant large enough to clean the city's water supply would have cost between $8-$10 billion and $250 million annually to maintain. In a radical change, the city considered letting nature do the work. Studies showed that preserving and improving the watershed would provide the same service for just $1.5 billion with much lower annual costs as well. So, in 1997, New York City embarked on a monumental plan to buy thousands of upstate acres, shield its reservoirs from pollution, improve treatment plants and septic systems, and support environmentally sound economic development to protect future supplies. This was a win-win solution.

The growing interest in payments for ecosystem services (PES) has led to many discussions of opportunities for limiting climate change with this approach. Costa Rica was one of the first nations to begin providing payments for farmers and foresters to adopt more sustainable management practices. Since 1997, nearly 2.5 million acres of forest in Costa Rica have benefited. Forest cover has risen from 20 percent to more than 50 percent.[14] When forest landowners in western Uganda were given a small cash reward for keeping forests intact, the deforestation rate was cut in half.

Governments too often assume responsibility for the problems caused by external costs. It is not enough that the party who caused the external cost problem gets off scot-free, but the victims are often compensated by the victimized—namely, taxpayers. Perverse government incentives further distort the market as policies reflect the goals of special interests to avoid paying external costs. The fossil fuel, mining, and timber depletion allowances are good examples. Rather than paying a depletion fee for destroying resources that are often irreplaceable and of potentially great value to future generations, they get tax credits and payments.

It is very easy to say what we should do: simply internalize the externalities. But this will not be easy. Special and powerful interests that benefit from incomplete accounting act quickly and aggressively to protect their entitlements and irresponsibility. Companies are not alone in this evasion as individuals and families are also reluctant to confront their external costs. The first step needs to be an intensive effort to improve our accounting practices and to develop a much better understanding of how large these external costs are and who pays them. While the effort to calculate costs and benefits more accurately is underway, estimates at the national or international level can be used to work back to approximate local costs. Many inequities in private externalities could be corrected if we did even rudimentary calculations of costs of common impacts and effects. The transfers of the costs and benefits between neighbors, polluters, victims, and communities will be further improved through negotiation, mediation, and litigation once costs are better understood. Ideally, these costs will be studied, refined, and validated by government and nongovernmental organizations (NGOs) and database developers. This will make it easier for accountants, sustainability report writers, and data-mining software developers to prepare balance sheets and improve true cost accounts.

External Costs of a Corporation

Very few analyses have considered corporate external cost. Forum for the Future has pioneered the development of external environmental cost accounting, and their model has been applied by a number of leading UK companies. Bulmers, a hard cider brewer worth £600 million a year, was the first to take up the challenge. Forum for the Future helped them complete a review of true costs in 2003.[15]

BULMERS ENVIRONMENTAL COSTS IN 2003

External costs	Million Pounds
Impacts to Air via . . .	
Energy	1.1
Transport	2.7
Production & Manufacture	0.1
Impacts to Land	0.2
Impacts to Water	0.2
Total External Environmental Costs	**4.3**

The accounting included road transport, factory emissions, farm operations, and water, chemical, and fertilizer use. Cost estimates used were $6.60 per ton for carbon and $5,500 per ton for nitrogen oxides (NOx) and sulfur oxides (SOx). For Bulmers, the environmental costs were significant enough to be approaching their net annual profit.

The social cost estimate for Bulmers was developed by starting with the national estimates of the social cost of alcohol and then working through the supply and distribution chain cost percentages and percent of total sales to arrive at Bulmers's share. Forum for the Future did not consider social benefits, so I have added a bit for the health and social interaction benefits of cider. The population of England in 2006 was 61 million. The government estimate of the social cost of alcohol was approximately £300 per citizen, which seems plausible.

BULMERS'S TRUE COSTS	MILLION POUNDS	
UK £20 billion social cost × 3.5%	−700	
Alcohol tax revenue		+100
Subtotal	−600	
Social cost	−300	
(less consumer share 50% × 530)		
Bulmers market share (265 × 19% revenue share)	−57	
Health and relationship benefits		+5
Total social cost	−52	
Total environmental cost	−4.3	
Total social and environmental cost	−56.3	
Annual internal profit		+7
NET LOSS	−42.3	

The social costs of Bulmers's operation dwarfed the environmental costs with the external cost recovery fee of $6.60 per ton for climate change emissions in 2003. If we use $50 per ton, considered more appropriate today, or the current Swedish carbon fee of $137.50 per ton—it would be a different story. The net loss is partially offset by the social benefits of the salaries for Bulmers's workers and suppliers. It seems likely that even if the social benefits were extended by multiplier effects, most liquor companies would be out of business if they considered their true costs. Many other apparently "profitable" companies cause irreparable harm with true costs several time greater than profits.

Bulmers deserve great credit for examining its footprint and taking up the challenge of being carbon neutral by 2025. They have continued to work toward more sustainable operations. They supported a thought-provoking look at the true value of the apple orchards that supply them and found the ecosystem and social benefits of orchards averaged three times the current profit.[16] Bulmers can claim some of these benefits in their annual accounts.

External Costs of Sea Level Rise

We can explore the social and environmental external costs of sea level rise in much the same way. Mean sea level (MSL) from global warming has been considered in more than 100 studies and reports, and scientists have been concerned about the risk of rising sea levels for over forty years. The rise is caused by the combined effects of melting ice adding more water to the ocean and the change in volume as ocean water warms up.

There is still considerable variation in predictions of the speed and height of the rise. We know global MSL rise accelerated from 1.4 mm/year over the period 1901-2009 to 3.6 mm/year from 2006-2015. In many areas, that rate had accelerated to 7 mm/year in 2020. In a 1989 *New York Times* article on climate change, EPA scientists projected a possible sea level rise (SLR) of 1.5-6.5 feet by 2100. Studies from 1990 to 2008 suggested a maximum SLR of 3 feet or less, but since then, most of the estimates have increased. The maximum SLR predictions from some experts now suggest 2.7 feet by 2050 and 10 feet by 2100. The melting rate of the Greenland Ice Sheet has increased.[17] In August 2021, rain—not snow—fell on Greenland's summit for the first time on record. If all of Greenland's ice melts, it will raise sea level by 23 feet. Some have suggested that if we fail to reduce emissions, we may see a sea level that is 33 feet higher by 2200.[18]

Better understanding of the ice sheets and glaciers has increased concerns about a more rapid rise. Improved monitoring equipment in the Arctic has revealed the ice to be much thinner than satellite observations suggested and to be melting faster. Melting floating ice doesn't change the sea level, but it can release and accelerate glacial melt rates. The ultimate SLR depends on our success or failure in limiting global carbon emissions. You can explore your own local flood risk with the National Oceanic and Atmospheric Administration (NOAA) Sea-Level Rise modeling program. You can set the parameters and see where the water goes with up to 10 feet of MSL rise with this program. FEMA and local agencies also prepare flood risk maps, often with 100, 200, and 500-year flood limits outlined. These tend to underestimate flood risk. New research suggests that nearly twice as many properties are at risk from a 100-year flood than these maps predict. Climate change and changes in urban hydrology from development are responsible. Houston, for example, has been hit with three 500-year floods in three years. The chance of this happening should have been about 1 in 1,000 before climate change impacts.

My experience leads me to the same conclusion as Michael Oppenheimer: "...climate skeptics and deniers have often accused scientists of exaggerating the threat of climate change, but the evidence shows that not only have they not exaggerated, they have underestimated." The recent Intergovernmental Panel on Climate Change (IPCC) chapter on sea level rise predicted a modest increase of 17-33 inches by 2100. This study involved eighty-seven authors and governments from around the world. Many participants are constrained in what they can say by the politics involved and understate concerns. This leads to squabbles and debate and slows efforts to reach consensus. The IPCC has the difficult task of gathering and evaluating all available evidence, and presenting a consolidated assessment of the state of scientific knowledge on climate change. This is particularly challenging for sea-level rise as computer model projections generally are unable to capture the abrupt and highly nonlinear dynamics that are being observed today.[19]

In 2019, climate scientist Richard Alley warned that the IPCC predictions were probably greatly understated, and that sea levels may rise 15 to 20 feet within the lifetimes of our children and grandchildren.[20] He notes the utter impossibility of predicting with any degree of certainty what will happen to ocean levels if large portions of the Western Antarctic ice sheet were to suddenly break off and fall into the Southern Ocean. What difference will the rainfall on the peaks of Greenland's ice sheet (happening for the first time in recorded history) have on melting rates?

The cost of sea level rise depends on the rate of change and the magnitude as well as the expenditures made in preparation. New Orleans has spent $14.5 billion to reduce flood risk, and in 2021, those efforts reduced damage from Hurricane Ida. But the area remains vulnerable because the levees are sinking as a result of ground subsidence. Year after year, they will provide less and less protection. Some areas of New Orleans are subsiding by an inch a year, but many areas are falling a fifth of an inch, and some just a tenth of an inch. Other areas face the same challenge and are considering protective projects. The cost of two northern European sea level defense dams has been estimated at $601 billion by the Royal Netherlands Institute for Sea Research.

A recent UK National Oceanographic Centre (NOC) study suggested that flooding from a sea level rise of 34 inches could entail annual costs of $14 trillion worldwide by 2100 if the global temperature rise isn't kept to less than 3.6 °F. As Dr. Svetlana Jevrejeva notes, " . . . sea level rise is one of the most damaging aspects of our warming climate."[21]

Higher sea temperatures result in increasing storm intensity, higher storm surge, and more powerful hurricanes that occur with greater frequency. These compound the impacts of sea level rise and will further increase costs. A recent study of surface elevations around the world found that as many as 230 million live in areas within 3 feet of current sea level. Jeff Goodell writes, "There are not enough economists in the world to calculate the trillions of dollars' worth of real estate that would be lost in a scenario like this. Nor are there enough social scientists to count the hundreds of millions of people who would be displaced."[22] Many coastal areas in the US, from California to Texas, Louisiana, and Florida, will be flooded. Many areas already flood regularly at the highest high tides.

A recent study suggests there has been a 6-inch sea-level rise in Miami since 1985 (sealevelrise.org). This makes every high tide or storm surge that much worse for a city where low lying areas already flood regularly. The risk is compounded by land subsidence. St. Petersburg, Florida, faces even worse problems. St. Petersburg saw two to three days of clear sky high-tide flooding in 2020, and this is expected to increase to 85 days by 2050. When high tides combine with heavy rains there is significant flooding. Some streets in the most vulnerable areas of Florida are already underwater much of the time. Some areas in San Diego County, California, flood regularly at highest tides.

External costs of sea level rise are both national and global. Millions of farmers will be displaced as sea level rises in Bangladesh, India and other low-lying nations. The burden falls hardest on the poor and middle classes as insurance covers at best only part of the cost in countries where flood insurance is available and affordable.

In 2005 the estimate for the annual future cost of sea level rise in the US was just $6 billion. Hurricane Ida alone inflicted $95 billion of damage in 2021. Nearly two million US homes will be lost if the oceans rise by six feet as scientists expect by the year 2100, according to a new Zillow® analysis. The endangered homes represent just under 2 percent of the national housing stock, and are worth a cumulative $882 billion. The US estimates suggest the British National Oceanographic Centre estimate may be low.

Governments have been slow to adapt, often providing support to rebuild in areas that will be devastated again and again. Dauphin Island, with 1,300 year-round residents off the coast of Alabama, has been devastated by storm after storm since 1979. At least $150 million (adjusted for inflation) has gone into patching up houses and utilities on the island. This is more than $100,000 for every permanent resident. This is folly. So is Palm Beach County's recent information sheet on flooding for residents, which manages to avoid mentioning the risk of sea-level rise. Denying the rising sea levels is like denying the earth is round.

There is some concern about future legal efforts by countries afflicted by flooding from sea-level rise to recover the costs from the responsible parties. If Americans' 14 percent of global climate change emissions (in 2021) is unchanged, our payment due might be about $2 trillion, or $5,000 per person. The share allocated for residential energy use would be $1,200 per person. It is likely the residential share of energy used will be considerably smaller by then, but the external costs per person will still be in the thousands. Global warming will also demand more air conditioning. For a family of four, the external cost of energy related to sea-level rise may be $2,500 a year more than current utility bills.

Sea level rise is irreversible. The costs will be extremely high if we do not take this risk seriously. This alone should provide the impetus to embrace true cost accounting. Emissions of climate change gases must be curtailed.

Completing the Market

More complete accounting has enabled many companies to discover new opportunities to reduce emissions, cut waste, limit pollution, and avoid pollution control costs while improving process management. Correcting internal accounting flaws that have led good products to subsidize bad ones in the past can also be very rewarding. True cost accounting has the potential to:

- Limit climate change
- Reduce risk and liability
- Improve employee morale and health
- Lead to better decision-making
- Highlight opportunities for cost savings
- Uncover opportunities for new products, processes, and services
- Improve stakeholder relations
- Improve reputation

- Lead to a more accurate pricing
- Provide value to the community and society at large
- Offer environmental benefits at the local, regional, and global levels

The potential benefits of true cost accounting would encourage increased commitments to environmental and social accounting. Increased effort and investment is needed in the academic world as well as for traditional financial and management accounting, policy accounting, and environmental management accounting (more in Chapter 4). Europe is leading the way. In an online analysis in 2006, I found that European accountants were 45 times more likely to address external costs than their American counterparts. By 2021, members of the Institute of Chartered Accountants in England and Wales were only twice as likely to mention externalities as the Americans start to catch up. The American Institute of CPAs now supports the Security and Exchange Commission's exploration of climate change and wider Environmental, Societal, and Corporate Governance (ESG) disclosures. In December 2022 the Labor Department expanded the use of ESG considerations by reversing Trump era rules and allowing pensions and retirement plants to consider climate change and ESG measures.[23]

There has been slow but measurable progress, but we need to speed it up.

The market is never going to be perfect, but it does work efficiently. Despite all the discussion, reports, regulations, and rules put in place, global climate change emissions have continued to rise. When external costs are deducted from an organization's financial profits (as shown in corporate annual reports and accounts), the organization's environmentally sustainable profits can be estimated. Linking social and environmental cost data to mainstream financial and management accounts is the key step. Managers of companies both private and public, for-profit and nonprofit, are usually familiar with traditional accounting and reporting systems. Including the financial impacts of social and environmental costs and benefits data can improve the organization's operations by reducing waste, identifying and eliminating costly external impacts and improving communication with clients, stockholders and stakeholders.

True cost accounting can enable governments, companies, and individuals to make better choices and invest more wisely. Climate change impact fees can provide needed funds to support improvements in education and accounting practice around the world, and speed the transition to more sustainable energy sources. It can also make reports on the state of the economy more realistic—by including the 75 percent of the economy that is currently ignored. Completing our picture of the market will give consumers the information they need to vote for sustainability with every dollar they spend. Ask your legislators today—for the sake of your grandchildren and the many generations yet unborn.

CHAPTER 3

ESTIMATING TRUE COST

Almost every action we take, every item we use, has environmental and social costs. They are incurred at every step along the path of creation and use, from materials acquisition and processing, through manufacturing, sales, distribution, use, maintenance, and disposal. True cost accounting and the better understanding that results will lead to innovative solutions to improve our quality of life. This new way of accounting rectifies the

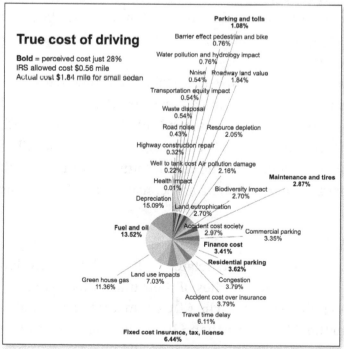

True cost of driving

Bold = perceived cost just 28%
IRS allowed cost $0.56 mile
Actual cost $1.84 mile for small sedan

Parking and tolls 1.08%
Barrier effect pedestrian and bike 0.76%
Water pollution and hydrology impact 0.76%
Noise 0.54%
Roadway land value 1.84%
Transportation equity impact 0.54%
Waste disposal 0.54%
Road noise 0.43%
Resource depletion 2.05%
Highway construction repair 0.32%
Well to tank cost 0.22%
Air pollution damage 2.16%
Health impact 0.01%
Maintenance and tires 2.87%
Biodiversity impact 2.70%
Depreciation 15.09%
Land eutrophication 2.70%
Fuel and oil 13.52%
Accident cost society 2.97%
Commercial parking 3.35%
Finance cost 3.41%
Residential parking 3.62%
Green house gas 11.36%
Land use impacts 7.03%
Congestion 3.79%
Accident cost over insurance 3.79%
Travel time delay 6.11%
Fixed cost insurance, tax, license 6.44%

We consider just a fraction of the costs of our actions. We often consider the cost of driving what we pay at the pump. But this is less than 10% of the true cost.

most serious flaw of neoclassical economics: the assumption that Nature and People don't matter and that everything can be substituted for, or technologically "fixed."

The tools for true cost accounting are improving. Many nongovernmental organizations along with the European Union, the US Environmental Protection Agency, and agencies in other countries have funded research to improve consideration of some types of external costs. Forum for the Future was the first to do a more complete analysis. Other consulting firms and NGOs have also started work.[24] Cost estimates and data resources are getting better, but still evolving. The complexity inherent in the work includes the issues of uncertainty, risk, and the potential cost of irreversible damage. How much will a three-foot rise in sea level cost?

We are often challenged by how little we understand about ecosystem structure, function, and resilience. We are equally uncertain of many concerns about human health. What are the long-term effects of chemical exposure? How fast will tropical diseases spread toward the poles? These and many more impacts will be intensified by increasingly severe and rapid changes brought about by global climate change.

True cost accounting must also deal with factors that aren't readily monetized, either for ethical reasons, attitudinal issues (like beauty and wilderness), or as a result of their complexity. Chapter 4 will describe the process of reporting. Chapters 5–12 will provide more detailed examples of true cost accounting for food, buildings, health, energy, water, products and consumption, forests and fisheries.

Social Costs

The enormous external costs related to ill health from drinking and smoking led to detailed studies of their uncounted, external costs, and then to policy changes. The CDC estimates the external costs of smoking in the US are more than $300 billion (and 480,000 deaths) per year. The CDC also estimates alcohol's external costs approach $250 billion. The CDC suggests the opiate epidemic may cost more than a trillion dollars a year.[25] Health costs matter because the US spends more on healthcare than any other country, approaching 20 percent of the gross domestic product (GDP).

External health costs can be developed from many available data sources. The United Health Foundation America's Health Rankings report on the health of women and children included 118 measures of health obtained from 35 data sources. The health impacts of power generation and transportation have been studied in some detail in Europe. However, many human health impacts from chemicals and pesticides have not been studied at all and certainly have not been monetized.

The Integrated Environmental Health Impact Assessment System Toolbox was designed to encourage better assessment methods to improve decision-making and more inclusive policy actions in the EU. This approach has been used to study the health impact and external costs of heavy metals. It has led to better understanding, and some surprises. Lead, arsenic, and mercury were found to be causing more significant health impacts and costs than cadmium, chromium six, and nickel. A more recent study found the external cost of mercury to be $52,800-$67,100 per pound. Mortality was the primary cost, followed by brain damage and lower IQ with a lifetime of consequences.

True cost accounting must also consider social capital, the building and protecting of which determines a society's sustainability. The external benefits of education are well studied and impressive. Estimating the value of empathy, community, and spirit will take some research. The Amish give us some idea, as their self-insurance and community support replace costly private insurance companies and government support with almost no administrative costs. External costs and benefits include family strength and integrity, health and well-being, empathy, caring, knowledge, skills, attitude, and community volunteerism.

Environmental Costs

Environmental costs include a wide range of impacts and outcomes such as deterioration of ecosystem services, loss of natural capital, and changes in ecosystem function and structure. The link between rising temperatures and increasing storm intensity is clear. NOAA reports that billion-dollar climate-related events of 2020 included a record seven disasters linked to tropical cyclones, thirteen to severe storms, one to drought, and one to wildfires. These twenty-two events cost the nation almost $100 billion in damages.

Many countries with few resources are also impacted by climate change and face high external costs. Those who have the least and who have played little role in changing the climate are being hit the hardest. Madagascar, for example, is being slammed by climate change with drought in the south and cyclone after cyclone in the north. In February 2022, northern Madagascar was hit by its fourth cyclone in a single month. Even though the country contributes only 0.001 percent of climate change gases, it is on the brink of experiencing the world's first climate change famine. Tens of thousands of people are already suffering catastrophic levels of hunger and food insecurity after four years without rain. The worst drought in four decades has devastated farming communities in the south, leaving families to scavenge for insects to survive. These famine-like conditions are being driven by climate, not conflict.

Climate-related crises are being seen in South Africa, Bangladesh, Rwanda, Zimbabwe, Malawi, Ethiopia, Kenya, India, Sri Lanka, the Philippines, Somalia, Australia, Guatemala, Honduras, El Salvador, Nicaragua, Puerto Rico, Haiti, Yemen, Mexico, and Mozambique. In California, a half-million acres of farmland will have to be taken out of cultivation in the near future due to lack of water. The ecosystems in these countries suffer as the people suffer. Ecosystem services are disrupted, and the value of Natural Capital declines.

True cost accounting helps us understand how much we depend on healthy ecosystems—and how often they are taken for granted or outright ignored in traditional economics. Ecosystem provisioning services (food, water, timber) are valued more highly by society, so these are often measured, counted, and fiscally inventoried; but others, including the oxygen we breathe, are not.

Regulation, support, and cultural services are often public goods or unowned resources that are considered free and limitless, but they are neither. When they are damaged or destroyed, the costs add up. The closer we look, the more expensive external costs become. The external costs across multiple categories rose 57 percent in a recent EU review.[26] The estimated costs of marine eutrophication increased from £0.7 to 2.9 billion from 2014 to 2020 as understanding has increased. We will likely find even larger costs as we look more closely.

True costs for ecosystems include the changes in:

- **Provisioning services**
  - Surface water and groundwater
  - Oxygen
  - Timber, wood, fiber
  - Fuel
  - Nuts, berries, mushrooms, truffles, ginseng, honey
  - Other minor crops—ramps (onion relative), acorns, etc.

- **Regulating services**
  - Water capture and storage
  - Flood reduction
  - Carbon sequestration
  - Erosion control
  - Pollination
  - Resilience
  - Air quality improvement
  - Microclimate benefits for summer cooling, winter wind control
- **Natural capital**
  - Groundwater reservoirs
  - Fish and other seafood stocks
  - Soil health
  - Wildlife

- Habitat biodiversity
- Locally adapted species
- Species biodiversity

Five primary approaches can be used to estimate true costs. The **damage cost approach** counts all the damage caused by an externality. Major costs may be incurred far into the future, as with sea-level rise.

The **avoidance cost approach** estimates external cost by calculating the amount required to eliminate or prevent the damage. A recent comprehensive study found the range of avoidance costs between $20 and $270 per ton of CO_2e (carbon dioxide equivalent).[27] A mid-range value of $125/ton CO_2e may be appropriate. The long-term impact cost will be much higher if changes are catastrophic.

The **replacement cost approach** values the external costs based on the total costs required to address and repair the adverse impacts. This can be very revealing. For one example, dealing with nutrient pollution (eutrophication) in fresh and marine water and on land is very costly. Nutrient pollution treatment costs may reach $2,000 per ton of nitrogen or phosphorus prevented from leaking into waterways. It costs even more to try to remove it from ecosystems. Land ecosystem restoration costs can be in the tens of thousands per acre and may take many years of work. Value can also be estimated by considering replacement cost, as is done for insurance value of collectibles. Given a patch of bare soil what would it cost to create a biodiverse old growth forest.

The **willingness to pay approach** can be used to estimate the value of environmental and social factors. How much people will pay for activities or resources that are not traditionally bought and sold? How much is a red rock slot canyon walk in Monument Valley worth? How valuable is a crystal-clear night view of the Northern Lights? What is a view of snow-kissed mountains behind golden aspen worth? We can estimate these by examining what people pay today, or asking them what they would be willing to pay.

The **resource value approach** considers the Natural Capital costs. These can be estimated by considering the past, current, and projected future value of the resource. For the 1.7 million tons of cod once found along the Grand Banks, the capital value at $3,000 per ton would have been $5 billion. Libya's Nubian aquifer, a "fossil" reservoir formed in a geological epoch when the region was wet, was being depleted at a rate of six million cubic meters of water per day before conflict slowed delivery. This water could be worth $320 per cubic meter if treated and sold as bottled water, or $1.9 billion a day. Because it was almost free, water use was very wasteful. The misuse of the Ogallala groundwater in the American west has been equally wasteful. Even today, the groundwater reflects a value of almost $4 billion in western Kansas. If no changes are made to how the aquifer is used and it continues its rate of depletion, the annual value of returns to land could decrease by $34.1 million by 2050 and $86.3 million by 2100.

Direct External Cost Recovery Fee Setting

Once we determine the external costs, we need to recover them. For this, it is often better to charge external cost recovery fees based on discharges (external costs) rather than production inputs. When fees are based on discharges, producers pay for their actual pollution. For example, it is easy to count and tax gasoline and diesel sales, but the actual impact of the fuel use depends on the design, maintenance, and operation of the vehicle.

The vehicle and use patterns determine the actual impact. Half of the smog in California is produced by motor vehicles. Gross Polluters, the worst 10 to 15 percent, are responsible for more than half of all vehicle emissions. In states like California with annual or bi-annual smog control tests, the external cost recovery fee could be based on actual emissions calculated from miles driven and engine performance. Many trucking companies have detailed data on these metrics already.

There will be some surprises. For example, small gas-powered lawn tools are very big polluters. A small gas-powered leaf blower can emit as many CCGs in one hour as a car driving 1,100 miles. The case for electric lawn appliances powered from photovoltaic (PV) panels is clear. Even if the electricity is from a gas-fired power plant, it will be a benefit. The polluting small gasoline-powered tools would be off the market if true costs were counted. The electrics are also quieter, reducing the impact on the user and the neighborhood.

For a regional true cost recovery fee linked directly to impact, we can go to the farm fields of California's Sacramento and San Joaquin valleys. The California Air Resources Board (CARB) estimated that agricultural burning in 2017 spewed fine particles equal to the emissions of 12 million cars. The smoke from agricultural burning causes suffering for people with asthma, chronic obstructive pulmonary disease (COPD), and heart disease. Human suffering is rarely counted as a cost, but it should be. Days with the greatest acreage burned in California have the highest hospital admission rates. Determining the cost would not be difficult. Today, the taxpayer, hospital, insurance company, and family picks up that cost—not the farmer. The CARB found that it would cost as much as $30 million to minimize vineyard and orchard burning. Rather than charging a true cost impact fee, they recommended a state subsidy of $600 per acre. Yet another transfer of external costs to taxpayers that further distorts the market.

Indirect External Cost Recovery Fee-Setting

An indirect fee is based on external costs that are less certain or harder to predict. Climate change gases are a good example. They affect everyone in the world, inflicting very significant costs on individuals, families, and nations, and the impacts will linger for tens of thousands of years.

As an example, incomplete accounting contributes to the ever more dangerous wildfires in the western US. These now cost more than $10 billion each year. Who is responsible? The oil companies like Exxon that have spent millions of dollars to suppress understanding about the risks of climate change are partially to blame. These and other major polluters as well as power-generating utilities should pay a charge based on fossil fuel consumption impacts. From 1965 to 2018, the twenty largest investor- and state-owned fossil fuel companies produced carbon fuels that emitted 35 percent of the global total of 493 GtCO$_2$e (climateaccountability.org). Consumers should also pay a share.

Questions for external cost recovery fee-setting and true cost accounting:

- Is it efficient—low administrative cost?
- How effective will it be—could it have more impact?
- Feasibility—can it be done?
- Does the polluter pay?
- Does it embrace the "precautionary principle, where manufacturers have to prove things are safe, rather than making the government prove they are not?"
- What are the economic consequences for the fee-payer?
- Is the fee large enough to change behavior? If not, what would be required?
- Is there support from environmental agencies, NGOs, health departments, and the medical sector?
- Can it be enforced? By whom?
- Will it cause minimal or tolerable income and property rights disturbances?
- How can it be shaped to fit with the culture, customs, and legal system?
- Can it be maintained over time?
- Will it become difficult for the government if the fee changes behavior and reduces revenue?
- How can trans-border issues of competition or smuggling be minimized?
- Can external cost impact fees replace or reduce taxes?
- What are the global impacts and opportunities?

Policy changes and policy evaluation can be very challenging because markets and prices are linked to world events, politics, tariff wars, pandemics, and climate variation. Agricultural and ecological field studies need to be continued for many years to gain confidence in the results—so does policy evaluation. In Europe, we have the added challenge of national programs interacting or conflicting with European Union directives and requirements. These have tended to derail or weaken external cost recovery efforts in the more advanced Nordic nations. Not a race to the bottom, but a slide down to the maximum acceptable for all twenty-seven nations.

To estimate natural system costs, it is possible to develop ecological health status ranking methodologies for ecosystem wellness and value. Indices of ecological integrity consider multiple factors, including biodiversity, and have been validated for consistency. The best examples of those currently in use have been developed for aquatic ecosystem health, designed to reflect an integrative and holistic assessment of a wide range of stressors.

A watershed index was developed as part of the Sierra Nevada Ecosystem Project. This work was requested by Congress. Funds were allocated for an in-depth study of the entire Sierra Nevada ecosystem by an independent panel of scientists, with expertise in diverse areas. The Watershed Index of Biotic Integrity[28] included 6 metrics rated from poor 1 to good 5. This information was then used to make policy recommendations.

Researchers can develop other indices to include related external costs and benefits. A consistent format for reporting ecosystem services and ecological integrity has yet to be developed. As a restoration ecologist, I know how valuable a better understanding of ecosystem function will be. This research is not expensive, but obtaining assured funding for long-term (ten years plus) interdisciplinary research projects will be needed to test the development and use of these indices. The National Science Foundation's Long-Term Ecological Research (LTER) and the Department of Agriculture's Long-Term Agroecosystem Research (LTAR) are well suited for this work, but both programs are woefully underfunded. We also need more of them—including a southwestern desert LTAR, northwest orchard LTAR, and three or four agroforestry LTAR projects.

In many countries, this research can be aided by specially trained workers who may not have advanced degrees but who have been trained and have local knowledge. Some can also be done by interested citizens, including students at the university, high school, and even intermediate school level. iNaturalist, a joint initiative by the California Academy of Sciences and the National Geographic Society, connects a community of over a million scientists and amateur naturalists. Easy online interaction helps with identification and enables people to develop quality data for scientists.

In addition to external costs, we also need to track environmental capital. These measures of nature's wealth have been ignored. We currently measure the annual value of fish catches, but usually fail to consider the economic value of the standing stock of fish. You can see what happens as a result in Chapter 12. We measure the water used in agriculture, but don't estimate the value of the groundwater that remains. If we don't value natural capital, we make big mistakes.

Follow the Money

Money is by far the most powerful and efficient way to guide the decisions of producers and consumers and to recover currently ignored external costs. External cost recovery fees are easy to understand and encourage innovation. True cost accounting modifies the price signal to encourage less harmful behavior. I use "fees" to mean external cost recovery when they are linked to impact. Taxes, by contrast, involve transactions that are not clearly related to impacts (income tax, sales tax, etc.). Court cases have supported this distinction. Many taxes can be cut when appropriate external cost recovery fees are collected.

The worst CCG-emitting companies and countries, like the US, should be held accountable and pay remediation fees to provide more sustainable markets and lifeways for poorer nations. If the US charged the same fee for CO_2e emissions as Sweden, the account for climate change protection and reduction would grow more than 700 billion dollars per year.[29] Half of that might be spent in the US, the other half abroad. Some could be used to offset Medicare and Social Security taxes.

Making the direct link between the fee and the benefits of external cost reduction very clear is important for compliance. These fees can be based on direct or indirect measured or calculated costs. The opposition to collecting uncounted costs can be reduced by designing them well. Options include reimbursement of tax revenue, offering control over where the revenue goes, and providing rewards for the best performance. External cost recovery fees might be set for an individual product, facility, organization, region, or nation.

External cost recovery fees can be levied at many points. The simplest approach, administratively, is to levy the fee upstream, where the fewest entities would be subject to it, such as at the manufacturers of plastic. Alternatively, the fee can be levied midstream; for example, at a power plant where a fossil fuel is burned. Or it could be downstream at the household or company where water is used. In some cases, all three should be assessed. When emissions are monitored, producers can pay for their actual pollution rather than input use. This allows for a cleaner facility or for the user to avoid paying for a dirty one—both using the same amount of fuel but with vastly different impacts.

The level and escalation of these fees should be related to the social cost increases over time. For example, for every ton of CO_2 emitted today, the rate may be just $50 per ton. This would rise over time to reflect the increasing harm a ton of CO_2 will do in the future. This might rise to perhaps to $100 per ton in 2030, $150 in 2040, $200 in 2050. Predictable increases in fees encourage everyone to do more because their investments in more aggressive remediation will be economically justified. Such design will also reduce opposition to them—markets like predictability and incremental changes.

The distributional impacts are also important. How will the external cost fee impact families with lower incomes and gas-guzzling cars? How will it affect households headed by women? Lower-income households spend a larger share of their income on energy than higher-income households. Should revenue from a CCG fee be used to improve the energy efficiency of vehicles and housing for low-income households? Should a threshold be set in place to offer minimal users a lower fee, no fee, or a credit? Should wealthy nations pay for improvements in impoverished areas and countries?

External cost recovery fees can raise revenue and encourage more sustainable behavior, but the implementation and use of the funds will always be political. Much of the money recovered for the external cost of smoking was diverted from the intended use (to reduce smoking and improve health) to the general fund. In Massachusetts, only 23 percent of funds collected in the first year were appropriated for programs that exclusively provided tobacco education, prevention, and cessation services.[30] This kind of drift can be avoided. The city of Burlingame, California, for example, established a citizens' oversight committee to ensure that storm water fees were used only for the city's storm drain program.[31]

The fees to recover external costs may be used to offset taxes, minimizing the impact on consumers and companies. Recovered funds can be used to improve health; reduce CCG emissions from housing, schools, and government facilities; repair damage to ecosystems; and improve education on sustainability. They could be invested in advancing low-emission technologies or building resilience to face future climate change disasters both in America and around the world. They could be used to prepare for rising sea levels. Many taxes can be cut when appropriate fees for external costs are collected.

A brief review of five important true cost recovery fees illustrates the opportunities and challenges of internalizing costs. These include: a Climate Change Gas emission fee, fees for pesticide damage, fees to address nutrient pollution from fertilizers, fees for stormwater pollution, and fees for the adverse impacts from plastics.

Global Climate Change Gas Emissions Fee

An indirect external cost recovery fee is based on costs that are less certain or hard to assign to an individual. Costs associated with climate change gases are a good example. These gases affect everyone in the world and are already creating very significant costs for individuals, families, and nations. Pacific island countries such as Tuvalu, Kiribati, and the Marshall Islands are already experiencing sea level rise, with ocean floods washing saltwater onto agricultural lands and contaminating sources of drinking water. Some of these nations will disappear beneath the sea unless climate change is halted.

Climate change gases are commonly reported as carbon dioxide equivalents (CO_2e), but carbon emissions and CO_2 are often conflated or confused. There is one ton of carbon in 3.67 tons of CO_2. Methane has 84 times the impact of CO_2, so it should have a much higher fee. Fees for CO_2e emissions provide incentives for process changes, energy conservation, and conversion to more renewable energy sources. Wind, solar, tidal, and geothermal energy is all greener, but each have external costs throughout their life cycle.

The first CCG fees were enacted in Finland and Poland in 1990, with more and more countries and governments having adopted CCG cost recovery fees since.[32] The 2015 Paris Agreement had 100 signatory countries pledging to reduce emissions, and today, 130 countries have net-zero carbon emission goals. New Zealand passed a Zero Carbon amendment to their Climate Change Response Act in 2019, setting a target for all greenhouse gases except for biogenic methane (from agriculture and waste) to reach net zero by 2050. In England, new rules require accountants to discuss emission levels of CCGs in annual reports for larger companies. They also have to report risks related to climate change. Worldwide, more than 3,000 companies have agreed to cut emissions over ten years, but few are including costs as a driver.

Globally, there has been more talk than action, and the 2021 United Nations Climate Change Conference (COP26) did little better than the past twenty-five meetings. As activist Greta Thunberg noted at the Youth4Climate summit in Milan, Italy, in 2021: "Green economy. Blah blah blah. Net zero by 2050. Blah, blah, blah. This is all we hear."

What should the cost for CCG emissions be? Recent research and analysis suggests it should be significant, in the range of $50-100 per ton or more. The importance of politics is striking even when the science is clear. Under Trump, the external cost of CCGs dropped to $1 per ton, but in early 2020, the Biden administration returned the estimated cost to $51 per ton of CO_2e, methane to $1,500, and nitrous oxide to $18,000 with a discount rate of 3 percent. Others have suggested that the CCG fees for CO_2e should be much higher.

Energy sources were first taxed in Sweden in the 1920s. Both a value-added tax on energy and carbon fee for climate change were added in 1991.[33] The carbon impact fee started at $25 per ton in 1991, rising to $137.50 in 2021. In 2021, the carbon fee was about 40¢ per gallon of gas. By increasing the fee gradually and in a stepwise manner, households and businesses were given time to adapt. This improved the political feasibility of maintaining and increasing the fee over time. The Swedish climate change gas fee is levied on all fossil fuels in proportion to their carbon content. This makes it easy to determine fees without complex emissions measurements. Sustainable biofuels are exempt. Sweden has demonstrated that a carbon fee can be easy to implement with low administrative costs to authorities and the public. In 2018, the Swedish CO_2e fee brought $2.73 billion into the general fund. The Swedish fee clearly makes a difference and has helped realize a 17 percent decline in CCG emissions from 1990 to 2017 while GDP grew 78 percent.

A recent study by the Congressional Budget Office (CBO) showed that setting a CCG fee at $25 per metric ton on most emissions of greenhouse gases in the United States, adjusted annually by 2 percent a year after inflation, would raise $1.1 trillion in ten years. Adopting the more appropriate Swedish fee level could bring in $1 trillion each year—enough to cover the full cost of Medicare.

The carbon emission fee in British Columbia rose from 10 Canadian dollars per ton of carbon dioxide in 2008 to $45 CD in 2021. It has reduced emissions with negligible effects on aggregate economic performance.[34] Boulder, Colorado, has a small carbon fee on electricity—a good idea for any city or state. The World Bank reported 61 carbon pricing initiative in place or anticipated in 2020. Most are still too low to effect meaningful change.

Some countries have adopted carbon emission trading as a way to be engaged without seriously tackling CCG emissions. Carbon trading involves buying and selling permits and credits that allow the permit holder to emit or offset emissions of CCGs. Some pollution trading markets have worked, but in general they are inefficient (although better than traditional regulations) and slow. Problems arise from the initial determination of allowable limits of pollution when system dynamics are not well understood. To me, the very idea of enabling polluters to trade pollution justifies pollution and is inappropriate.

Denmark's Pesticide Impact Fee

Denmark adopted pesticide impact fees[35] in 1996. From 2011 to 2015, the goal was to reduce the pesticide load by 40 percent. In 1998, the fees were 54 percent for insecticides and 33 percent for fungicides, herbicides, and growth regulators. In 2015, this structure was changed to levy a specific fee for each chemical based on impact. Base rates are now 40 percent on insecticides, 30 percent on herbicides and fungicides, and an added toxicity-based fee determined with a Pesticide Load Indicator that considers three different factors: toxicity load, environmental fate, and human health risk. The goal is to have the lowest possible amount of pesticide residues in Danish food, and no pesticides in groundwater above set values. All commercial use of pesticides now has to follow Integrated Pest Management (IPM) principles. Efforts to control illegal imports have increased. The revenue from the fee was about $143 million in 2014.

Experience has demonstrated that pesticide fees can be very effective if they consider economic, political, and environmental circumstances. Today, many areas subsidize pesticide use. They don't even collect sales tax on pesticides. Impact fees should be implemented and raised incrementally to allow farmers to adjust their field practices and equipment. There are tradeoffs in maximizing revenues with a simple and uniform tax instead of using a more complex differentiated rate based on toxic impact. More complex impact-based fees can be more effective from an environmental and economic standpoint, but the difficulty involved can be seen in Sweden, with 677 approved chemical pesticides and 203 approved active substances in 2012. The wide variety of farm sizes and operations makes it a challenge to avoid unexpected consequences.

Nutrient Impact Fees

Nutrient runoff from farmland causes severe problems in many areas of the world. Many waterways and coastal zones are naturally nutrient-limited, so when fertilizers reach these waters, they can cause catastrophic algal blooms. Nutrient leakage from confined animal feeding operations (CAFOs) is also a problem. These operations can have up to 150,000 cows generating 10 million pounds of manure a day, which is very hard to dispose of without leakage into the environment.

Algal blooms can occur in fresh, marine, and brackish waters, and they are becoming more frequent with temperature increases. People can get sick when exposed to algal bloom toxins by swallowing or swimming in affected waters, eating poisoned fish or shellfish (even when cooked), or inhaling airborne droplets of affected water. Depending on the level of exposure and the type of algal toxin, health consequences range from mild to severe and fatal. Dogs are very vulnerable because they love to swim and can't read warning signs. The CDC reports the rare brain-eating amoeba, *Naegleria fowleri*, grows best in warm waters, up to 115 °F, and is moving north with rising temperatures.

Dead zones happen when agricultural runoff sends nitrogen-rich fertilizer downstream into the sea. The fertilizer feeds harmful amounts of algae at the surface that eventually die and sink to the bottom. Bacteria feast on the dead algae, removing oxygen from the water. Fish, crabs, and shrimp leave or die. Reducing the flow of nutrients has to be done upstream in the watershed with better agricultural management practices.

The "dead zone" in the Gulf of Mexico is the result of a catastrophic nutrient overload with external costs estimated in the billions of dollars.[36] These costs could be minimized by limiting nutrient leakage from farms into the full length of the Mississippi River. This is not technically difficult, but it is political, and efforts have failed since 1997. Staff at the US Army Corps of Engineers, Department of Agriculture, Department of the Interior, Environmental Protection Agency, the National Oceanic and Atmospheric Administration, and many state agencies have tried to make it better. However, regulations and education have provided little relief, even after nearly twenty years. Hundreds of millions of dollars have been spent, but control efforts have been offset by the continued massive subsidies to corn farmers that encourage greater use of fertilizer. External cost recovery fees for fertilizer sales and use are needed to offset environmental and health costs. Instead, US policy has primarily taken the form of added government subsidies. External cost recovery fees could meet this challenge much faster and more efficiently. We can see what has worked elsewhere.

Fertilizer impact fees were adopted in Sweden in 1984, Austria in 1986, and Norway and Denmark in 1988. They have low administrative costs and can be part of an effective policy mix to help address nitrogen, phosphorus, potassium, as well as unwanted cadmium (average 32 milligrams of cadmium per kilogram of phosphorus), lead, cobalt and other pollution problems resulting from fertilizer source rocks. Many of these very toxic elements build up in the soil and waterways and are very damaging for human brain development, leading to lifetime loss of earnings. They are also harmful to ecosystems.

External cost recovery for the adverse impact of fertilizer surplus leakage into the environment in the Netherlands was based on detailed farm measurements.[37] The *Mineralen Aangiftesysteem* (MINAS) was the accounting system developed to track the nitrogen and phosphate content of manure and fertilizers, and to compute levies on surplus nutrients being generated by farms. Levies were imposed on nitrogen and phosphate surpluses above a certain level per hectare. When nutrients exceeded allowable levels, farmers were charged a fee that increased in steps to $10 per kg of phosphate and $10 per kg of nitrogen. Farms were required to develop a nutrient input and loss account of their mineral balance. By 2001, all farms (including crop farms) had to participate. The calculations and measurements were complex and led to frustration by farmers. Although the mineral balance requirement and fees were effective in reducing the environmental burden they increased the administrative burden, for both farms and the government. The Dutch fee system was working but was cancelled by the European Union Court, which determined it was in conflict with the EU Nitrates Directive.

Nitrogen leakage from Dutch farms is still a problem, particularly from dairies and other confined animal production. Nitrogen deposition from all sources still exceeds ecological risk thresholds in 118 of 162 Dutch nature reserves by an average of 50 percent.[38] The EU National Emissions Ceiling Directive did help reduce emissions of ammonia, with health benefits estimated between one and four billion dollars per year for EU nations. In December 2021 the new Dutch coalition government announced that it was going to reduce livestock numbers by a third to reduce nitrogen pollution from manure. The €25-billion plan will either offer to buy out farmers, relocate them, or resort to expropriation if farmers are unwilling to sell. Although many farmers share the vision to clean up the environment, they naturally oppose the controversial expropriation measures. The new Minister for Nature and Nitrogen faces a difficult challenge.

The USDA reports we use about 21 million tons of fertilizer a year, 13 million for nitrogen. The estimated external costs have ranged from $15 to $1,400 per ton.[39] To reduce excess use and external costs we might start with an impact fee of 20 percent of the sales price, about $200 per ton—this would be comparable to the Swedish fee of $270 per ton and would raise $4 billion a year. Fees might increase 10 percent every 3 years. Animal waste pollution is also a problem in the US. When the NGO Mighty Earth, analyzed water pollution data collected by the Environmental Protection Agency for the 2012-2017 period, they found the top meat companies collectively discharged nearly 220 million tons of manure and facility waste into the environment, either directly into waterways, onto land, or by storing it in earthen impoundments. That's about 500 times the sewage waste generated by New York City each year. Three quarters of slaughterhouses were found to be violating EPA rules in 2018.[40] Tyson Foods was the leader, discharging a ton and a half of nitrogen into the Missouri River every day. When floods occur, these wastes are spread far and wide.

Fee revenue from nutrient inputs (low administrative cost) or measured nutrient surplus could be used to offset health costs and environmental damage, improve monitoring of aquatic ecosystems and air quality, and support improved farming systems research in the University of California's Sustainable Agriculture Research and Education Program (with a budget of just $19 million a year, about twice what a top athlete or football coach earns).

External Cost Recovery for Stormwater

Rain leads to runoff. The amount of runoff increases with urbanization, and the issues with runoff are exacerbated as the water collects a wider range of pollutants, from chemicals to viruses that harm ecosystems and people. Stormwater pollution reduction in the US has been limited despite extensive regulations and considerable investment. More paper, but not much progress. In some areas, property owners, industries, and government agencies are required to develop and report total maximum daily load (TMDL), meet the rules of the National Pollutant Discharge Elimination System, and the MS4system for collecting or conveying stormwater. They are also supposed to apply for permits for industrial stormwater and submit other permits and reports. Too much emphasis has been put on failed historic regulatory approaches, and too little on innovation, monitoring and performance-based financial incentives.

Stormwater is well suited for external cost recovery accounting because impervious surfaces are readily quantifiable. True cost accounting will facilitate adoption of development guidelines that minimize impervious surfaces and encourage above-ground water collection and retention. Some cities and agencies are adopting stricter rules for runoff. For example, in San Luis Obispo, California, runoff retention requirements apply to general projects of 15,000 square feet or more of new and replaced impervious surface, and to single-family home projects of 15,000 square feet or more of net impervious area.

Stormwater runoff in urban areas around the world contains a host of chemicals and contaminants that flow into the waterbodies that are used for recreation, fishing, and drinking. Starting in the 1980s, twenty-eight sites in the US Nationwide Urban Runoff Program (NURP) identified more than 100 pollutants in stormwater. Although the final NURP report[41] was delivered in 1983, almost 40 years ago, data is still limited, and comprehensive reviews of specific sources and impacts of pollutants in different waterways are still not available. Many pollutants not currently included in routine monitoring studies have no regulatory standards, but are considered contaminants of emerging concern. The materials picked up in stormwater flows include oils, grease, antifreeze, pesticides, salt (from deicing), pet and human feces, microplastics, phthalates, nutrients, paint, lead, copper, zinc, viruses, bacteria, and other hazardous materials. External costs can be very high for the restoration of damaged waterways and ecosystems.

The conversion of natural areas to urban and suburban use results in many changes that increase health risks and healthcare costs, damage infrastructure, and cause extensive environmental damage. Changes in flood frequency and intensity are the most visible consequences, and perhaps the most important. Considering the pollution and hydrologic impacts of stormwater makes it possible to develop stormwater external cost recovery fees, which were first introduced in the US in the 1970s, but not widely used until the 1990s. They are now used in forty states as well as Canada, Australia, Europe, and other countries.

Stormwater impact fees are often based on a measurement of impervious surfaces. Ninety-two percent of the agencies surveyed in 2018[42] used geographic information systems, aerial photos, LIDAR or other methods to determine impervious surface area. The stormwater utility fee bill in Alexandria, Virginia, is typical of its kind. The fee is charged by billing unit and the impervious surface of a parcel is determined by the city using aerial photography, as-built drawings, final approved site plans, building permits, field surveys, or other appropriate engineering and mapping analysis tools. For a large residence with a driveway and patio, the area might easily be 4,000 square feet, which would carry a fee of $560 per year.

When the impervious surface area of a parcel increases or decreases (using stormwater reduction techniques, cisterns, swales, etc.), the fee should be adjusted—this would enable homeowners or businesses to reduce their fee to near zero. For an example, in the city of Portland, Oregon, you can receive up to a 100 percent discount on stormwater fees for effective on-site stormwater management.

Stormwater fees will lead to design changes that provide other benefits as well. The Village Homes development (200+ units and commercial space, built in the 1970s) in Davis, California, reduced their area of impervious surfaces by reducing road widths, minimizing parking, and moving to above-ground drainage into swales and ponds.[43] These design features also reduced urban heat island impacts, pollutant runoff, and energy use. The city engineers fought these features tooth and nail, but the development performed well even while it was under construction. Village Homes did not flood while conventional developments did. As a result, future developers found it much easier to propose stormwater management activities. More recently, a developer in San Diego told me that he saved $1 million by changing from stormwater drains and pipes to swales and retention basins, in just one development project.

Capturing rainwater provides many benefits. It helps provide better water quality, irrigates landscaping, recharges groundwater, and reduces water costs. The almost salt-free rainwater helps rinse salt out of planting areas in the arid Southwest. The state of Texas and the city of Tucson, Arizona, have been particularly active in promoting stormwater as a resource. For more information, see Brad Lancaster's rainwater harvesting books.[44]

Stormwater impact fees should not be limited to private lands. City, county, state, and federal highways should pay stormwater fees for buildings, roads, sidewalks, and parking lots. These impervious surfaces are often major contributors to both runoff and pollutants. Portland, Oregon, estimated that streets and rights-of-way make up 42 percent of the impervious surfaces in the city—yet in the 2018 stormwater utility survey, 64 percent of stormwater agencies exempted public roads, medians, and rights-of-way from stormwater charges.

External cost recovery fees should be prioritized based on local stormwater pollutant loads determined by stream and stormwater monitoring. The city of Portland's fees are related to estimated pollutant loads by customer classification for seven pollutants, including nitrogen and phosphorus (nutrients that damage waterways), zinc, lead, copper, suspended solids, and oxygen demand.

Stormwater revenue can be used to help support better delivery of information for landowners to aid in improving the management of hazardous materials, fertilizers, pesticides, herbicides, and other common pollutants. Improving collection and recycling of common pollutants from materials related to automobiles, roads, and trucks can be funded from point-of-sale fees on these materials.

Plastics External Cost Fee

Plastics have proliferated and spread around the world. Since they were first developed, more than eight trillion tons of plastic have been produced, and very little has been recycled.[45] Global plastic production has quadrupled over the past four decades, and humanity now adds over 300 million tons of plastic each year. Half of that is single-use plastic, much for packaging. More than 100 billion plastic beverage bottles are used every year in the US—only a third are recycled.

Plastics are commonly made from petroleum (a nonrenewable resource), and most will last for tens or thousands of years. There are many types of plastic with very different properties, which makes recovery and recycling difficult. Plastics often end up in the ocean and are found on even the most remote islands. They harm bird colonies and marine life throughout the world. Ocean currents concentrate plastic debris in several locations.[46] The estimated 100,000 tons of plastic in the Great Pacific Garbage Patch covers an area three times the size of France. No viable method of cleanup has been suggested. And that pales in comparison to the estimated 940 million tons of plastic produced in the US between 1960 and 2017, with 83.6 percent ending up in landfills.

As plastic wastes are burned in Europe, China, and the US to produce electricity they also emit CCGs. In the US, more plastic waste is currently burned than recycled. More than 40 percent of the plastic waste in the EU is burned. Globally, in this year alone, researchers estimate that the production and incineration of plastic will pump more than 850 million tons of greenhouse gases into the atmosphere.[47] Toxic and hazardous emissions from burning plastics include dioxin and micro-particulates. Research suggests a strong link between dioxin and esophageal cancer, larynx cancer, kidney cancer, non-Hodgkin's lymphoma, myeloma, and soft-tissue sarcoma. These often sicken nearby residents, but their suffering, treatment costs, and lost productivity are not reported. Even when there are laws to control pollution, enforcement is often weak. Burning so much plastic makes no sense, except as a sign of desperation.

There is virtually no control on plastic manufacturing at the moment. The global plastics industry is spending billions every year on new plastics-production capacity. Much of this is produced as microplastics in the form of fragments, pellets, beads, fibers, and film. The average person now probably consumes 70,000 microplastics a year.[48] The health risk and health costs are not yet known, but are expected to be significant.

Plastic bags are particularly problematic. Some 160,000 of them are used every second. That's five trillion bags a year, and fewer than

3 percent are recycled. One option has been to ban them outright, but this has been difficult. The second option is an external cost fee per bag. In 2016, a ban on free plastic bags was enacted in the Netherlands.[49] A year after the ban, there was a 71 percent decrease in plastic bag usage and 40 percent decrease in resulting litter. A Beijing Normal University study examined the effect of a mandatory plastic bag fee in supermarkets in China. They found an overall reduction of 49 percent in self-reported new plastic bag consumption, and a 64 percent reduction of the number of new plastic bags used.

There are some potentially more sustainable options, including biodegradable bags. One such product is the Earthnest Bio Bag, certified as biodegradable by TÜV in Germany's Rhineland and by UKAS in the United Kingdom. However, many biodegradable options are not compatible with current waste management systems in the US. Boomerang bags make shopping bags out of scrap fabrics (more in Chapter 13).

The problems of plastics can be managed by increasing external cost fees that will need to be levied at the refineries and production plants as well as at the distributor and consumer level. Production fees could be assessed per ton, starting at 10 percent of current cost and increasing by 10 percent every three years. Today, costs for a simple plastic might be about $1,000 per ton, so the fee would be about $100 per ton. More than 50 million tons are produced in the US every year, so this fee would bring in $5 billion. This could fund research on alternatives, health impacts and care, and environmental cleanup.

With extended product responsibility, distributors can be held responsible for recovering bottles and bags and returning them to the manufacturer. Consumers should pay a fee for each bag, wrapper, bottle, and roll of plastic wrap. In August 2014, California became the first state to enact legislation imposing a statewide ban on single-use plastic bags at large retail stores. The bill also required a ten-cent minimum charge for recycled paper bags, reusable plastic bags, and compostable bags. Washington DC's five-cent tax per bag has raised $2 million per year. Even California's 10¢ fee is still too low—it should perhaps be 25¢ cents per bag, rising 10 percent every three years.

Internalizing External Costs Drives Change

Adding external cost recovery fees gets results. In the past decade, we have learned more about external costs, ecosystem services, and the current and emerging costs of climate change. Internalizing these costs will be a big political challenge. Different segments of society have quite different views about the benefits and costs of products and services. Do they care about external costs? Perhaps not, unless they are directly affected with allergies, asthma, cancer, wildfires, flooding, or other disasters.

How do business owners feel? Most have been taught to select enterprises and practices that maximize private benefits and transfer external costs to the public. However, change is coming. Companies are establishing internal carbon fees even where governments do not. In most cases, the key issues are relatively clear. The question becomes: how do a company's options meet the policy criteria of efficiency, effectiveness, fairness, and social acceptability used to weigh the alternatives for internalizing costs?

One of the potential benefits of true cost accounting is reduced administrative costs. The Tax Foundation reports tax compliance cost the US economy $409 billion in 2016. Add to that the cost of the IRS (more than $10 billion), congressional staff time, lobbying to reduce taxes, and tax enforcement, and the costs probably exceed $500 billion. This is 6 or 7 percent of federal tax collected. Add in state and local governments, and the overall administrative tax burden may be 10 percent. Many of these costs are related to subsidies and payment made to address external costs. If true costs are charged directly many of these taxes can be reduced. The Swedish climate change gas fee program has had an administrative cost of just 1 percent. But the nutrient management fee program in the Netherlands showed that addressing the complexity of farm operations can be expensive for both farmers and the government.

Accurate accounting combined with social action, education, and moral persuasion may enable us to stabilize the climate before it is too late for us. In any case, the environment will be cleaner and safer, and we will be healthier in the face of a more hopeful and sustainable future.

Internalizing costs drives innovation and changes behavior! True cost accounting is a powerful tool that can reduce the current and future risks to the climate, people, and the environment. We need to apply this approach NOW!

CHAPTER 4

TRUE COST REPORTING

T
rue cost accounting requires true cost reporting. This will be easy for some companies and more challenging for others. The first step is describing what the business or organization does and what the many impacts might be. A business can find guidance for this in the work of the Global Reporting Initiative (GRI), the Sustainability Accounting Standards Board, the B-corps impact assessment guide, the International Integrated Reporting Council, and Forum for the Future. In June 2021, the International Integrated Reporting Council (IIRC) and the Sustainability Accounting Standards Board (SASB) merged to form the Value Reporting Foundation (https://www.valuereporting-foundation.org); this should be a useful source as well.

True cost accounting is based on integrated reporting that includes an organization's strategy,

Would you like to restore the social & environmental impact of your coffee?
Pay the True Price at the coffee bar

Take a look at the True Price gap (€0,81) for a medium cappuccino with cow milk.

€0,096
Climate change

€0,001
Water use

€0,124
Land use

€0,492
Air pollution

€0,034
Water pollution

€0,030
Material use

€0,010
Child labor

€0,023
Poverty

Learn more about the true price

True Price   Deloitte.   Hutten

True cost accounting is gaining acceptance. Reporting should be clear, concise and engaging.

governance, performance, and prospects and which reflects the commercial, social, and environmental setting where it operates. It should provide a clear and concise representation of stewardship and value, now and in the future. Integrated reporting combines the most material elements of information currently reported in separate reporting strands (financial, management, governance and remuneration, and sustainability) into a coherent whole. The report should identify the connections between these strands and explain how they affect the ability of an organization to create and sustain value in the short, medium, and long terms.

GRI reporting encourages greater transparency and organizational accountability. Their standards were developed to help organizations discover, disclose, and manage their most significant impacts on the economy, environment, and people. Although the GRI encourages consideration of a wide range of external impacts, it does not, as yet, report the costs. Still, knowing how many kWh are used, how many gallons of water are consumed, and how many tons of CCGs are emitted is important. The relevance of these many impacts is also analyzed. In GRI lingo, this is referred to as "materiality." The GRI standards do, however, tend to limit discussion of external costs by narrowing the scope to boundaries at or close to the organization.

Thousands of companies have now completed GRI reports, and the organization has worked hard with stakeholders to improve both the quality of these reports and the ease of preparing them. The GRI has three sets of standards: **Universal** standards that can apply to almost any operation; **Sector** standards (by industry or organization type); and **Topic** standards on specific issues. A preparer's job will be much easier if they are able to find a comparable company or organization that has already done a comprehensive GRI report; costing impacts will still have to be calculated—but made easier by having an example to follow. GRI training courses are available at www.isosgroup.com/.

Interested businesses may also find a company that is related to their work in the growing list of so-called "B-corporations," which balance profit and purpose for a sustainable future. They are in many ways the opposite of Milton Friedman's profit-only corporation. These companies recognize that society's most challenging problems cannot be solved by nonprofits or governments alone. They meet high standards of verified social and environmental performance, public transparency, and legal accountability. The B-corp community works toward reduced inequality, the eradication of poverty, a healthier environment, stronger communities, and the creation of high-quality jobs with dignity and purpose. In 2021, there were 4,000 B-corporations. In their 2021 annual Best for the World lists 767 from organizations from more than fifty countries were honored. More than 100,000 companies have tried their assessment guide (it's free), and many will eventually join. But the B-corps still need to add external costs to their certification system.

Developing a solid foundation for true cost reporting will involve the organizations now working on the critical issues of true cost accounting. Many NGOs are involved, and so are the regulators and developers of accounting standards. These include: the International Sustainability Standards Board (ISSB), the IFRS Foundation, the Climate Disclosure Standards Board (CDSB) and the Value Reporting Foundation (VRF). Prototype climate and general disclosure requirements will be developed by the IFRS technical readiness working group (TRWG), the International Accounting Standards Board (IASB), the Financial Stability Board (FSB), the World Economic Forum, and the International Organization of Securities Commissions (IOSCO). These groups will help lay the technical groundwork for a global sustainability disclosure standard for financial markets.

To help determine the true cost of social and environmental impacts in their balance sheets, a business or organization needs to select a discount rate for economic calculations. The discount rate reflects the consideration of the importance and value of the future and future generations. Many different approaches have been used to develop discount rates, but most have ignored the goal of equal treatment of all generations, and failed to support consistent and efficient policy and investment choices.

The social discount rate represents the rate at which we are willing to conserve now to consume later. Depletion considers resources that may be nonrenewable and without easy substitutes or alternatives. These are both important for true cost accounting.

A social discount rate of 10 percent was once used by the EPA to consider emissions control for locomotives. With the power of compounding interest this suggested that the future seven years from now was worth only half of what it is today. Many government studies have used 7 percent, where the future drops to half today's value in just 12 years. High discount rates used in many historic economic studies have devalued the future and future generations, and made it clear that planting trees and pollution control were not "economic." These high rates have also supported investments in unsustainable resource management, investment and policies with high environmental and social costs.

Ethicists often argue that future use should not be discounted— that the well-being of future generations should count as much or more than the current generation. The case can be made to employ a positive (but very low) use discount rate to reflect extinction risk (the meteorite or nuclear conflagration effect).

A few economists have even suggested we consider using a negative discount rate when the poorest contributors to the policy are richer than the poorest beneficiaries.[50] Many climate policies satisfy this condition, and mitigation efforts should put the financial burden on the high emitters—typically the most affluent countries, communities, and families of the present generation. Climate policies must avoid imposing a burden on the poorest members of society. Low discount rates favor sustainable practices and ethical behavior.

True Cost Report Preparation

Here is a short introduction to the steps for developing a True Cost Report. These will vary by site, region, government, operation, and culture. Preparers should be able to find general information on emissions, health issues, and environmental impacts, but will likely have to determine the costs for themselves.

1 The first step is defining what will be evaluated. Where is it? What is it going to cover? Manufacturing concern? Product? Farm? Community? Region? Country? What is the life cycle from raw materials to waste disposal? What will the boundaries be? How much of the value chain will be considered relevant, both upstream and downstream? Historically, many studies have limited themselves to the property boundary—but impacts extend much further, from the mining of ore to the product's disposal at end-of-life. A farm in the Midwest, for example, should consider their nutrient flow to the dead zone in the Gulf of Mexico. Facilities getting electricity from coal-fired plants should consider the impact of downwind acidification and eutrophication from plant emissions, the health impacts of mercury and particulates, and the global climate change impacts of CCGs when they are burned and from leaks during mining, drilling, refining, processing, and transportation.

2 The second step is to do a careful review of the **full cost** of current operations.[51] This may seem odd, but understanding the current economics (not including external costs) of the family, farm, forest, product, company, organization, or government is very important. A study in Canada[52] found the combined annual operating budget for water and wastewater facilities underestimated the full cost of water supply and sewage treatment by a factor of 16–55 percent. Full costs are rarely well understood by smaller firms and family operations and are often a contributing factor in business failures. Enterprise-based accounting can help identify areas where processes and products can be improved and where external costs can be slashed. This can stop a good product or service from subsidizing a costly or harmful one.

3 The next step is deciding what level of detail is possible and desirable. How much information is available? How much time is there? What issues are likely to be most important? Are there regulations, fees or rules in effect that the report must address?

Ecological impacts are very important and entail very high costs. Many have been studied but very few have been monetized. Improved understanding of the cost of these is very important.

- Changes in land use
- Abiotic (nonliving) resource depletion
- Ozone depletion
- Land eutrophication
- Water eutrophication
- Water quality index
- Biodiversity index
- Ecosystem health
- Native/alien species ratio
- Soil health
- Terrestrial ecotoxicity
- Freshwater ecotoxicity
- Saltwater ecotoxicity
- Teratogenic human toxicity

You may find the International Sustainability Standards Board (formerly SASB) listing of ESG issues they feel are most relevant to financial performance in seventy-seven distinct industries helpful. The European Commission has also been developing product environmental footprint category rules (PEFCRs) and organization environmental footprint sector rules (OEFSRs), and has been supporting research on external costs.

The PEFC rules can help identify the most important processes and direct material flows. This will help engineers, designers, managers, accountants, and others find ways to reduce external costs and external cost recovery fees, either by process changes, anti-pollution technology, replacement or elimination of certain products, improvements to maintenance and operations, or revisions in procurement. The most relevant impact categories are those that cumulatively contribute to at least 80 percent of the total environmental impact. Toxicity-related impact categories should be considered carefully even if the risk appears minor because the long-term impact may be significant.

Environmental groups, environmental regulatory agencies, health departments, and finance agencies in the US and Europe have acknowledged the many adverse impacts that climate change, poor natural resource management, alcohol consumption and smoking, and manufacturing have on the environment, human health, animal welfare, soils, biodiversity, and ecosystem health. But recognizing the problems and understanding them are different issues.

US efforts to analyze risks to health and the environment have been weak. In the US, risk is determined by the regulators. Government agencies have to establish and list harmful materials and actions, but when money is tight, they often ask industry to supply the data, and industries have been very effective in resisting efforts to isolate or ban harmful chemicals. In 2016, a study found that American agriculture used 322 million pounds of pesticides that have been banned in the EU.[53] An additional 40 million pounds were pesticides banned in China.

Because industries are very powerful and effective in their lobbying, the government has also failed to reduce the risk of contaminated foods. Although the USDA has pledged to reduce illness from salmonella contamination for more than a decade, *Consumer Reports'* tests[54] showed that more progress is clearly needed. *CR* found salmonella in 31 percent of the samples of ground chicken it tested, all of which were resistant to at least one antibiotic and 78 percent of which were resistant to multiple drugs. As a result, nearly 1.35 million Americans get sick from salmonella every year. The FDA requires poultry processors to test for salmonella—but a plant is allowed to have salmonella in up to 9.8 percent of the whole birds, 15.4 percent of the parts, and 25 percent of the ground chicken it tests. If producers exceed those levels, they are only given what amounts to a warning: they are not told to stop selling the meat. This is almost completely avoidable, but the true costs are ignored, and the regulators are controlled by the regulated—not the public. In Sweden, less than 1 percent of all food-producing animals and foods are infected with salmonella.[55]

Monitoring is essential to understand risk, but government support for monitoring has never been adequate and has declined in recent years. This has led to greater reliance on self-reporting from the companies that generate the harmful pollutants or create risks. This is asking for trouble, as the catastrophe with Boeing's 737Max8 passenger jet has shown. The decline in government funding for basic research on environmental and social problems has encouraged university researchers to seek corporate funding. To maintain this funding, researchers are often less willing to report adverse events or problems with chemicals, products, and processes.

In much of Europe, the government doesn't have to prove that a new product or production practice is harmful; instead, private firms or NGOs have to prove that they are safe, and the Precautionary Polluter Pays Principle (or "4P") holds firms responsible if a technology or production practices prove to be harmful. The 4P approach is cautious and considers that external costs are likely higher than expected rather than lower. In some European countries, there is also an implicit "social impact" hurdle that expands the consideration to future generations beyond the questions of product efficacy, safety with respect for human health, and safety with respect to the environment and animals.

4 Develop an outline of the True Cost accounting report and spreadsheet. What does the organization or company do? How do people use the products or services? With careful consideration and review of available information (see appendices and suggested resources), list the possible environmental and social impacts and costs. Develop a flow chart of materials and resources, incoming and outgoing. Appendix 1 on Material Flow and Life Cycle Analysis should help. Quantify these flows, if possible. How much electricity from what source? How much water from what source? Worker injury and illness? Nitrogen deposition, nutrient flows, and eutrophication of land and water? Any toxic or harmful chemicals? Drug flows, prescription and illegal? Illness? Focus on what matters. What

stages matter most? What impacts do they have on health, communities, and the environment? This should consider both local and global impacts.

5 Once the outline is set, it is time to estimate the external costs. In the future, online databases of external cost factors for different actions will be available by region, country, product, and service to make this task much easier. Until then, the preparer must become a True Cost detective and analyst.

Environmental Cost and Natural Capital

A great deal can be learned from previous studies. As an illustration of potential true costs, CE Delft has developed external cost estimates for the European Union.[56] The importance of climate change is clear, but analysis of ecosystem costs is weak and, I would say, is actually much higher. Terrestrial eutrophication is not included but could easily approach the cost of climate change.

EXTERNAL COSTS IN 2018 FOR THE COUNTRIES IN THE EU28	BILLIONS
Climate change[57]	159.8
Particulate matter	90.1
Resource use fossil fuels	39.6
Human toxicity, non-cancer	20.6
Land use soil quality index	9.3
Photochemical ozone formation, human health	5.3
Human toxicity, cancer	3.2
Eutrophication, marine	3.1
Acidification	1.6
Water use and depletion	0.9
Ionizing radiation, human health	0.7
Total	334.2

ExternE was one of the first comprehensive studies of the external costs of electricity.[58] For the report, estimating external energy costs should be straightforward. What are the billed amounts? How was the electricity generated? What global warming CO_2e gases were emitted? What is the impact cost at $50 or $100 a ton? In California, for example, at the simplest level, we could simply take the state emissions of 60 million tons and divide by the population of 39 million to find about 1.5 tons per capita. For a family of four, this is 6 tons with an external cost of $300-600.

We can easily refine this to the household level. In California, the Utility Power Content Label sent to utility customers tells us how our electricity was generated. In San Diego in 2020, electricity was generated by natural gas 26.2 percent, solar 17.9 percent, wind 11 percent, biomass 2.1 percent, and unspecified 40 percent.

The unspecified and untraceable energy was purchased. This loophole allows utilities to evade the goal of transparency that the legislature intended with the labeling requirement. California-based utilities can claim to be almost 100 percent clean energy while still using coal! In 2015, 17,000 GWh were imported from power plants in the Southwest. The California Air Resources Board (CARB) uses a default emissions factor of 0.9 lbs/kWh of CO_2e for this untraceable electricity. Wind and solar are in the level of grams per kWh (1-2 percent of natural gas) and can be ignored. For my house, the annual use of 3,600 kWh of electricity has an impact of about 1,200 pounds CO_2e. My use of natural gas for heating and hot water would add another 1,400 pounds. At $50 per ton of CO_2e, my external cost recovery fee for electricity generation and heating would be about $65 a year.

Other true costs of energy are less certain. These include issues like the wildfires started by PG&E, ecosystem disruption by hydroelectric dams, erosion and water quality problems from utility right-of-way maintenance, and off-road vehicle damage using utility rights-of-way.

The California Air Resources Board has developed a pollution mapping tool that allows users to locate and view emissions of CCGs and criteria pollutants from large facilities in California. Users can select facilities by name, location, or industrial sector; view their reported emissions using maps, charts, and tabular formats; and download the data. This background pollution may increase the impact of home or company emissions.

Transportation is thought to cause about a quarter of global CCG emissions,[59] a third of US CCG emissions, and 40 percent of California's CCG emissions. Reporting CCG from transportation is important for companies and organizations because it is often a major source of emissions. It is best to be expansive and consider CCG from employee commuting. Proctor and Gamble recently reported 117,000 tons of CO_2e from employee commute miles and 151,000 tons for business travel.[60] At $50 per ton, their external cost recovery fee would be $13 million for transportation energy use alone.

Many studies have been done on the wide range of external costs of transportation. You may be able to find estimated external costs for your specific car model. Other true costs of transportation include impacts related to mining ore, processing, transporting material, manufacturing emission and wastes, climate change gases, health costs, the cost of crashes and repairs, ecosystem disruption, and fuel sourcing. Congestion, land use for parking and roads, and end of use disposal are also important. The external cost of vehicle ownership in the EU in 2008 was estimated at $548 billion per year, or $1011 per person.[61] In the US, a detailed study found external costs were more than 40¢ per mile for many vehicles but just 11¢ per mile at the lowest end.[62]

The current **full cost** estimate for driving a car in the US is 58¢ mile, without considering external costs. The cost of the gasoline, even at California's $6 per gallon, is $0.25 per mile for my 2002 Toyota Tacoma. The EPA footprint calculator has a car emission estimator that considers only the energy impact for driving. For my Tacoma, the CCG cost for fuel use on a per-mile basis is 3¢ mile, and accounts for about 10 percent of the total external cost. As Lemp and Kockelman reported in 2008, the external costs related to crashes turn out to be very important. These are vehicle-specific, either because of the vehicles or the types of drivers who are attracted to them. In 2008, the crash-related external cost was estimated at 23¢ per mile for large Ford and Dodge pickup trucks, but only 8¢ for the Toyota Prius.

If we paid the full cost for driving cars and trucks, we would be paying an additional $1.50 per mile. As we start to pay costs closer to the true cost, we will see the economic incentive to redesign our cities and suburbs for light rail, electric buses, pedestrians, and bicycles. In San Diego, arguably the best climate for bicycling in the United States, only 1.2 percent of the commuting is done on bicycles. Many, like me, will not use bikes because it is too dangerous to share the roads with motor vehicles. In the first ten months of 2021, more than one cyclist per month was killed in San Diego. Poor design and maintenance of facilities and roads, inattentive drivers, and general disregard for others leads to too many bicycle fatalities. In 2018, cyclist fatality rates per km in the USA were 4–7 times higher than 4 European countries.[63] Between 1982 and 2007, the car share of trips in Freiburg fell from 38 percent to 32 percent during a period in which the car's mode share was increasing rapidly almost everywhere else in the world. At the same time, the bike share of trips in Freiburg almost doubled, from 15 percent to 27 percent.[64] There are twice as many bikes as cars in the city. In the Netherlands, some companies buy bicycles for their employees, and the country offers tax credits to people who commute by bicycle.

Stormwater volume can be estimated from climate data, rainfall, flood frequency, and ground cover. The risks and costs can then be considered and estimated. There are costs related to ecosystem disruption, damage to property and infrastructure, and health risks to humans.

Emission impacts from other chemicals and compounds are related to quantity and concentration. For larger companies, some types of emissions are already reported or can be determined by monitoring air and water. Cost impacts can be found for many common pollutants. If US data is not available, a useable cost may be found in Europe—try the 2018 Environmental Prices Handbook EU28. This may only provide a generic cost, but is still better than "no cost." These true cost estimates are from different years using varied assumptions and levels of analysis, but they are still instructive. The wide ranges suggest how little we know. Some of the impact-reporting companies have large databases that may be of use. More complete details are found in Appendix 2.

EXTERNAL COSTS	$/TON
aluminum ϵ 18 tons CO_2 per ton	$1,600
lead 23,000 ϵ/kg	$21 million
mercury 29,000–74,867 ϵ/kg	$26 million
platinum 2–78 tons CO_2 kg	$100,000–$3,900,000
steel at 1.9 tons CO_2 per ton	$190
cadmium 236,691 c/kg health	$21 million
coal	$9–$2,689
carbon dioxide	$50–150
carbon dioxide long-term	$10,000–$750,000
cement manufacturing at 0.59 tons CO_2 per ton	$59
methane 2.5% discount 2020	$2,200
CFC_{12} (refrigerant)	$1 million
particulate PM<2.5	$29,000–199,630
N_2O at 2.5% discount rate 2050	$96,800
NH_3	$82,514
NOx	$31,941
phosphate PO	$4
SO_2 all	$5,600–42,588

More location-specific estimates of external cost can be found. Often, the rural and urban differences are significant because more people are exposed in urban areas. The BeTa database[65] was developed twenty years ago by NetCen for the European Commission to provide external cost calculations for the health costs of air pollution in Europe. To calculate the cost for Stuttgart, the short-range (urban) external cost was calculated, and then the longer-range (rural) external cost was added. The external cost of 1 ton of sulfur dioxide released in a city of 100,000 people was estimated to be $6,600. To scale up to Stuttgart, a city of 500,000 people, they multiplied by five (5 × $6,600 = $33,000). Adding the long-range effects from rural figures ($6,710), the total external cost of 1 ton of SO_2 emitted in Stuttgart was estimated to be $39,710.

For products, buildings, and facilities that may be used for decades, the impacts over the full life cycle are important (more details in Appendix 1). We need a concerted global effort to create easily accessible high-quality life cycle external cost data. These databases would improve sustainability explanations on environmental product declarations, improve eco-labeling criteria, encourage eco-design, and improve product-oriented environmental management systems.

External costs for some environmental impacts, such as land eutrophication, may be challenging because they have rarely been studied. As a proxy, we might use estimates of marine eutrophication. The European Union estimates the cost of marine eutrophication at $3,200 per metric ton.[66] As mentioned earlier the Gulf Dead Zone cost of nitrogen pollution ranges may be as high as $2.4 billion from 1.2 million tons of nitrogen, or about $2,000 per ton. This suggests these estimates may be plausible. Treating land or waterways with excess nitrogen from emissions and leakage can cost thousands of dollars per acre, year after year. The affected areas may show a potential annual cost of $12 million per square mile. These costs should not be simply footnoted as unavailable.

Social Cost and Capital

Social cost and social capital are also essential parts of true cost accounting. The social costs of global climate change are already high and growing day by day. Organizations that are making an effort to fully balance their books with True Cost Accounting should consider issues of social costs and capital. This can help identify policies and practices that are harmful. Sufficient detail should also be developed to identify, reduce and hopefully eliminate the impact of harmful and costly products or services on communities and families. The benefits a company or organization provides are also important and should be included.

Government agencies and nongovernmental organizations can play an important role in estimating social costs by assisting with research, putting pressure on the worst offenders (as has happened in the cigarette and alcohol industries), and publicizing the efforts of companies that make good faith efforts to prepare true cost accounting reports and implement suggested changes. These moves would help companies and organizations create and implement programs that improve quality of life, strengthen families, and enhance the vibrancy of communities. Basic social information may include:

Employees
    Salary and benefits
    Number of employees
By position, age, and sex
    Equity—median, mean, average
    Industry competitiveness
    Retention
Health
    Days missed work
    Injury and accident
    Chronic disease
    Outcome of health innovation
    Pollution-related health impacts
Product-related health costs
Education
    In-house
    Support for training and college
Volunteers
    Support for volunteers
    Volunteer numbers
    Hours volunteered
    Value of contributed time (for volunteer organizations, schools, etc.)

Many economists seem to feel $10 million is an appropriate value for a human life.[67] One quality year of life is valued at between $50,000 and $129,000. Social cost and benefit calculations are essential for true cost accounting.

6 The final step is putting this all together with an executive summary and spreadsheet. What are the most important external costs? What is the total external cost estimate and how does it compare to company income and profit? Is it a sustainable operation? If not, what changes could be made to make it better? Then add the cost or benefit to the year-end annual report and balance sheet.

True Cost Report Outline

1. Introduction

- Organization profile, strategy, ethics and integrity, certifications, governance, stakeholders, engagement practices, and reporting process
- Employees (number, gender, location, education, commutes)
- Pay and benefits packages
- Childcare

2. Operations

Description of facilities, operations, services

3. True cost (overall, by division, by product line, etc.)

Social

- Employee working conditions (accidents, days lost, chronic conditions related to work)
- Supply chain working conditions
- Potential health risks to family and community
- Educational support, internal training and mentoring
- Contributions to community
- Taxes paid
- Government costs for low pay employee healthcare, food, childcare

Environmental

Energy (use, supply, source) kg/ton/liter	CO_2e, nitrogen, PM<2.5 in tons
Travel business (vehicle, rail, air) miles	CO_2e, nitrogen, PM<2.5 in tons
Travel commute (bike, vehicle, air, rail) miles	CO_2e, nitrogen, PM<2.5 in tons

• Water use (supply, source, treatment, release)	gallons, acre feet, cubic meters
• Stormwater runoff	gallons, acre feet, cubic meters
• Impervious surfaces for stormwater	square feet or square meters
• Air emissions	pounds, tons, kilograms
• Ecosystem services	as appropriate
• Potentially harmful materials (input, output, leakage)	pounds, tons, kilograms

4. Products

Life Cycle

Supply chain (materials, sources-certifications, transport, treatment)	tons, CO_2e
Manufacturing (input, output, waste)	tons, CO_2e
Waste (recycling, disposed, return to nature, stored)	tons, methane
Potentially harmful materials (input, output, leakage)	pounds, tons, kg
Hazardous waste	pounds, tons, kg
Plastics for products and packaging type and amount	pounds, tons, kg
Distribution network	CO_2e nitrogen, particulate matter

5. True costs

This analysis can be very simple and generic or it can be specific and focused. Transportation-related external costs of energy are readily available. Specific flights can be identified, but energy use would vary depending on the jet stream orientation. CO_2 calculators are readily available and relatively consistent. Car model and year data is often available. For the energy a bicyclist expends the CO_2e impact is related to diet: a beef-heavy diet could lead to energy and CO_2e costs similar to an electric car. Some estimated external costs of materials are included in Appendix 2.

Here is an example of transportation reporting for a hypothetical company.

EKOTEK CONSULTING—TRANSPORTATION TRUE COST

	Miles	Pounds CO_2e/mile	CCG Fee $50/ton CO_2e	Other ext. costs
airplane	10,000	0.009	90	
commuter train	2,000	0.003	6	
electric car	5,000	0.008	40	
gas car	20,000	0.02	400	$4,000*
bicycle (food & mat'l)	2,000	0.0017	3.4	
electric bike	4,000	0.00125	5	
CO_2e fee for transportation			$544.4	
Total external cost for transportation			$4,544+	

*crashes, medical, highway maintenance, air pollution damage, noise damage, water pollution, ecosystem damage, land use, congestion, lost time, depletion of nonrenewable resources, waste, end-of-life pollution, and energy cost for crushing, shredding, and sorting.

The life cycle true costs can be estimated using the best sources of cost data. Develop a spreadsheet and list emissions, then estimates of social and environmental cost per unit or activity, and finally overall cost for the company or organization. You may choose to start with just a true cost estimate for energy and water, but try to expand beyond that. The true cost of health impacts might be the next step. Or go all in and attempt a comprehensive true cost assessment. Consultants can help.

Next Steps

Developing true cost accounting is a critical challenge for the world. Growing interest and work in this field is inspiring and will make a difference. Even rudimentary calculations of the external costs of common impacts and effects will lead to changes. Transactions between consumers, companies, organizations, and communities will be more sustainable and lead to a more positive future.

External impacts and costs need to be studied, refined, and validated by government and nongovernmental organizations (NGO). We need to make True Cost Reporting and Accounting easier for accountants, CEOs, CFOs, engineers, designers, sustainability report writers, and database and data mining software developers. We also need to make these reports consumer-friendly, with information included on product labels, bundled in utility and water bills, and added to waste disposal and recycling charges. The growing number of digital devices and PV home energy systems can be used to create impactful displays on smartphones, computers, and thermostats. These reports can further encourage improved behavior by showing comparisons with others, highlighting progress over time, and offering rewards. For example, the lowest energy use in a neighborhood might lead to a refund of the year's energy bills, a credit card for the farmers' market, a bicycle tune-up—any number of incentives toward reducing the friction of engaging in ecologically friendly practices.

Young innovators with the energy and skills to address these problems are working on them, and I am confident they can succeed!

True Cost Accounting Examples

The following chapters will begin to detail true costs in different sectors of the economy. Almost all of the 7.8 billion people on Earth participate in the world market at some level. There are more than 500 million small- and medium-sized enterprises that trade 5 to 6 million different products internationally. There are also a comparable number of farms. Each one is likely to emit climate change gases or cause environmental and health problems. Our future will depend on the changes we make in what we do and the materials and processes we use to make, grow, distribute, and dispose of our products. These farms and enterprises operate in more than 200 countries with differing climates, resources, politics, economies, histories, and cultural realities, but all depend entirely on the health of a single system—the Earth.

True Cost Accounting can help us reduce the damage we cause and ensure more sustainable economies and communities. I start with Food and Agriculture because we are all participants in the food market every day. This is the most detailed section because

I know it best and it suggests what could be done with further research on the other sectors of the economy.

Food is followed by Buildings, the biggest source of health-related problems, a major energy user, and in many ways the easiest to fix. Next is the most publicized and biggest source of climate change gases, Energy Production. This is followed by Water, the most essential threatened resource. Consumption looks at the things we buy and throw away. The chapters on Forests and Fisheries are less detailed as fewer people will be directly involved, but they illustrate several important aspects of True Cost Accounting. Transportation is not included because the true costs are already well described and available online—down to individual car models in some cases.

We should all do our own accounts. As you will see in the following sections, it is not too hard to begin accounting for energy, water, and food. We will pay more for what we buy. The "lowest price at any cost" mentality will be consigned to history. The subsidies we have been getting will slowly go away, but price increases will be accompanied by true cost savings. Each of the following chapters has an example of best practices that show how dramatic the change can be. In almost every case, it is possible—and sometimes relatively easy—to cut the true costs in half. Often, true costs can be reduced even further. Each chapter ends with suggestions for action. We can all choose to invest our personal internal true cost fees in ways that reduce our impact and improve our health, comfort, and quality of life by upgrading our homes, improving our workspaces, using fewer fossil fuels, and improving our food choices. We can pay to offset our impact by supporting tree-planting or other projects that sequester carbon. We can cut CCG emissions and reduce other types of environmental and social costs. First, we must understand them.

CHAPTER 5

FOOD AND AGRICULTURE

The primary cause of our failure in farm management has been the lack of adequate consideration of true costs and asset values. While true costs can be considered for each foodstuff produced, we also need to consider the external cost for the entire agricultural system. This requires accounting for Nature's Services and Natural Capital on farms, which are related to the farm ecosystems structure and function. They may be broken down into provisioning services (food, vegetable oil, feed, water, oxygen, wood, etc.) and regulating services (climate balancing, air and water pollution amelioration, flood reduction, wind erosion control, waste treatment) as well as Cultural Services (recreation, fitness, health, aesthetics, spiritual recovery).

Natural Capital may include both renewable (crop) and nonrenewable or finite (fossil fuel, fossil groundwater) resources. Unfortunately, even potentially renewable resources are currently being mined instead of sustainably managed. The longer the history of on

Farmer's markets help reduce the true cost of food. A dedicated, covered space helps. Davis, California.

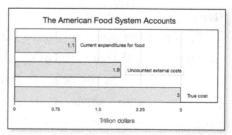

The American Food System Accounts

1.1 Current expenditures for food
1.9 Uncounted external costs
3 True cost

Trillion dollars

The Land Institute is bringing a perennial grain to market. Kernza© can reduce the true cost of grain. No plowing and reseeding required.

farm or regional data that can be developed, the better the chance we will be able to understand slow but significant changes. Is historic data available? Is information available at the appropriate scale?

In most areas, farming has been neither stable nor sustainable from the earliest days of settlement. The story has been about exploitation and survival, not sustainability in the long term. Farming and ranching won't be restructured until true cost accounting is done. Too many farms in the US, Asia, and Europe rely on government subsidies to survive. Most American farms and ranches have such slim profit margins even with subsidies that they have to have at least one source of off-farm income to survive. Unfortunately, farming and ranching today are more often lifestyles or hobbies than sustainably profitable businesses. Sadly, factoring in true costs shows they are even more problematic.

To better understand the performance of farms and farm communities, we need to consider all financial, environmental, and social costs and benefits. The costs related to farming and food production are very large and commonly transferred from private farms and supply firms (pesticides, nutrient leaks, GMOs, misuse of antibiotics) to the public and future generations. Farmers and ranchers with limited resources struggle to make a living as agricultural mega-firms make more and more money while ignoring external environmental and social costs. In 2017 Monsanto's net profit was $3.3 billion. It was acquired by Bayer in 2017. Bayer Crop Science revenue was $20 billion in 2020, more than the GDP of many countries.

This is a problem not only for the US, but for the world. Three hundred and thirty million small farms make do with one hectare of land or less.[68] Many of these families have small irrigated gardens (kitchen or home gardens) that provide food for domestic consumption and for sale.[69] Almost a billion people are undernourished, with caloric intake below the minimum energy requirement. More than two billion face food insecurity. Even here in the US, one in ten households is food insecure.

The war in Ukraine will make it much worse. In 2021, Ukraine exported more than $27 billion in agricultural products to the world, including wheat, corn, and sunflower oil. Russian exports will also decline. Millions of people around the world will be affected by rising prices and shortages. But most Americans don't know or think about how secure the food supply may be or where their food comes from until, for example, a global pandemic leaves empty supermarket shelves highlighted on the nightly news.

Many areas that were once productive have been ruined by unsustainable management.[70] Degraded lands may no longer offer any products for use or sale. Soil erosion, salinity, loss of nutrients and organic matter, damage to soil structure, and overuse of groundwater have all played a part. True cost accounting that tracks the value of natural capital would have minimized this damage.

Every time we go shopping, we make choices about food, farming, and the future. Agriculture has some of the highest external costs of anything we do, and the system is unsustainable. This has led to a rapidly growing interest in the true costs of food.[71] The profit and production of crops, meat, dairy, and other foods and food products has always waxed and waned in response to national and international events and market forces. Environmental and social collapses, government intervention, wars, and financial panics have often devastated farmers. The only consistent theme over the years has been a decline in water supply, deterioration of ecosystem health, and loss in value of Natural Capital. Farm land prices have often risen, but this reflects a scarcity of land, not the health, productivity, or ecosystem services the land can provide.

Failed accounting is a major factor in the crises now emerging in our food supply system: human ill health, damage to ecosystem structure, decline in ecosystem function, falling farm asset value (including ecological assets), and marginal profit—or more commonly, loss.

Health and Well-Being

Unhealthful foods have contributed to the astonishing levels of obesity in America. The Centers for Disease Control reported the obesity rate had passed 40 percent in 2020. These same foods contribute to diabetes, which now afflicts one in every ten people. By 2050, the rate of diabetes is expected to reach as high as 30 percent. The Milken Institute estimates the total cost of chronic diseases due to American obesity and overweight was $1.72 trillion in 2016. Much of the cost is paid by the government. The cost of suffering and death is paid by consumers, families, and communities.

American farmers use about a billion pounds of chemicals on crops every year, and 90 percent of Americans have detectable levels of pesticides in their blood. The fruits, nuts, and vegetables many parents beg their kids to eat are often tainted with chemicals. This is outrageous. Much of the problem is the result of flawed government subsidies and failed policies. The Environmental Working Group research shows the US government paid $425 billion in farm subsidies from 1995 to 2020, much supporting unsustainable practices and crops with adverse health effects.

Food is intimately linked with health. Health benefits should be considered in true cost/benefit studies. The quality of food and access to healthful food help determine long-term health and medical costs. Many poor communities are "food deserts," where only budget and packaged food are available within a reasonable commute. By the same token, organic foods without pesticide residues are increasingly available, but usually cost more. Supplemental nutrition programs with good food have decreased the risk of chronic disease, the risk of medication nonadherence among adults with diabetes, hospitalizations and nursing home placements among older adults, and visits to the emergency department for pregnancy-related diagnoses, hypertension, hypoglycemia, and childhood asthma.

After controlling for factors expected to affect spending on medical care, low-income adults participating in Supplemental Nutrition Assistance Programs (SNAP) incur about $1,400 (or roughly 25 percent) less in medical care costs in a year than low-income non-participants.[72] The difference is even greater for those with hypertension (nearly $2,700 less) and coronary heart disease (over $4,100 less).

A detailed study in California found that when schools contracted with a healthy lunch company, students at the school scored better on end-of-year academic tests.[73] The test score increases were about 40 percent larger for students who qualified for reduced-price or free school lunches. These are the students who are most likely to eat the school lunches.

The Farm to Table and Slow Food movements strive to offer higher quality foods that preserve cultural cuisines and associated food plants and seeds, domestic animals, and farming in an ecoregion. Consumers are encouraged to buy from farmers' markets, direct from farmers at farm stands, or as part of a Community-Supported Agriculture (CSA) agreement. A university study in California comparing farmers' market prices with those of conventional grocery stores found that contrary to many consumers' perceptions, farmers' market prices were competitive with regular supermarket prices."[74] Some prices were slightly higher, some slightly lower, but they were in the same range. Produce at a farmers' market is usually sold the same day or the day after it is harvested, has a shelf life that is two to three times longer than supermarket produce, and will have less thrown away. And because it is so fresh will taste better and be more healthful. Buying local also supports the local economy. California was the first state to allow their supplemental nutrition program[75] (the Golden State Advantage Card) to be used at farmers' markets, most of which have enrolled in the program. Many states continue to encourage purchasing lower quality, higher cost processed foods instead.

Getting harmful chemicals and antibiotics out of food has been an ongoing struggle in competition with farmers and food producers that ignore external costs. The Environmental Working Group analysis of foods in 2020 found more than 90 percent of the samples of nonorganic strawberries, apples, cherries, spinach, nectarines and grapes tested positive for residues of two or more pesticides. Kale, collard and mustard greens, as well as hot peppers and bell peppers, had the most pesticides detected, 103 and 101 pesticides in total, respectively. A single sample of kale, collard and mustard greens had up to 21 different pesticides. On average, spinach samples had 1.8 times as much pesticide residue by weight as any other crop tested. Kale was contaminated with a chemical called dacthal, classified by the EPA as a possible human carcinogen and which has been banned in Europe since 2009. Over 400 pesticides were found in 76 oregano samples collected across Europe.[76]

Permethrin, a neurotoxic insecticide found on spinach, has been linked to ADHD. To gauge pesticide exposure, University of California researchers had teenage girls living in the intensively farmed Salinas Valley wear wristbands that pick up environmental chemicals.[77] Dacthal and chlorpyrifos were among the most frequently detected pesticides for these young Latinas. The concentrations of dacthal and permethrin were three times higher for those who lived close to fields.

The misuse of antibiotics in meat production is contributing to the rise of antibiotic-resistant bacteria that are transferred to humans. There is a good chance the meat will be contaminated with potentially deadly Salmonella or E. coli bacteria at the farms and slaughterhouses that cut corners to increase speed and reduce costs. Consumers Report's tests found one ground beef sample with E. coli O157:H7 that causes severe illness and death. This triggered a federal recall. A third of the ground chicken was contaminated with Salmonella, and 78 percent of these positive tests were resistant to multiple drugs.[78] A Salmonella strain found in pork was resistant to 16 antibiotics. This misuse has eroded the natural capital value of antibiotics. Developing a new antibiotic can take ten to fifteen years and cost a billion dollars.

Growing concern about pesticides and antibiotics in food has led to improved regulations, but most external costs are still ignored. As a recent study showed, buying organic foods can dramatically reduce our dietary exposure to pesticides.[79] Organic products are cleaner, but some contamination can still drift over from crops in adjacent fields, be introduced through legacy contamination of the soil, be picked up in post-harvest treatment, or simply be from allowed organic pesticides.

Oregon passed the first organic law in 1973. California Certified Organic Farmers started work on organic standards in 1974, and the state passed those standards into law in 1979. The USDA National Organic Program passed in 1990. In 2018, the Trump administration rejected the proposed animal welfare standards (referred to as Organic Livestock and Poultry Production) that the National Organic Standards Board (NOSB) and the organic community had worked on for a decade. The Federal organic cost share program used to pay up to 75 percent of the certification costs up to $750, but this was reduced to $500.

Certifications are taken seriously by inspectors. In Canada, organic certification is done under the Canada Organic Regime. International organic rules include the International Federation of Organic Agriculture Movements. In Europe, the EC 834 Regulation on Organics covers both grown and imported foods. Global G.A.P. sets standards for good agricultural practices, and their Integrated Farm Assurance (IFA) standard covers agriculture, aquaculture, livestock, and horticulture production. It also covers additional aspects of the food production and supply chain, such as chain of custody and compound feed manufacturing. The IFA standards are revised through an extensive stakeholder involvement and consultation process.

Organic farming still occupies a small share of US farmland, but in 2020 organic sales broke the $60 billion mark for the first time.[80] The USDA reports the overall sales of organic commodities overall rose 31 percent from 2016 to 2019. More than 16,000 certified organic farms were counted. Organic farming and gardening can be much better than high input, chemically intensive farming, but still can be less than sustainable if management neglects the true costs. Major challenges remain, including climate change gas emissions from livestock and soil erosion.

A detailed analysis of true external costs would reveal that organic prices fall well below chemical-intensive products—consider, for example, the difference between a "low-cost" burger and a "high-value" organic burger.

Two Burgers

A comparison of the estimated true costs of a budget burger (which might cost just $4) and a bison burger from an organic restaurant (which may cost $10 or more) shows the difference in true costs possible between seemingly comparable food items.

The Lowest Cost Burger (up to 40 Ingredients)

The budget burger is made from the lowest-cost-at-any-price meat that may be imported from Brazil or from a barren feedlot with tens of thousands of cattle in Nebraska, Texas, California, or Colorado. Before it goes to the feedlot, the cow will likely have come from overgrazed rangeland (often subsidized by the public) that has resulted in biodiversity loss as well as increased runoff from storms resulting in increased erosion, dust, and flooding.

Transportation to the feedlot is stressful for cattle, but the stress is nothing compared to the conditions in many feedlots, which may hold 20,000 cattle or more. Feedlots for cattle are dangerous, dirty, and inhumane. The cows are fed soybeans and corn so that they will gain weight faster. It takes more than five pounds of taxpayer-subsidized soybeans or corn—and thousands of gallons of water—to produce the cheap fast-food burger.

The concentration of thousands of pounds of cow manure at a feedlot fouls the air and water as much as a small city, yet sewage treatment requirements are often minimal. The stress of crowding and filthy conditions may lead to disease, so cattle may be fed antibiotics even when they are not sick. This misuse of antibiotics is contributing to the rise of antibiotic-resistant bacteria that can be transferred to humans. The slaughterhouse is also inhumane for workers, who develop repetitive motion injuries and psychological problems. With crowding, stress, and low pay, meat processing workers were very vulnerable to COVID-19. Perhaps a hundred thousand have been sickened, and more than 500 have died. After processing, the meat must be refrigerated in storage, during transit, and at the fast-food site before being cooked, which uses significant amounts of energy and has environmental and health consequences. Refrigeration impacts include global warming gases, nitrogen pollution from power generation, and chlorofluorocarbon (CFC) leaks from refrigeration systems.

The fast-food tomato will likely have been grown in Mexico with intensive use of machinery, synthetic fertilizers, herbicides, pesticides, and fossil fuels. It may have been irrigated with water that is being used unsustainably and causing salt water intrusion. In San Quintin, Mexico, this has led to a problem with community water supplies becoming salty. The farmers get government support to treat this brackish water—the communities do not. The lettuce will probably come from California and will also be a chemically intensive product: another of the dirty dozen. The lettuce must be kept cool or it will wilt. In the case of the tomato and the lettuce, the farming and harvesting laborers are likely to be underpaid and mistreated. More than half of the farm workers in California may be undocumented. Lack of restrooms may lead to food contamination with dangerous germs. The tomato and lettuce will be trucked to a central distribution center and then to the fast-food outlet, so a long storage life is important.

The wheat for the bun will be the lowest-cost-at-any-price and it may be old, imported, or lower grade. Domestic wheat production is too often subsidized by US taxpayers. Synthetic fertilizers, herbicides, and pesticides may be used, and soil erosion and chemical contamination are inevitable. In addition to the wheat, the bun will contain a wide range of chemical stabilizers that are not well studied or understood. Many may come from China, the lowest-cost-at-any-price source of an increasing number of chemicals, additives, and even vitamins.

The mayonnaise will be made with eggs from industrial-caged chickens that may also have been fed antibiotics and mistreated. The soy oil will be from genetically engineered crops and grown with extensive chemical inputs and federal subsidies. The lemon "juice" will be imported and may have very little real lemon in it. Corn syrup, which is also produced from chemically intensive farming and subsidized by taxpayers, will be used as a sweetener. The vinegar for the mayo will be the lowest cost product.

The cucumbers for the pickles will have been grown with chemically intensive methods, harvested by poorly treated laborers, and shipped long distances. The USDA pesticide survey in 2010 found residue from eighty-six pesticides on cucumbers. Ten were known or probable carcinogens, thirty-two were suspected hormone disrupters. Seventeen were neurotoxins, and ten were developmental or reproductive disrupters. In addition, a quarter of all cucumbers had pesticide residue harmful to honeybees.

External costs of the budget burger include the energy used and pollution caused by the transportation of the food, manufacturing of the farm machinery, diesel fuel for the trucks, chemicals, and fertilizers. The overuse of chemicals reduces the population of the natural predators that help control pests and leads to higher costs on the farm and for neighboring farms.

After the salty, fatty—and tasty—burger is eaten, the external costs of health impacts begin. They may include hardening of the arteries, heart disease, intestinal and digestive problems, and obesity. The feedlot beef includes more harmful fat and less beneficial omega-3 oils than range-fed beef or bison. The health costs for each individual burger will not be very high, but the cumulative costs matter. The annual costs for obesity in the United States were estimated by the Milken Institute at $481 billion for healthcare and $1.24 trillion for indirect work loss.

The external costs of the budget burger are staggering. Soil, water, and energy resources are depleted. The misuse of antibiotics, erosion, sedimentation, air and water pollution, and related impacts diminish the value of Natural Capital and Nature's Services. The less costly burger is not a bargain after all.

The Better Value Burger (15 ingredients)

The better value burger will be made of bison meat from a native co-op. Bison are better at using the land. When they graze, the bison herd moves in any direction (like an amoeba) instead of following a lead cow. This limits damage to the rangeland and reduces overgrazing and erosion. The bison can be range-fed and slaughtered by a mobile processing van. They do not suffer the trauma and indignity of being shipped, and spend no time in a feedlot. They are also healthier, need no antibiotics or supplemental feed, and are leaner and healthier to eat. The meat will travel a shorter distance and be fresh. There are still, however, the external costs of transport and refrigeration.

The tomato for the bison burger will be a locally grown organic heirloom tomato. No chemicals or pesticides will be used to grow it, and it will come from a small farm where the workers are paid better (if not well) and are treated as human beings. The lettuce may come from a local organic farm, but is more likely to come from a larger organic grower in California or Mexico. The fresh, high-quality wheat for the bun will be organically grown and processed.

The mayonnaise will be made with eggs from free-range chickens that are not fed antibiotics and are better treated. Organic olive oil (most likely from California) will be used. Under the California Olive Oil Council program (COOC), California Department of Food and Agriculture officials collect samples of olive oil from member producers that are sent to independent accredited laboratories for chemical and sensory analysis. Members also have to send samples of their olive lots to an accredited lab of their choosing. The UC Davis Olive Center then compares test results to ensure the highest quality. The lemon juice will be from organically grown lemons; therefore, little sugar will be needed. The vinegar for the mayo will be artisanal, made locally with high-quality ingredients. The cucumbers for the pickles will be organic and locally grown. The budget low-cost burger may include two to three times as many ingredients and even more types of pesticides.

The bison burger uses only 15 ingredients and will have very low levels of pesticides. Even for the bison burger, the external costs of the meat are significant, but they are low when compared to the lowest-price-at-any-cost burger. The climate change gas emissions for feedlot beef are estimated at perhaps 15 pounds per pound of meat.[81] The bison would be less than half as much. So for the meat in a 1/3-pound budget burger, the CCG would be 5 pounds versus 2.5 for the bison. Bison meat is also lower in fat content, has more omega-3 fats than beef, and a better omega-6 to omega-3 ratio. It has a much lower chemical contamination level, is less likely to include disease-causing organisms, and is healthier to eat. These all lead to savings realized in external health benefits.

Both burgers also have many additional external costs. Both unsustainable and eco-friendly cafes will use energy, water, chemicals (for cleaning), and many other materials in their operations. Fast-food restaurants are some of the most energy-intensive buildings in America, with an on-site use of 120 kwh/sf/yr.[82] Disposal is unlikely to be very sustainable for either burger, although the "eco-friendly" cafe may pledge to reduce their use of plastic materials. Food waste in both cases is likely to go to a landfill, although it could be composted and recycled. The other ingredients and operation of the cafe would add perhaps 30 percent or more to the CCG.

The external costs of travel to the diner in an automobile may be comparable to the CCG emissions from growing the meat. If the best value burger diner drives 6 miles round trip in a Ford F150 pickup, the CCG emitted will be about 9 pounds CO_2e or 3 pounds for each burger; If the lowest cost burger buyer arrives in a Nissan Leaf the CCG impact will be only 0.7 pounds per burger. Choices matter. If cooks are commuting in older cars they would add even more CCGs, distributed across hundreds of servings during the day.

Although many people will be able to understand the external costs related to growing food for a burger, most are unaware of the many and varied external costs of the global food supply chain. There are crop-specific CCG emissions—but again, these are highly dependent on the skill and intention of growers. Try keeping a food diary and estimating your CCG emissions for a week or two. Include how much food is wasted and how many pounds of food packaging there are.

POUNDS OF CCG EMITTED PER POUND OF FOOD[83]

Peas	0.09
Apples	0.2
Potatoes	0.37
Carrots and root crops	0.37
Onions and leeks	0.40
Broccoli	2.0
Lentils	0.9
Bottle of wine	1.28
Yogurt	2.2
Greenhouse tomato	2.5
Rice	2.7
Beer six-pack	3.2
Chicken	5.4
Canned tuna	6.1
Pork	12
Cheese	13.5
Coffee	16
Dark chocolate	19
Beef	27

For almost any food product, the range of impacts is large depending on how and where it is grown. In one comparison coffee CCG emissions ranged from 5 to 68 grams per kilogram of coffee. The BBC online food calculator makes it easier to review the CCG of specific foods. If I have an apple a day, the calculator says this will generate 26 pounds over one year. Beef once or twice a week would add 1,328 pounds.

Growing tree crops like apples (50 grams CO_2e per apple in one analysis), storing them, and shipping them to market all generate

CCG emissions. These are offset by the 20 tons of CO_2 removed from the air and the release of 15 tons of oxygen each season. Well-managed fruit trees can be productive for more than a hundred years while sequestering carbon in their roots and wood.

Locally grown food is usually the best option. Truck transportation CCG emissions can cause 296 grams of CO_2 per ton-mile—air freight may release four times as much. Studies have suggested that on average, the food eaten in the US may have traveled 1,500 miles. Eat local, seasonal crops instead of imported out-of-season foods.

The EPA reports six billion tons of CO_2e are emitted by agriculture every year in the US. This is not just from the production of the food itself, but also includes the ethanol and other industrial products from corn, methane from cows, and more. For the 329 million US residents, this amounts to 18 tons per person every year, or 1.5 tons each month. If we paid the Swedish CCG fee of $137.50 per ton, we would be paying $200 every month to cover our share of the external CCG costs from agriculture.

Ecosystem Structure

Assessing the health of a farm ecosystem includes not just the farm but the whole region. Water, nutrients, CCG emissions, chemicals, antibiotics, and other materials flow onto and off of the site. Food production affects the distribution of species, their population sizes, organization (nearest neighbor, nurse plant), richness, seasonal occurrence (migration stopover), and the ability of native plant species to resist invasive species.[84] The architecture of the ecosystem (its size, shape, pattern) and eco-diversity according to multiple indices are also affected.

Photographs and satellite images can provide low-cost information on ecosystem structure and change in some areas. Paired photographs, particularly aerial photos over many years or decades, can reveal large-scale changes over time. LIDAR (similar in operation to radar but using pulsed laser light) mapping can provide very accurate details of land surface configuration, even under vegetation, that help examine environmental history. In some areas, detailed maps are available from ArcInfo and other geographic databases. Some excellent work has been done in the Netherlands. An accurate understanding of changes in ecosystem structure may require field studies and surveys across the seasons, years, and decades, and we need to get started now. Many farmers already pay careful attention to such changes. This type of analysis is not costly, but it does take time.

A wide range of factors may need to be considered in agroecosystems, including species diversity and richness, population dynamics of many species, soil health, seeds, seed banks, pollinators, symbionts, and so forth. In aquatic systems, the focus may shift to understanding seasonal flows, food webs, invasive species, and biodiversity.

Ecosystem Function

Ecosystem structure influences ecosystem function. The key ecosystem flows that must be understood include energy, water, and nutrients. Nutrient cycling is particularly important because many native ecosystems are nutrient-limited, and nutrient leakage from farms can cause damage and costly disruption to waterways. Water flow and quality are two of the easiest functions to track and can be good indicators of farm ecosystem health. Resilience to disturbance, or stability, will be increasingly important as climate change worsens.

In aquatic systems, we may measure ecotoxicity, biological oxygen demand, nutrient flow, temperature, biomagnification, invertebrates, fish, amphibians, birds, and other vertebrate species. The influence of chemicals on hormone systems, reproduction, and survival are of special concern. For larger operations, it may be possible to sample soils, water, and air to refine the estimate of external costs.

Ecosystem function also includes the ruminant bacteria in farm animals. A single cow releases around 200 pounds of methane a year. The US legislature has suggested valuing the external cost of methane from fossil fuel systems at $900 per ton.[85] If this was applied to cows it would represent an external cost of about $90 per cow. New food additives are showing great promise in reducing cow gas emissions, up to 60 percent with a sea weed based supplement.[86]

Soil erosion is a persistent problem that may have a true cost of $37 billion a year.[87] Soil erosion costs are related to both on-farm and off-farm impacts. Reduction of soil depth can impair the land's productivity, and the transport of sediments can degrade streams, lakes, and estuaries. Flooding from rapid runoff of bare soils can destabilize streams and accelerate bank erosion, damaging bridges and filling reservoirs. The bank erosion can be severe, studies showed bank erosion could be on the order of 430,000 tons a year for a 44-mile reach of the Nishnabotna River in Iowa.[88] Typical monoculture cropping in the Midwest can have erosion rates of 10 tons per acre year after year, but up to 65 tons acre have been lost in dry and windy years.[89]

These sediments add to nutrient flows in waterways and the ocean. The dead zone at the mouth of the Mississippi River is primarily caused by fertilizer and sewage leaking from farms in the river's watershed.[90] Nutrients feed algae blooms and bacteria that consume all the oxygen in the water, which kills off fish, shellfish, and other organisms. In 2017, this dead zone measured nearly 9,000 square miles: about the size of New Jersey. The cost in loss of ecosystem services was estimated at $2.5 billion.[91] The seafood and tourism businesses pay a high price for farm mismanagement upriver. The cost for farm improvements to minimize this pollution could reach $3 billion, but the runoff of nitrogen represents a loss of $400 million worth of nitrogen fertilizer a year.

An Estimate of the True Costs of American Agriculture

It is possible to consider not just a particular food or farm but to explore the true costs of the entire agricultural system. I have been interested in this approach for more than forty years.[92] This has led me to work on a variety of projects involving true cost, the use of rice straw to avoid field burning, biological cleanup of selenium, more efficient irrigation systems, and more sustainable crops. I have found that external costs can usually be estimated if we take a good look at the farm's operation and region.

Calculating the true costs of agriculture on a larger scale is sometimes easier than for a specific farm or landowner. Scientific evidence and data, an understanding of linkage and causation, and the challenges involved in pricing risk and uncertainty are all involved. The EPA estimates that agriculture accounted for 11.2 percent of US greenhouse gas emissions in 2020.[93] Of the 11.2 percent, electricity-related CO_2 emissions accounted for 0.6 percent. Other agricultural emissions include N_2O from cropped and grazed soils, methane from enteric fermentation and rice cultivation, N_2O and methane from managed livestock manure, and CO_2 from on-farm energy use.

The external costs of food and agriculture are often global, with pesticides banned in the US or Europe transferred to poor countries and returned to us in imported foods. In 2017, the FDA found that roughly 51 percent of imported fruits and 47 percent of imported vegetables carried pesticide residues. Overall, the imported foods had more illegally high levels of pesticide residues than domestic foods. Imported foods also often have a large transportation footprint of CCGs.

Farms are a major source of pollutants when flooding occurs. Pesticides, oil, diesel, gas, and fertilizer are washed out of barns and sheds. Animal manures and sludge are picked up along the way. When animals die during floods, the mess is compounded. Hurricane Florence killed as many as 3 million chickens and 3,000 pigs.

Risk and resilience in agriculture will become increasingly important as climate change adds ever more intense droughts, water shortages, storms, and flooding, as well as higher temperatures in most areas and perhaps much colder temperatures in Europe if the Mid-Atlantic Overturning Circulation weakens or fails.

Estimates of the true costs of agriculture in the US are listed by declining true costs.[94] Full details and notes on sources are available at www.truecostalways.com. The results are clear and disturbing, with a staggering net loss year after year for agriculture as currently practiced.

ESTIMATED TRUE COSTS FOR AMERICAN AGRICULTURE	MILLION DOLLARS
Biodiversity loss cost	453,000
Cost related to subsidy-related obesity: 20% of $1.7 trillion	344,000
Reactive nitrogen leakage from agriculture	210,000
Terrestrial ecosystem function disruption	200,000
Lost livelihood, underpaid, displaced, health and safety	134,000
Diabetes costs probably related to corn subsidies: 33%	107,000
Damage to aquatic ecosystems	90,000
Food pre and post production GHG at $100 ton	69,600
Resistance to antimicrobials	55,000
Fuel combustion at $100 ton	40,400
Crop cultivation at $100 ton	34,000
Value of lost soil: 1.5 billion tons at $20 ton	30,000
Federal crop support and other programs, average 1995-2019	28,000
GHG emissions livestock at $100 ton	25,400
Cost related to cancer pesticide exposure: 33% of $57 Billion	17,100
Cost from food borne pathogens	15,600
Drinking water treatment for nitrate (N)	14,250
Other costs of undocumented farm workers: 20% of $50 billion	10,000
Drug trafficking displaced farmers: 5% of $193b	9,650
Cost to replace lost reservoir capacity	8,462
Cost related to fine particulates	4,800
Damage to recreation	4,457
Flood damage (10% attributed to agriculture)	3,200
Remittances by farm workers: 10% of $28.8 billion	2,800
Administrative and compliance cost for tax used to pay subsidy	2,800
Bird kills due to pesticides	2,200
Salinization of soil	2,000
Crop damage from air pollution related to agriculture	2,000
Habitat conversion: 1 million acres, restoration cost as value $20,000 acre	2,000
Cost of undocumented farm worker medical care: 20% of 10 billion	2,000
Subsidies for water and water project energy	2,000
Instream impacts to fisheries	1,706

Pesticide resistance	1,500
Crop loss due to pesticides	1,400
Cost to water industry for added processes	1,164
Water conveyance costs	1,106
Dead zone in the Gulf of Mexico: 8,000 sq. miles	1,000
Loss of beneficial predators from pesticide	934
Off-stream impacts: industrial users, steam power plants	616
Cost to navigation: shipping damages, dredging	474
Honeybee and pollination losses from pesticide use	283
Treatment of surface water for microbial pathogens	166
Facility infrastructure needs to remove pesticides from water	157
Ethanol program subsidies	150
Harmful algal blooms	100
Cost to comply with hazard control rules	92
Fish kills due to pesticides	72
Conversion of natural areas and CRP to cropland	52
Consumptive water use	43
Fish kills from manure spills	17
Total external cost of agriculture and food in the US	$1,936,699
Uncounted external cost per acre	$2,152
Farm net income per acre 2019	$88
Net loss acre	$2,064

This tremendous loss year upon year is a sign of failure in our current accounting and management of farms and ranches. The "get big or get out" of Secretary of Agriculture Earl Butz led them into a trap.[95] It is not hard to see why children are reluctant to stay on the farm.

The USDA estimates we spend $1.77 trillion a year on food and beverages, slightly less than my estimate of external cost at $1.9 trillion. The Rockefeller study estimated the true costs of food were even higher, at $3.2 trillion.

The true cost can also be explored for a crop or farm. Data on crop production and farm income are not hard to find, but the results will surprise many readers. The annual average **loss** per acre for corn in Illinois from 2015-2019 was $39,[96] so the net loss after considering external costs would be $2,191 per acre. Even in a good year like 2020 with a nominal profit of $137 an acre, the net loss would be $2,015. With a banner year of 200 bushels per acre and a price of $9 bushel, there is still a net loss of $1,100. The picture gets even worse if we consider the energy, social, and environmental costs of food transport (processed food typically travels over 1,300 miles) before it is consumed.[97]

This closer look at the true costs of American food production and agriculture highlights the need for changes in the agronomic practices of most of the Nation's farmers and food producers. It also illustrates the need for major revisions in policy and funding for the US Department of Agriculture and the nature of future support for farm research and farm welfare.

This rather surprisingly high true cost does not mean we should stop producing food. Our challenge is to do it more wisely.[98] The external costs often look much better on an organic farm. For a German organic farm, the net was a **profit** of $560 per acre.[99] For an intensively managed conventional farm, the **loss** was $280 per acre. The complete transformation of the farm/food system will benefit farmers in many ways,[100] but will take time and policy changes.

Restructuring American Agriculture

We need to ease into new ways of thinking and methods of operation while giving farmers and ranchers time to change equipment, crop selection, and management. We need to reduce the external costs while helping to meet the food demand here in the US and around the world. This restructuring can be done, and it needn't affect the food supply. It will create hundreds of thousands of satisfying jobs.

True cost accounting will help level the global playing field and improve profitability for many smaller farms. In most cases, the external costs of imported foods are much higher than those of locally grown foods. First, there are the very high social costs of underpaid and exploited workers. Second, there are the external costs of transportation over thousands of miles. And in many cases, there has been land conversion from biodiverse forests to plantations of oil palms, corn, and soy beans. Replacing the mangroves that once protected coastlines from storms with aquaculture ponds has led to tragic social and environmental costs, all so that Americans can eat "lowest price at any cost" shrimp.

The lack of regulations (or lack of enforcement) in developing countries encourages chemically intensive operations, and imported foods are often contaminated. Small farmers may prefer to work differently, but they may be trapped. One farmer I talked with in Sonora, Mexico, regretted that the bank would not loan him money for crop production unless he agreed to use high-input, high-yield corn seed instead of locally adapted corn seed. He also had to buy and use commercial fertilizer and pesticides. In this arid area, these both made it more likely his crop would fail. Farmers and farm families are most likely to be hurt by the misuse of pesticides, antibiotics, and fertilizers. These can have tragic, long-term impacts when used without proper protection. In many cases, the damage to people and wildlife is irreversible.

True cost accounting for American agriculture will help restructure and eventually eliminate subsidies. In the US today, highly paid special consultants help rich farmers milk these subsidies, and the costs are staggering. Since 1995, $400 billion in subsidies have been paid to American "farmers." Over the same period, just $500 million was spent on the kinds of sustainable agriculture research we need (a tenth of 1 percent of misguided subsidies). Most of the subsidies flow to the largest farmers, who grow crops like wheat, soybeans, and corn in over-supply. Many who get subsidies live in cities and never touch the soil. The top 20 percent of farms, as measured by crop sales, received 73 percent of all Market Facilitation Program payments in 2018 and 69 percent in 2019. They also received 76 percent of all crop insurance subsidies. From 1995 to 2014, the Environmental Working Group found that 50 people on the Forbes 400 list of the wealthiest Americans had received farm subsidies. Today, some of the worst subsidies are funneled through insurance companies to mask the identities of recipients. The Government Accountability

Office found that at least four recipients of crop insurance subsidies had a net worth of more than $1.5 billion.

Stewart Resnick (aka the Nut King) and his wife Lynda have benefited from many subsidies and incomplete accounting. In 2018, they owned 180,000 acres in the San Joaquin Valley, an area larger than the city of Chicago, and their farms were using more water than all the residents of Los Angeles. The Resnicks have returned some of their profits to universities for research on more sustainable agriculture. In 2022 UC Davis received a $40 million donation from the Resnicks to fund a center for agricultural innovation and sustainability to better respond to the impact of climate change.[101] Another $10 million will fund research grants on these topics at UCD. In 2019, the couple donated $750 million to Caltech to aid research on climate change and sustainability.

Small farm families, people of color, and Native Americans get little or nothing in the way of subsidies and find it hard to compete with heavily subsidized big farms who benefit from very skilled lawyers and political connections. When an effort was recently made to help farmers who are people of color, the outrage from white farmers was disturbing—particularly when contrasted with the lack of criticism for unconscionable subsides to rich white people and mega-corporations.[102] Monsanto's profits exceed $2 billion a year; the Organic Consumer's Association budget is $4 million a year.

Small farmers sell their products at reduced prices because they have to compete with large subsidized farmers. These effects are global. Selling subsidized corn, soy beans, and wheat at prices below the local cost of production in other countries has bankrupted millions of small farmers. This has added to the pressure to emigrate to the US and Europe. Many of the undocumented workers and refugees in the US are victims of American farm subsidies.

If we look at the heavily subsidized and environmentally costly corn operations in the Midwest, we find the average profit/loss for an Illinois corn farm (on high productivity land without land rent but with external costs included) was a loss of $84 per acre from 2012-2019. If we include land rent, the loss would be $356 per acre each year. For a relatively small farm of 1,500 acres, that represents an effective loss of more than half a million dollars a year even before external costs are counted, which will boost the loss up to one million dollars a year. It is no surprise that the average age of American farmers rose from 50 years in 1982 to 59.4 years for primary producers in 2017.[103] A third of the farmers are over 65, and many are now in their seventies and eighties. Their children have not replaced them because they understand the system is unsustainable, even with all the subsidies.

Using TCA to Improve Farm Management and Profitability

The summary of costs and returns for our hypothetical Heartland Farm is based on a range of studies done in the Midwest.[104] It assumes a $4 per bushel price for conventional corn and $12 per bushel for organic corn. The organic corn production costs as much as $100 more per acre, but averaged $133 more income per acre Adding external costs more clearly illustrates the long-term value proposition. Adding some beef cattle[105] to diversify operations adds some security for years when the corn crop is damaged by severe weather events or pests.

TCA HEARTLAND FARM

Current Conventional Cropping System	Cost	Income
Internal operating cost 300 acres GMO corn	-$285,600	
External cost	-$72,000	
Income 250 bushels acre @$4.40[106]		+$330,000
Year end loss	-$27,600	

Improved management with true cost accounting		
200 acres organic corn expense	-$240,000	
100 acres, 20 grass fed beef	-$20,000	
Internal Costs	-$260,000	
External cost corn	-$36,000	
External cost beef	-$5,000	
Income organic corn: 200 bushels acre @$12		+$480,000
Income beef		+$30,000
Income total		+$510,000
Apparent profit		+$250,000
Year end profit		+$209,000

The conventional Heartland Farm appears profitable if we only look at profit in relation to internal operating cost, ignoring external costs and land cost. A better operating plan, like the organic operation, could make a tremendous difference. Change is inevitable.

Asset Value in Agriculture

Asset value, another important consideration in food production, considers the change in the value of the land and resources over time. Failing to consider these changes leads to mismanagement. Once again, we can compare two hypothetical farms with the same land base but different management. One farm is more "profitable" in today's economy, while the other is a "marginal" performer but a truly profitable operation over time.

Bob's farm has adopted a high-input, high-yield cropping system and has shown good profit on paper for some years. Equipment—up to $700,000 for a large tractor—is bought on credit to ensure that the large monoculture fields can be harvested quickly. Erosion is high. Nutrients and pesticides run off into nearby streams and seep into the groundwater, contributing to the Gulf of Mexico dead zone. High risks of crop failure are taken, encouraged by federal farm subsidies and crop insurance, which are essential to keep Bob's farm afloat. Bob is often held up as a model farmer in the news because he has a new truck, a new tractor, and apparently high profits. His highly variable (and growing) debt load is ignored. In a drought year, his farm may be bankrupted and auctioned off even with crop insurance.

Nora's farm is a mixed operation that produces a range of organic food and medicinal herbs as well as chickens and eggs. Even if one income stream has problems, the others can pick up some of that slack. Nora maximizes local inputs to minimize environmental costs. Soil fertility is maintained with biological nitrogen fixation by bacteria on plant roots and the use of manure. Crop rotations, chickens, and biological controls are used to minimize pest problems. She maintains and repairs her old equipment. More labor is needed but is spread across the year. Capital costs are much lower.

Year-to-year income fluctuation is much larger for Bob's farm, with some years of considerable profit (thanks in part to federal support) and some with large losses from weather, pests, or market price collapse (offset to some extent by crop insurance). Nora's farm has higher labor costs and lower input costs; profits still vary, but even in a bad year, there is income and little or no debt. A study of long-term farm ownership in the Midwest found that the conservative farm families lasted, while the risk-takers didn't.

The profits and asset value for the two farms would be much different if the full costs of soil erosion, soil health, ecosystem damage, and health impacts were subtracted, and the value of improved human health, vitality of the farm community, and the environment were added. Bob's farm may show a decline in asset value every year while Nora's farm builds the value of Natural Capital by enriching soil, sequestering carbon, and supporting pollinators and other beneficial insects. True cost accounting favors the sustainable farm and puts the unsustainable farm out of business—the reverse of what happens today.

Steps to Sustainable Farming

When accounting rules are changed to more properly consider true costs and asset values, the farm economy will favor more sustainable practices. These operations will require and support more farmers per acre, enabling more people to enter the industry and make a living as farmers. It will also encourage farmers to return to complex mixed-farming systems, rather than the extensive high-risk monocultures of today that see hundreds of thousands of acres growing the same cultivars, vulnerable to the same pests and diseases.

Small towns across rural America are dying as a result of incomplete and distorted accounting. The land base that supported them is also declining as farmers succumb to the pressure to grow bigger, to grow fewer varieties of crops, and to increase inputs. These pressures will abate when true costs are counted, and direct and indirect subsidies and other perverse government incentives are reduced, and then eliminated. Improved accounting can repopulate the countryside and make local food the first choice.

The nominal price of food will go up, but the true cost of food will go down. True cost accounting will have an impact on prices, but perhaps not as much as you might expect. Farmers currently receive an average of only 10-20 percent of the retail price. Even if we increased the farmers' price by 25 percent, the retail price in the package at the store might increase just 2.5-5 percent.

In California, where regulations have begun to encourage more realistic (although still incomplete) cost accounting, wine grape growers have rapidly converted to more organic operations. Sixty growers, including many of the giants, switched to organic practices in just ten years, largely to avoid potential liabilities for environmental contamination. They also found this gave them a marketing advantage and justified higher prices for more sustainable organic wines.

True cost accounting for transportation would also emphasize local supplies and home gardens. It would increase direct farmer-to-consumer sales on-farm, at farmers' markets, and with consumer-supported agriculture agreements (CSAs). Markets that purchase directly from local farms (as Whole Foods often does) would also help reduce consumer costs and increase profits for farmers. Savings in energy and chemical inputs would also help offset cost increases. True costs of transportation savings would be significant, both in energy use and environmental and social costs.

The value of most high-input farm land typically declines year over year with the loss of organic matter and nutrients, loss of insect predators that helped control pests, loss of pollinators, and loss of soil by wind and water erosion. The national USA annual average farmland soil erosion rate for sheet, rill, and gully erosion is 7.6 tons per acre of farmland. This soil would cost more than $150 an acre to replace.

Research on reducing some impacts from farming have been en-couraging. About 5.7 percent of global greenhouse gases may come from methane released by ruminant animals. Research at UC Davis and in Australia on food additives to reduce methane production from cow burps has found that a small amount of seaweed in the feed can cut emissions by as much as 82 percent. Other food ad-ditives are also being studied. Producing the necessary volume of seaweed would have to be carefully developed to minimize external costs and environmental impacts.

Food production doesn't have to be destructive and detrimental to the environment, farmers, and consumers. Increasing consid-eration of true costs will lead to change. Crops that taste good and are healthier can increase profits. Home gardens and small farms are already growing more food every year, even in urban areas. The challenge of counting true costs is important not just in the US, but globally. Lessons from the best practices and systems around the world need to be better studied and supported.[107] Farmer-to-farmer information exchange can be particularly effective.

Policy-making to address the problem of external costs of agricul-ture will be ideological, partisan, and contested like any other issue in contemporary politics. The powerful groups that have benefited from dumping their costs on the public and future generations will not give up easily. It will require active education and support from NGOs, communities, and ethical politicians. But it can be done.

The growth in numbers of younger farmers following more sustainable paths is very encouraging. Seventeen percent of all organic farmers are thirty-four years of age or younger. In 2008, there were around 11,000 certified farms; by 2019, there were more than 16,500. Sales of organic food increased 31 percent from 2016 to 2019. Three and a half million acres were certified organic in 2020. More than 10 percent of the farmland in Vermont is now certified organic. In 2015, the Organic Trade Association estimated US organic retail sales reached $43 billion, representing double-digit growth in most years since the USDA established national organic standards in 2000. In 2020, organic sales reached $56 billion.

What You Can Do!

Advocate for true cost accounting at the state and national level. Support NGOs, farms, and programs that promote true cost accounting and restorative agriculture.[108,109] True cost accounting will help drive a rapid change in agriculture to improve the quality and security of our food supplies. Food production will become more healthful, profitable, sustainable, and resilient in the face of climate change. Farm organizations and advisors can begin to include external cost information in their educational and marketing materials. Universities and training centers need to start the research that will provide detailed external cost information. We also need more funding for locally adapted, sustainable farming research that will clearly identify and reduce external costs. The USDA Long-Term Agricultural Research Network (LTAR) has tackled this challenge on a shoestring budget of $20 million per year with about a million dollars for each research site.

The goal—which is achievable—is to create an accounting system that promotes healthy and ecologically sound food production while rewarding farmers and consumers for doing the right things. As the noted farmer/philosopher Wendell Berry puts it:

... an economy worthy of the name should begin with proper care of its sources in the natural world and in the local cultures of land use. Beyond that it should be based upon the principle of a reasonable self-sufficiency, from the household to the local community and on through the categories of political organization.[110]

You can reduce the True Cost of your food by half or more today. One of the most powerful options to reduce your impact is by changing what you eat. By itself, eating less (or no) meat won't halt climate change, but it will make a difference. It will also improve your health and reduce your environmental footprint. A diet with less meat will reduces CCG emissions, and a vegetarian or vegan diet has even less harmful impacts. The Environmental Working Group estimates that if everyone in the US chose a vegetarian diet, it would have the same benefits as taking 46 million cars off the road. You can also reduce your share of methane emissions by composting all your food waste instead of sending it to a landfill.

DIET	CCG POUNDS MONTH	CCG FEE MONTH @ $137.50/TON
Vegan	201	$13.80
Vegetarian	263	$18.08
Low meat eaters	319	$21.93
Medium meat eaters	387	$26.60
Meat-centric	480	$33.00

Home gardens are important. Two pounds of carbon emissions can be prevented with every pound of homegrown vegetables consumed, according to David Cleveland at the University of California, Santa Barbara. If most families in California had a garden at home or access to a school or community garden and were benefiting from the advice of the state's excellent Master Gardener program—emissions for food could be cut significantly. This could be done very rapidly when we assume a war footing for CCG. The 20 million "Victory Gardens" of WW2 grew 40 percent of the nation's vegetables on 20 million acres. American families had grown approximately 8 million tons of food by the time the war ended in 1945.[111]

If you can't garden, buy fresh produce at a farmers' market or direct from the farm if you can. Support local markets that sell organic foods. Organic foods may be little different in nutrition, but they are much lower in chemical contamination. Sadly, they are not always completely free of biocides that can drift in from adjoining nonorganic farms, be found in irrigation water, or remain as residual in the soil.

Join a community garden. Participate in an organic farm's Community Supported Agriculture (CSA) network. In a CSA, you subscribe to a farm and get food every week or month. If no CSAs exist in your area, you might consider starting one. You can reduce your impact by shopping at a responsible store that offers a wide range of organic foods. Take your own reusable bags. Ask retailers and producers to start listing the CCG impact of their food offerings. Some companies have already taken this step, and consulting firms are emerging that can do these calculations.

If conventional markets are your only choice, look for their growing selection of organic foods and ask them to do more. In food deserts, it will be tough, but it may be just the ticket to start a community garden—local public schools are prime territory for such initiatives.

You can also help by supporting organizations that are currently working to improve the sustainability of the food system here in the US and around the world. Calculate your CCG emission true cost. Invest a third of that cost in improving your gardening skills and supporting your local school or community gardens. Donate another third to a group working on sustainable agriculture and the true cost of food. And give the final third to international efforts to reduce the true cost of food, to cope with drought, and to improve water use efficiency for small farms and home gardens. The countries hit hardest by climate change are suffering as a result of our emissions.[112]

One of the best organization worthy of support is the Environmental Working Group (www.ewg.org). Other notable organizations include the National Sustainable Agriculture Coalition, the Agroecology Fund, The Land Institute, New Forest Farm, Ecoagriculture Partners, the International Federation of Organic Agriculture Movements, the Global Alliance for the Future of Food, the Food and Environment Program of the Union of Concerned Scientists, the Slow Food School Garden Network, and Native Seeds Search. There are many more worthy organizations. Look for a local food or farm program to support as well—there are more every year.

CHAPTER 6

TRUE COST ACCOUNTING FOR BUILDINGS

We spend more and more of our lives inside buildings. Their construction and operation have involved enormous impacts on our health, ecosystems, and the global climate. External costs from buildings arise from energy use (nitrogen pollution, CCGs, and acid rain from fossil fuel burning), toxic runoff, waste water, disruption of hydrologic flows, bird mortality, and much more. Poorly designed, built, and maintained buildings are a common cause of human suffering, illness, and death.

Building design and well-planned land use matter even more in countries where there is no power grid. Good design and careful choice of materials enable the simplest buildings to perform better. They can be warmer in winter, cooler in summer, safer in earthquakes, fires, or typhoons, and they pose less risk for mold and asthma.

The San Luis Obispo Sustainability Group designed this naturally heated, cooled, lit and ventilated synagogue. It uses 80% less energy than a conventional design and is more comfortable.

Indigo Architects remodeled a Dairy Queen for their office in Davis, California. They optimized natural heating, cooling, ventilation and lighting. Adding PV panels brought the building to zero net energy - even while charging two electric cars.

Estimating true costs begins with design and construction, then operation and maintenance, and finally demolition or deconstruction. Site acquisition, clearing (logging), and ground-shaping with heavy equipment lead to habitat destruction, soil compaction, and erosion. Studies have demonstrated erosion loss may be near zero up to 100 tons per square mile in native cover, but with road building, utility trenches, cutting trees, grading and other activities soil loss can increase to 100,000 tons per square mile. This has catastrophic effects on streams, lakes, and waterways.

External costs of buildings can be shaped by custom, design standards (if any), rules, and regulations. These have neglected environmental and social costs, such as comfort, health and productivity, while focusing on energy savings. The Center for the Built Environment database reveals that throughout the 897 buildings surveyed, occupants reported air quality problems (25%), temperature control problems (39%), noise (34%), and poor lighting (14%).[113] The building codes have made it much less likely buildings will collapse, but have clearly missed the mark on comfort.[114]

Building Energy Use

In 2020, the combined end-use energy consumption by residential and commercial sector buildings was about one third of the US total. Energy also costs energy, and if we add the losses that occur in the electrical production and distribution networks, the residential and commercial buildings may rise to 40 percent of total US energy consumption. Buildings are energy guzzlers that harm the environment and people especially because fossil fuel energy has been heavily subsidized. These direct subsidies enable the enormous costs that are transferred to the environment, the poor, and future generations to be ignored. Energy has been so cheap that there has been little incentive for innovation or change in how buildings are designed, built, and operated. Buildings have also grown because we have ignored true costs. Home sizes grew—from 1,000 square feet in 1950 to 1,500 in 1970, 2,349 in 2004, and 2,261 square feet in 2020. All the while, family sizes have been decreasing.

Buildings have not improved much because building science research has been underfunded. Many of the basic flows and impacts of buildings are still not well understood. Environmental costs have not been studied carefully either, and may well exceed health costs. Indeed, the external costs of buildings have been almost completely ignored. Solar pioneers and energy specialists have demonstrated that windows, thermal mass, and insulation can be used to meet most if not all heating, cooling, and ventilation needs. But architectural schools have rarely selected professors who understand and study these proven strategies. The notion of the architect as an artist first and foremost still holds sway in many programs. As a result, many students graduate with little exposure to cost-effective designs and material choices.

The Department of Energy reports the average annual energy use for a commercial building is about 22.5 kWh per square foot. This includes 8 kWh/sq. ft. for refrigeration and equipment, 7 for lighting, 3 for cooling, 2 for heating, 2 for ventilation, and 0.5 for hot water heating. The average energy use for a 150-square foot office would be about 3,375 kWh per year, costing $338 at 10¢ kwh. The external cost of climate change emissions at a gas-fired power plant to meet that need would be about $456 at 13.5¢ per kWh. The true energy cost would then be $338 plus $456, or $794. For electricity from a coal-fired power plant with an external cost of 40¢ per kWh, the true cost would be $1,320 for a total energy cost of $1,658.

Life cycle costs are important for buildings that may be in use for 50 to 100 years or more. In the US, most commercial and residential buildings are designed and built on speculation, and future occupants have little say in design, energy use, material choices, comfort, lighting, or health issues. In Europe, where buildings are more often owned by occupants, the incentives are different. Long-term costs and health impacts are more often considered. In Switzerland, mortgages of between 50 and 100 years are common, so the quality of materials and skill of labor are critical.

Construction of homes, offices, and industrial buildings is important. Retrofitting for energy efficiency is generally more expensive and less effective than getting it right in new construction. External impact cost recovery will often double the price, suggesting the level of hidden subsidy we all benefit from—which many will fight to retain. But change is coming.

Office buildings are similar to residential buildings, but typically are used more during the day. The higher occupational load along with computers, printers, and other equipment often makes cooling more important than heating. Institutional buildings vary widely, but usually require the same services as commercial and residential buildings. Some, like churches, have more unusual patterns of energy demand.

True Costs of Building Materials

The external costs of construction materials are also important. Cement production may account for 8 percent of global climate change gas emissions. Stefan Brincrezu and coworkers computed the resource intensity of the fifty-eight sectors of the German economy and concluded that buildings and dwellings consumed between 25 and 30 percent of the total nonrenewable material flow. The Dutch National Environmental Database (*Nationale Milieudatabase*) contains product environmental profiles in the Netherlands. It was created to develop a uniform calculation of the environmental performance of buildings and civil engineering works. Similar work should be done in other nations and states.

Homes and commercial buildings shed or leak toxic materials from roofing, paints, and other components. We need to look at the inflow and outflow of these materials. Copper and zinc ions in runoff from roofs and architectural elements cause ecosystem disruption even at very low levels. Asphalt and composite shingles use copper, arsenic, and other biocides to minimize growth of moss and algae—these leach into the runoff. A study in Washington State found cadmium in runoff from one-third of the sampled roofs, arsenic in 90 percent, lead in 99 percent—and copper and zinc in all water samples. Cleaners, detergent, solvents, hormones, antidepressants, antibiotics, viruses, bacteria, chemicals and other compounds enter the sewage from homes and offices.

Environmental costs throughout the life of a building and perhaps long after that if waste materials, hazardous materials, and pollutants remain. Most attention has been placed on energy, but this is rarely the primary cost. Health, lost productivity, and environmental costs may exceed energy costs by a factor of five, ten, or more. As with most true cost considerations, the impact depends very much on the skill and intent of the people along the value chain. Wood, for one, can be sourced from a well-trained sustainable logging operation or from a "scorched-earth" logger pushing their crew to go faster and faster with no concern for environmental damage or risk of injury.

The cost of building materials also includes the energy used in mining, processing, and transportation. All of these have global climate change emissions as well. Information may be found on CO_2e costs, but much information is more available in energy units. Investing in better materials may cost more up front, but will save money over the lifetime. By one estimate, the energy used by a well designed and built conventional home wouldn't match the construction energy for eighteen years. The energy required to make a product is called its embodied energy. Lower energy-use materials like straw bales can cut building energy and impact.[115] Using more wood sequesters carbon. Using recycled materials can offer dramatic savings, compare aluminum roofing in the following table.

EMBODIED ENERGY OF BUILDING MATERIALS

	Unit	Embodied BTU[116,117]	Other costs/ benefits
Wood	cubic foot	9,000	carbon offset
Softwood	board foot	5,399	
Softwood plywood	square foot	3,790	glues outgas
Glue-lam	board foot	14,673	
Glass	square foot	11,895	
Concrete	cubic yard	2.58 million	mining

Aluminum roofing	pound	82,115	mining, processing
Aluminum roofing	recycled pound	6,362	
Strip asphalt shingles	square foot	24,792	
Paint	gallon	413,600	disposal
Brick	square foot	133,000	
Cooper sheet	pound	70,000	aquatic damage
Steel roofing	square foot	55,000	mining processing
Zinc	pound	22,000	aquatic damage
Composite shingles	pound	24,000	biocides
Polystyrene insulation	pound	9,180	oil depletion
Cellulose insulation	pound	1,508	carbon offset
Adobe straw-stabilized	pound	201	carbon offset
Straw bale	pound	103	carbon offset

If we look at all the materials used in a wall system or building, we can estimate the total embodied energy cost. Here is one analysis of different typical construction types.

EMBODIED ENERGY FOR A FINISHED BUILDING

	BTU/square foot
Single family residential	702,000
Educational	1,400,000
Office	1,600,000

GLOBAL WARMING POTENTIAL PER WALL TYPE[118]

	Pounds CO_2e Square foot
Brick wall	12.6
Straw bale wall	-10.3 sequestration

Lower Price Materials at Higher True Cost

Historically, the developer's goal has usually been to seek the lowest first cost, ignoring life cycle problems and future costs. Most houses are designed and built by developers who leave after the homes are sold. In one neighborhood where I lived, the developer was known as a least-cost champion. He saved a couple of dollars with each water fitting to the main line. These were not durable, and within thirty years, almost every one was replaced—at a cost of more than $1,000 each, some as high as $4,000. He saved a few hundred dollars and cost homeowners and taxpayers $100,000.

The high costs of using lower-cost materials have been clear in many cases. Between 2004 and 2007, an estimated 100,000 homes in more than twenty states were built with toxic drywall imported from China. Emissions from the drywall corroded plumbing and electrical systems. Homeowners also blamed it for illness, headaches, and respiratory ailments. Many homeowners have paid $40,000 or more to have all of the drywall replaced, as well as damaged wiring, A/C, and other hardware. Others simply walked away from their homes. The estimated total cost for replacing the Chinese drywall in the United States was more than $25 billion.[119] In part, this material was imported to meet the demand for sheetrock to repair buildings damaged by Hurricane Katrina. Some builders stepped forward and replaced the defective drywall, but thousands of homeowners were forced to wait until 2020 for a settlement. Ultimately, many victims got nothing, and others will recover pennies on the dollar for the damage to their homes and possibly to their health. The emotional strain of a decade lost will not be compensated.

In the 1960s, builders tried using aluminum wiring because it was cheaper and more available than copper wire. A national survey conducted by the Franklin Research Institute for the Consumer Product Safety Commission found that homes wired with aluminum before 1972 were fifty-five times more likely to have one or more wire connections at outlets reach "fire hazard conditions" than homes wired with copper.[120] Replacing the wire can cost more than $10,000.

The quest for lower costs has also led to the use of different types of plastic pipe instead of copper. The low costs of these materials have earned them the moniker of "the pipe of the future" and led to their widespread use. Unfortunately, when water with high levels of chlorine flows through polypropylene pipe, the protective antioxidants are stripped off the inside surface. Once that protection is gone, the surface layer becomes degraded and brittle. Cracks form and pipes fail. The newest plastic pipe, PEX, is more stable but has an estimated lifetime of only 30-40 years—maybe half the life of copper. On the upside, PEX is considerably cheaper and more resistant to freeze damage. But millions of homes may need to be repiped by the year 2050.

Construction Worker External Costs

There are external costs for construction labor as well. These include energy for food, miles of commuting to the site for many days, weeks, or months, and travel for medical care. The US relies on undocumented workers for much of its construction labor. In Texas, more than a quarter of construction workers are undocumented. They operate dangerous equipment, often with no training, and work in extreme weather conditions, from heat to freezing snow or rain. Safety rules and regulations to prevent falls and injuries are often ignored. The undocumented can't afford to complain. As a result, many construction workers are killed each year. In 2019, the recorded construction-related deaths in Texas reached 123, with more than 11,000 injuries and illnesses. Costs are often paid by the government, which is to say, the taxpayers. In California, 330,000 construction workers rely on government safety nets at a cost of more than $300 billion a year. These are significant external costs.

TRANSPORTATION COSTS

Transportation energy use and CCG in buildings can be calculated for an annual report.

Materials	truck ton/mile times	4,009 BTU
Diesel fuel for tractors	gallons times	140,000 BTU
Gasoline	gallons times	125,000 BTU
Construction workers	miles travelled times	3,600 BTU
Maintenance/commute	miles travelled times	3,600 BTU

Operational Energy Use

The embodied energy is just the first energy cost. Operational costs are high as well. Energy for heating, cooling, cooking, hot water, lighting, and other uses can be found on your monthly bill for electricity, gas, solar, and/or propane. This can be done for home, apartment, condo, office, or workshop. Compare this with the EIA report for the average American home that uses 11,000 kWh a year. A super-insulated passive solar design may use less than 2,000 kWh. Maintenance energy use is relatively minor, but can have health and environment impacts.

End of life Energy Use

At the end of the life of a building's life, more energy costs are added. This involves heavy equipment, transporting wastes, and the energy used in the landfill operation. The embodied energy of lost materials for a light frame wood building may be 3,000 BTU square foot. For a masonry/concrete building it may be five times as much.

In 2009, the Construction Materials Recycling Association estimated that about 350 million tons of construction and demolition material is generated in the US every year, considerably more than the total amount of municipal solid waste. When buildings must be removed to make way for new development, many types of buildings can be deconstructed instead, with much of the material saved, reused, or recycled rather than buried. When true costs are considered, it will be preferable to unbuild almost every kind of building instead of having them demolished and sent to landfills. Taking a house or building apart piece by piece creates jobs and saves reusable materials such as metals, windows, doors, and wood. Old wood is often much higher quality than that available today, but an old true 2"×4" may need to be processed to match today's lumber that is 1.5"×3.5".

When I helped deconstruct the dilapidated ranch buildings on my parents' place in Colorado, the discoveries included beautiful clear 18-inch-wide pine planks from the late 1800s. My parents recycled almost all of the wood, pipes, insulation, and other materials into their new home. My father organized all the wood by size and length and was able to minimize waste. My mother helped straighten the larger nails in the evenings.

There are a number of programs that can help. In 2014 Vancouver, British Columbia, enacted a deconstruction bylaw that required all pre-1910 and heritage-registered buildings to be deconstructed, as the Canadian law says, " ... systematically dismantled, typically in the opposite order to which it was constructed." This was later extended to houses built before 1950, recycling 75 percent of materials by weight and 90 percent for homes built before 1950 and deemed character houses. The ReBuild Hub in Vancouver provides assistance in this area, and the organization used salvaged material to build their office.[121] The Hub has the resources to guide building owners through the assessment process and tax benefits. A study in metro Vancouver suggested the potential volume of salvageable wood a year with this new law would be worth approximately $340 million.[122] Many other cities as well as Habitat for Humanity help to recycle and repurpose building materials.

When a building's life ends in a fire or flood, the external costs are very high. A burning building creates both toxic air and water pollution. The ash that remains often includes heavy metals including antimony, arsenic, cadmium, copper, selenium, lead, and zinc. Building materials found in older houses, including stucco, sheetrock and joint compound, cement pipe, exterior home siding and shingles, often contain asbestos that remains on site to be blown in the wind.

A burning building also creates polycyclic aromatic hydrocarbons (PAHs), chlorinated polycyclic aromatic hydrocarbons, and other harmful compounds. If heavy rains or winds come after the fire, these nasty materials can spread far and wide to contaminate fields, streams, and lakes. Benzene and other volatile organic compounds were found in the water distribution networks of areas hit by the Tubbs and Camp wildfires in 2017 and 2018.[123]

Getting rid of this wildfire debris is very costly. In California's 2017 fires, the cleanup cost per parcel at the Valley Fire was $77,000 when done by the state, and a staggering $280,000 for the North Bay fires done under contracts from the Army Corps of Engineers.[124] In 2017, two million tons of fire debris were removed from 4,500 parcels—more than 400 tons each.

Floods can create equally hazardous and difficult-to-manage debris. Flood waters pick up sewage, manure, gas, oil, cleaners, pesticides, chemicals, fertilizer, drugs, paints, and other pollutants as they enter, damage, and destroy buildings. Flooding also increases medical costs. Wounds, gastrointestinal diseases, and skin or soft tissue infections (primarily staph and strep) occur after floods. Anxiety and stress also take a costly toll. Flood-damaged and contaminated personal belongings, fixtures, appliances, furniture, and other material are piled up on the streets to be carted off and buried.

Hurricane Katrina destroyed or damaged more than 850,000 homes, more than 300,000 vehicles, and 2,400 ships and vessels. Fifty levees and floodwalls failed. The cleanup took more than a year and cost more than 2 billion taxpayer dollars. More than 23,000 homes were demolished and cleared in the New Orleans area.[125] Hurricanes Harvey and Irma also left millions of tons of debris. Houston officials expected the cleanup costs would reach $200 million to dispose of 8 million cubic yards of storm debris. Hurricane Harvey also damaged about 1 million vehicles; many could not be repaired. In 2022 Hurricane Ian devastated parts of Florida with damage estimates as high as $50 billion.

In 2021, flash floods in Germany and Belgium left hundreds of thousands of tons of debris. The tsunami of trash was so large that the main priority was getting rid of the stuff before it posed a worse risk to human health. It couldn't be recycled and reused as called for by EU guidelines. In addition, between 40,000 and 50,000 vehicles were damaged.

Other Energy Costs

Other external costs of building energy use include the emission of climate change gases, ecosystem damage from dams built for hydroelectric generation, and disruption of ecosystems from constructing power lines, pipelines, generation plants, substations, and other fa-cilities. As noted in Chapter 1, wildfires have become the critical ex-ternal cost of energy in some areas. Because many of the external costs of energy production are known and power plant generation data is available, the true costs can be estimated.

The tragedy of this energy misuse is that much of it could be elim-inated at little or no cost with better design, more skilled craftsmen, and more judicious choice of building materials. Buildings using low-impact design strategies (natural heating using window place-ment and thermal mass, cooling with microclimate resources, and ventilation by wind flow) have demonstrated energy use reductions of 90 percent with noticeably improved comfort.[126] When true costs are counted, these design principles will be used in almost every new building and building renovation. Today, most "net-zero en-ergy use" buildings follow the same old designs but add large arrays of PV panels. These are more costly and less sustainable.

Health Costs in Buildings

Energy use is often considered the most important external cost of buildings, but this is rarely the case. The value of human health im-pacts and loss in productivity can be five to ten times higher than the cost of energy. A worker earning $70,000 a year in a 150 square foot office with poor air quality and mold may experience a 7 per-cent cut in productivity. The external cost from the loss in produc-tivity would be $4,900. Treatment for building-induced asthma could easily add another $3,000 a year for a true cost of $7,900—ten times the cost of energy.

In many cases, the health costs and productivity loss will be even higher. Outgassing from building materials, furniture, and other components also add external costs. Chemicals used for cleaning, painting, and pest control can add to health risks. We have known this for decades, we know how to avoid these problems, but it hasn't been done. The benefits have been demonstrated in field studies.[127] In controlled environment tests, the cleanest air with lower CO_2 and volatile organic compounds led to a performance increase of 101 percent. It also improved decision-making.

One office complex I worked in for several years had mold problems from poor roof design, least-cost construction, inadequate repairs, and minimal drainage maintenance. One of the seven workers in this complex was more afflicted and had serious breathing problems with repeated lost work days, medical care, and misery. This may have degraded her performance by 20 percent for the year. Three of the others, including myself, suffered to some extent. I would say it cut my productivity by 5-10 percent. Saving a few thousand dollars on construction and maintenance cost tens of thousands of dollars in healthcare and productivity loss.

True cost accounting for buildings can provide health benefits for everyone—whether you own or rent, whether you work at home, in a factory, or commute to an office. The commercial and residential building stock in America ranges from health-giving to deadly. Too often, people are hot in summer, cold in winter, and face real danger if and when the power goes off. More people die of heat stroke than from storms or tornadoes. People also die in the cold—both from freezing and, more commonly, from carbon monoxide generated by improvised heaters.

One and a half million people were without power in Louisiana, many for weeks, after Hurricane Ida roared ashore in 2021. Puerto Rico's energy system was shattered by hurricane Maria in 2017, when people went for days, weeks, and months without electricity. This can be catastrophic for people who rely on energy to provide water or medical support.

Power outages also stop sump pumps in basements, leading to flooding and water damage. Power failure from ice storms can lead to frozen pipes and water damage. Heat waves can create power demands in excess of capacity, leading to rolling blackouts, brownouts, and equipment failures. Every climate disaster reveals the vulnerability of current building designs.

Many people—especially the poor, but from all segments of society—suffer at work or at home from poor air quality. Sealed buildings, inadequate ventilation, flawed building materials that off-gas, and poor design leads to leaks and mold. In 1998, World Health Organization research suggested that 30 percent of all new and remodeled buildings in the world were afflicted with sick building syndrome (SBS).[128] The symptoms are mainly allergy-like, including nasal, eye, and mucous membrane irritation, dry skin, respiratory distress, fatigue, lethargy, headaches, and fever. Chronic or cumulative exposure to the microbiota (molds and other organisms) that thrive in damp indoor air can make SBS potentially life-threatening and leads to irreversible dampness and mold hypersensitivity syndrome (DMHS). This results from dysregulation of the immune system, leading to hypersensitivities and reduced immunity that increases susceptibility to infections. This has happened in my family, and it is a terrible burden with a very high external cost!

The CDC estimates that from 2008-2013 the annual economic cost of asthma was $81.9 billion, much from buildings. US adults miss about 14 million workdays per year as a result of asthma, often from moldy buildings at home or at work. Students miss an estimated 14 million days of school from asthma, often caused by mold, mites, or other allergens in their home or school. The annual medical cost per person with asthma in the US is over $3,000. Of that, more than half is for prescriptions, with about equal amounts for office visits and hospitalizations, and some for outpatient visits and emergency room care. Asthma triggered by bad buildings can become a lifelong challenge, costing as much as $100,000 over a lifetime.

The annual cost of poor indoor air quality in the US has been estimated at as high as $168 billion[129]—several times the cost of energy and more than the gross national product of most countries. In a survey of 215 office buildings with 34,000 responses, only a quarter of the office workers expressed satisfaction with the air quality, and a tenth for thermal comfort.[130] Improving indoor air quality could bring substantial economic benefits.

The COVID-19 pandemic has highlighted the need for better ventilation. Some buildings can be cured, others need to be replaced. Older buildings that have been modernized and sealed can often be returned to more natural space conditioning, ventilation, and day-lighting. Better design and material use can return large dividends in human comfort and health while improving productivity. The value of productivity gains alone is often 100 times greater than the energy savings.

Climate Change, Extreme Storms, and Extreme Temperatures

Global climate change will lead to more frequent and intense storms. The changes in hydrology from impervious surfaces around buildings will combine with storm surge and sea level rise will make it even worse. More and more buildings will suffer flood damage and increased mold. The longer a building is flooded, the worse the problem becomes. When Hurricane Harvey flooded 150,000 homes in Texas, cleanup took months in many cases.

Mold exposure can be hazardous during cleanup and often will persist for the life of the building. Repairing mold damage is difficult and expensive. Treatment may require stripping out all wall board and insulation, then cleaning, drying down the building, blasting with dry ice, spraying with anti-mold coating, and finally sealing with impermeable paint. Some buildings have materials that are hard to treat or areas that are impossible to reach.

The cost of a professional cleaning can be $10,000-30,000 for a house. After a major hurricane and flood event, cleaners may be booked for months or years, and the longer buildings sit untreated, the more expensive remediation becomes. If all the homes flooded in Harvey had been professionally cleaned, it would have cost three billion dollars. Mold remediation is rarely done well when homeowners try to do it themselves. Even professional treatment may prove inadequate, and homeowners or workers may suffer from asthma and allergy for decades.

Increasing carbon dioxide levels in the atmosphere have been found to cause subtle changes in many aspects of the environment. One of the many surprises was the large impact this increase has had in stimulating fungal spore production.[131] Mold grown in current carbon dioxide levels produced 8.5 times as much allergenic protein as those grown in pre-industrial carbon dioxide levels. The extra carbon dioxide induces changes in the bacteria's respiration and growth processes. This provides a very important warning, and suggests that there will be more unexpected impacts of global climate change that cause severe and costly problems.

Record-high temperatures also harm residents, degrade building materials, and increase energy use intensity. Overheating in buildings without air conditioners in Europe has led to thousands of deaths. The European heat wave of 2003 was blamed for more than 70,000 deaths. Subsequent heat waves in 2006, 2010, 2015, 2018, 2019, 2020, 2021, and 2022 have killed thousands more.[132,133] Some experts think global deaths from heat exposure now may reach one half million people a year.[134] Several cities, including Phoenix Arizona, have established Heat Response & Mitigation Offices to address this risk.[135]

Demand for air conditioning will increase the environmental cost of manufacturing and operation. New energy demand for cooling will further stress energy grids—with the potential for more frequent and longer-lasting power outages. Extreme high temperatures also increase the risk of wildfire and degrade building materials. When buildings burn, a wide range of toxic materials are released. Climate change gases are also emitted.

Along with extreme highs, we can expect more extreme lows as a result of meridional flow from the more erratic jet stream. Extreme cold events threaten people. They also damage buildings as frozen pipes rupture and lead to water damage to building materials with the potential for mold. Widespread low temperatures can also overtax fragile energy grids, leading to cold-related deaths and suffering.

Disruption of the Hydrologic Cycle

Streets, parking lots, sidewalks, and roofs dramatically increase the percentage of the soil surface that can no longer absorb water. In industrial areas, these impervious surfaces can cover 75 percent of the area and malls can cover 95 percent. Residential areas may still have 65 percent impermeable surfaces. Instead of filtering into the ground, a high proportion of rain water runs off quickly into streets and streams, causing much more frequent and higher peak flows than exist in the natural watershed.[136] Scientists found that not only are floods more likely to be severe in the future, but that they've become more intense. Mean flood heights have increased by nearly four feet over the past 1,200 years.[137] Flooding from the more intense floods of a new, more intense "100-year rainfall event" today can be catastrophic and will reach far beyond the historic 100-year flood plain maps calculated and drawn before urbanization and climate change.

Climate change has increased flooding in many areas. The area of West Houston called Memorial City was outside of Houston's calculated 500-year floodplain, but has flooded three times in the past decade. With climate change, we may see flooding at levels never seen before. For example, heavy flooding occurred on June 26, 2022 after more than 12 inches of rain fell in 8 hours from Hawk Point to St. Peters, Missouri.[138]

High stream flows destabilize streambeds, mobilizing sediment, which in turn can destabilize lower stream reaches and cause additional problems. Bridges and roads can be damaged or washed out, power may be knocked out, sewers can break, and transportation can be interrupted by damage to railroads and highways. Sediment and debris can block drains and pumps, causing even more extensive flood damage. Sediment can also fill ponds and reservoirs, reducing storage capacity. Water quality is degraded as stormwater collects pollutants from streets, homes, farms, and industry, even before it gets mixed with overflow from treatment plants in high rainfall events. People are sickened by exposure to this toxic stormwater. Recreational use of streams and beaches may be curtailed for months, at high economic cost to the tourism industry. Fishing may be banned as well until water quality improves.

The solution is to minimize or eliminate runoff by incorporating stormwater management in the design of every home, facility, city, region, and transportation infrastructure. Porous pavement, infiltration wells, and surge storage ponds all can help. Homes, schools, and commercial buildings should include cisterns to capture rainwater. These tanks can also provide needed drinking water in emergencies after storms or earthquakes damage water supply systems.

Stormwater management techniques are proven and inexpensive. Some areas now mandate a net-zero increase in runoff. Developers can actually save money by doing the right thing. The innovative 220-unit solar subdivision known as Village Homes in Davis, California, minimized impervious surfaces and used above ground water collection and retention basins instead of storm sewers.[139] My own research enabled the development to use streets as narrow as 20 feet. These features all saved money. The city engineers fought these features, but the development has performed very well. Village Homes did not flood after a major storm just after the features were installed—while much of the city did. After this success, other developers found it easier to adopt stormwater management design. One developer in San Diego told me that he saved $1 million by moving from a storm drain and pipe solution to aboveground drains, swales, and infiltration basins in one of his developments.

In Texas, rainwater has been captured in large cisterns at schools where water resources are limited. The Roy Lee Walker school in Texas, built in 2000, has 68,000 gallons of storage. The Wimberley Blue Hole primary school in Texas approached design and construction of the primary campus using a "One Water" concept, which looks at drinking water, wastewater, stormwater, and greywater as a single resource. The campus collects and stores up to 200,000 gallons of rainwater. In addition 600 to 1,300 gallons of air conditioning condensate is collected per day. This water is used for toilet flushing and landscape irrigation through an advanced reuse system. The system reduces the campus water consumption footprint by 90 percent. The University of California in Davis installed rainwater harvesting in their new viticulture building complex, where the 36,000 square foot roof will collect and store 250,000 gallons of water for use in the teaching and research winery. General Electric

Power and Water donated the reverse osmosis system and key instrumentation.

True cost accounting will reduce stormwater runoff and pollution. Charging impact fees based on runoff water quantity and quality can limit flooding while funding stormwater retrofits and more resilient natural stream and river channels. Stormwater impact fees can also support educational programs to help landowners understand how to minimize stormwater runoff and reduce their fees. (More on stormwater and external cost recovery at www.truccostalways.com).

Environmental Impact from Building Runoff

Runoff from building roofs is often laced with copper, zinc, lead, arsenic, and cadmium. The concentrations in water are not high enough to pose much of a risk for people, but can be very damaging to aquatic ecosystems. Very low concentrations can be biomagnified hundreds of times to levels that sicken or kill organisms higher on the food chain.[140] For example, if the concentration of a pollutant is 2 ppm in lake water, then it might be 5 ppm in phytoplankton, 200 ppm in fish, and 1600 ppm in a fish-eating loon or merganser. Biomagnification is often suggested to be about ten to twenty times for each step up the food chain, but has been found as high as 2,000 for one step.[141]

Copper is considered a pollutant of concern by the Environmental Protection Agency because of its widespread occurrence and impact on the environment. Copper roofing, gutters, and downspouts are good examples of seemingly sustainable products with a very long service life, but they have a hidden cost in the shedding of copper ions. Roofing may release 1.3 pounds per thousand square feet.[142] Concentrations of copper in runoff from buildings has been measured at 3 parts per million.[143] Levels as low as 1.5-10 parts per billion, 1,000 times less, can be detrimental or lethal to aquatic organisms. Trout are particularly sensitive. Biofilters on downspouts using peat[144] or crushed crab shells can capture most of the copper ions, but these are rarely used. They could be very helpful if installed when new roofing or copper flashing and gutters are installed.

Zinc ions from galvanized roofing are another common pollutant from buildings. Zinc is used in many other applications to reduce corrosion of pipes, railings, fixtures, and other elements. It is effective but does have external costs. Roof runoff may approach 1 pound of zinc per 1,000 square feet of galvanized roofing per year. Zinc runoff is very toxic in aquatic ecosystems. *Daphnia magna*, a common bioassay test organism, started dying within 24 hours with 0.5 ppm zinc in soft water, reaching 100 percent mortality in 72 hours.[145] Coatings such as urethanes, epoxies, and acrylics can be used to seal roofs and limit release of harmful material. They should be carefully selected as they may have problems of their own.

Other roofing materials may also leach arsenic, copper and other harmful compounds. These are applied to reduce growth of moss, mold and other unsightly stains or damaging growths. Wood shakes treated with copper arsenate released arsenic (692 to 4,690 ppb) and copper (601 to 3,190 ppb). Tests showed one type of asphalt shingles also leached copper 30 ppb, zinc 6.4 ppb, arsenic 0.21 ppb, cadmium 0.005 ppb, and lead 0.05 ppb.[146]

Other types of infrastructure, like parking lots, roads, and utilities, also add to pollution loads and ecosystem disruption. Pavement is usually identified as the most significant source of metals above natural background levels.[147] In addition to metals from car brake pads (copper, zinc, nickel, lead, and more), runoff may include antifreeze, lead from the weights used to balance tires (in older cars), oils, and other compounds. Tires also contain zinc, which is released onto highway surfaces as the tire wears down.

Copper, zinc, and other pollutants enter streams and lakes where they kill or disrupt a wide range of organisms. Every step up the food chain can increase concentrations by ten times or more, easily reaching a thousand times the base level in high-order predators. Even low levels can be harmful. Pacific salmon are particularly susceptible to copper-induced olfactory injuries that inhibit behaviors critical to their survival. In general, insects are more tolerant than fish and shellfish to copper, zinc and other pollutants.

Water Use in Buildings

Buildings use water inside and out. Single-family homes may use more water for landscaping, while multiunit dwellings, commercial and industrial buildings, use more water inside. Public supply withdrawals account for about 14 percent of the total freshwater used in the US. Almost 300 million people on public water supplies use 39 billion gallons per day. External costs are involved in water extraction, transport, supply, treatment, and disposal.

Buildings also cause very significant environmental damage related to water. The building site is stripped and converted to hardscapes of roofs, concrete sidewalks, asphalt roads and parking lots with no water infiltration. This leads to fast runoff with quick and much higher flood peaks.

Water diversion leads to the deterioration of ecosystem services. Streams and rivers may run dry. The price we pay for water ignores most external costs, but when true costs are determined, water use in buildings can often be reduced with relatively simple changes in equipment and habits. Rainwater capture can reduce imported water use. Some cities have approved rainwater for non-potable uses like flushing toilets—some even encourage the widespread use of rainwater. Pliny Fisk and the Center for Maximum Potential Building Systems started Austin and Texas on the path to capturing and using more rainwater back in 1996. Since then, Texas has supported rainwater harvesting, and the Texas Commission on Environmental Quality doesn't regulate the use of rainwater for indoor uses in private homes if it is their sole source of water supply (i.e., homes that are not connected to a public water system). Filtration, disinfection, and testing are required for homes on public water systems as well as for schools and commercial buildings.

Nutrient Pollution

Building design and land use planning affects energy and fossil fuel use, which in turn determines nitrogen pollution. Development design choices can minimize transportation impacts and encourage bicycling, e-bikes, walking, and public transit. Nitrogen deposition can be reduced by making better choices for building design, land use planning, and choices of electric rather than gas-powered garden tools. Nitrous oxides from burning fossil fuels that generate electricity and provide space heating and hot water in buildings contribute to the problem. So do cars, gas-powered tools, trucks, and power plants. The nitrogen falls back to earth as dry particulates and in rain. Deposition rates in auto-dominated areas like Southern California are considerably higher than the world average application of nitrogen fertilizer to farmland.[148] Decreasing the emissions from cars, trucks, and other vehicles is critical.

Phosphorus pollution can cause similar problems. In aquatic systems, it can compound the effects of nitrogen pollution and create super blooms of algae. Phosphorus is a common constituent of home and agricultural fertilizers, manure, and organic wastes. About half of the total input of phosphorus coming in to the city of Gothenburg, Sweden, was in food and beverages.[149] Detergents made up 6 percent of the total phosphorus input and pet food 4 percent, while goods for agriculture made up only 2 percent. Wastewater and solid waste represent the main flows and sinks for phosphorus. Sewage sludge and incineration residues each contained 40 percent of the total output of phosphorus. Ten tons of pet feces-related phosphorus was estimated to have been dropped in the environment. Only 4 percent of the phosphorus input was recycled to agriculture as manure and 0.3 percent as certified sludge. These phosphorus flows are very out of balance, and levels in soil and water will continue to increase.

Bird Kills from Windows and Reflective Walls

We often see information about birds killed by windmills, but we should remember that buildings are more deadly. Glass can be invisible to birds in many situations, and conservative estimates suggest that 100 million birds die as a result of hitting glass in the US every year. Nearly half of all window strikes are thought to occur at residential houses (44%), and over half at low-rise buildings (56%).[150] Fewer than 1 percent occur at high-rise buildings.

The bird kill risk of buildings can be reduced by simple steps. Move plants away from windows because interior landscaping by windows can increase the risk. A leafy plant inside a building can be seen as a refuge, and a panicked bird will smack into a window as it attempts to hide. Designs with glass on both sides of a room or building can create the illusion of an unobstructed corridor. Tilting glass out at the top to give a ground reflection helps (and keeps glass cleaner), as do shades and shutters (best when installed to the exterior) and markers on the glass. Bird strike prevention tape is readily available, and has worked very well on my own patio doors.

Additional sources of bird kill are affected by design and planning decisions. Longer commutes or many long-haul truck loads lead to vehicle collision bird kills. These are estimated to be as high as 100 million per year. Birds also die in collisions with towers, guy wires, and transmission lines. Mine and industrial operations can also kill birds. Solar concentrating mirrors at "power tower" electricity generating plants create extremely high temperatures in the area around the collector that vaporize birds. They appear as little puffs of steam.

Light Pollution

Buildings and development also create more complex ecological problems. Many organisms rely on light polarization to determine locations for migration, nesting, breeding, or feeding. Pavement, dark cars, glass, and other shiny building materials can polarize light and confuse this behavior. Birds that cannot take flight unless they are on water have been known to land on asphalt at night because it can have a polarized light signal similar to water. Insects that lay eggs near ponds may lay eggs near parking lots for the same reason.

Light has such a strong biological impact that artificial lights at night can adversely affect foraging, sleep, migration, immune response, cortisol, testosterone, and melatonin levels. It can affect glucose metabolism in birds, animals, and other organisms. The impact of light differs by species. Lights rich in short-wavelength blue and green light (metal halide, mercury vapor, fluorescent, and LED) tend to be more disruptive than those emitting long-wavelength pure yellow-orange light (high- or low-pressure sodium).

Lights contribute to the death of millions of birds a year. Many migratory bird species fly at night and they are confused by or attracted to artificial lights. Light pollution levels during the past two decades have gone up over roughly 16 percent of the land area in the Western Hemisphere.[151] Ten million birds a year may be killed by communication towers, both from attraction to the lights and hitting unseen guy-wires. More than 174 million birds may be killed by transmission lines, with additional deaths from power plant stacks and towers. After it was discovered that the 9/11 memorial lights were disrupting navigation of more than a million birds a year, a monitoring program was set up. Volunteers watch the lights, and when the number of birds crossing through them reaches 1,000, the lights are turned off for 20 minutes to give the birds time in the darkness to resume their natural migrations.

Lights may also encourage migration in the wrong direction for other species. They can lead baby turtles to walk away from beaches, stop fish migration, and cause many other problems for a remarkably wide range of organisms. Artificial lights are often bright enough to induce a physiological response in plants, affecting their phenology, growth form, and resource allocation. The physiology, behavior, and ecology of herbivores and pollinators are also impacted. Understanding the ecological consequences of artificial light at night is critical to determine the full impact of buildings and development on ecosystems.

Buildings, lights and other hazards have contributed to the alarming decline of once common birds. The Audubon Society's Christmas Bird Count and Breeding Bird surveys have revealed the crises facing many of our most common and beloved birds. Since 1967, the average population of the common birds in steepest decline has fallen by 68 percent; some individual species have dropped 80 percent.

True cost accounting will include the value of birds, other species, and ecosystem stability in design. This will shift building and development design and lighting choices to reduce the risk. The choice of lighting type, fixture design, light placement, shielding, and time of operation all matter. The International Dark Sky program has helped many communities reduce lighting impacts and preserve the dark night sky so residents can see stars and planets. This helps migration and reduces other risks. Towns, cities, municipalities, and other legally organized communities that have shown exceptional dedication to the preservation of the dark night sky are recognized for their efforts.

Noise Pollution

The 2000 United States Census found that 30 percent of Americans complained of noise, and 11 percent found it to be bothersome. Urban areas are particularly noisy, which affects human health along with that of many other species. Gas-powered lawn tools can hit 100 dB while electric models may top out at 75 dB. Several cities have banned gas-powered garden equipment to cut noise.

Humans can barely perceive a one-decibel difference, but one study found that for every 1 dB increase in noise, owls in the area were 8 percent less successful at catching prey.[152] Noise can also impact feeding and navigation of many species. Buildings don't emit too much sound, but transportation to and from buildings can.

Disease Vectors

Pets contribute to the external costs of buildings and communities. Although a favored companion with significant health benefits for owners, cats are among the world's most destructive predators. One study suggested free-ranging domestic cats kill a median estimate of two billion birds and 14 billion mammals annually. Un-owned cats, as opposed to owned pets, cause the majority of this mortality.[153]

Dog and cat feces add nutrients, but also bacteria, parasites, and viruses to the environment. Although seemingly insignificant, the half a million tons of cat feces produced a year introduce parasites such as the single-celled *Toxoplasma gondii* organism in people and if outside, into stormwater. This parasite has wreaked havoc on California's endangered southern sea otter population. Post mortem studies found almost 10 percent of more than 100 sea otters examined died primarily due to *T. gondii,* and in another 20 percent, the parasite was a "contributing" cause of death.

This single-celled parasite enters the brain and changes the behavior of prey animals like rats, which develop a strange attraction to cat urine. From 10 to 20 percent of Americans also harbor the parasite, which can be absorbed through contact with litter boxes, drinking contaminated water or eating undercooked meat. Scientists now believe that *Toxoplasma* may actively change the connections between neurons—shifting dopamine levels, altering personalities and even triggering diseases.[154]

The external cost of a dead bird is not easy to compute, but a simple bird from a pet store may cost $25. For buildings and other structures the cost at $25 each for 300 million birds would still reach $7.5 billion. Cats are in another league altogether, with certainly more than a billion birds killed or a nominal cost of $25 billion. But the cost of the native bird species lost is really much higher, perhaps $100 or even $1,000 or more for replacement cost. The cost of efforts to save the California condor, a species that has been done in by poison, lead bullets in carrion, antifreeze, hunters, and habitat loss, has passed $35 million. There are now 337 flying free and 175 in captivity at a cost of about $68,000 each.[155]

Transportation Costs of Design Choices

When commercial buildings are put outside of towns and developed areas where construction costs are lower and regulations are weaker, the buildings increase commute time and distance, add stress on drivers and families, and increase energy use and CCG emissions for transportation. All of these have external costs.

Very few architects and designers have the opportunity to participate in location decisions. The designer of the NMB Bank in Amsterdam did, and he used worker home locations to determine the best placement for their new building. Even a minor difference can have an enormous impact. Imagine an office with fifty workers and a 260-day work year. The developer places the building outside the city limits to minimize cost and regulations. If the average worker has to drive an extra seven miles each way, this design choice leads to 182,000 miles driven by the workers in the office every year. Because there are detailed studies of auto external costs, we can estimate these external costs.[156] If the workers all drive Dodge Ram pickups, which have an external cost of 40¢ per mile, it will total $72,800. If they all drive Lexus RS350s at 20¢ per mile, it would still be $36,400—enough to make a difference. Over the thirty-year life of the building, it could make more than a million-dollar difference and increase CO_2e by 250 tons.

Toxic and Hazardous Compounds

True cost accounting for buildings also includes releases in sewage and the use of pesticides in and around the building. The drugs found in sewage include hormones and hormone mimics, antibiotics, antidepressants, and other legal drugs as well as cocaine and other illegal drugs. These have caused a range of problems in aquatic ecosystems, including changes in fish development.[157] Fish may be affected by estrogen from birth control pills at 0.1 nanogram/liter, well below the concentrations found in some streams and lakes. Researchers found that 50 to 75 percent of male smallmouth bass collected in the South Branch Potomac River exhibited signs of feminization, as did 100 percent of those collected at sites in the Shenandoah.[158] Other types of hormones and hormone mimics are also released from livestock farms, CAFOs, and natural sources.

Pesticide use around and in buildings is excessive and can be reduced by better building design and use of materials, wiser landscaping, better maintenance, and true cost accounting. More than four billion pesticide applications are made every year to American homes, gardens, and yards. According to surveys by the US Environmental Protection Agency, more than three quarters of American households use pesticides, with 66 percent treating major living areas in the home one or more times per year. Sales exceed $2 billion a year. Health costs from pesticide use in the US (including agricultural use) have been estimated as high as $1.5 billion. The share of that cost for pesticides used in homes, buildings, and gardens would be $225+ million based on use. Frequent use of any household pesticide has been found to increase the odds of getting Parkinson's disease by 47 percent.

Insecticides are the most commonly used pesticides in and around homes and buildings and carry some of the largest health risks for humans. Residential pesticide exposure significantly increased risks for all types of leukemia, and specifically for exposure during pregnancy, indoor exposure, prenatal exposure to insecticides and whatever the age at diagnosis.[159] The impact falls hardest on the poor, Black, and LatinX people. The six million children living in poverty in America's inner cities are at high risk of exposure to pesticides used extensively in urban schools, homes, and daycare centers to combat roaches, rats, and other vermin.[160] The rate of use of fumigants is markedly different depending on location. Neighborhoods that have been under-invested and have older, poorly maintained buildings may have less trash pickup as well. These factors can lead to more common pest problems and increase the use of fumigants. This was reflected with blood levels of fumigants six times higher in Black and four times higher in Mexican Americans.

True cost accounting will reduce the use of pesticides in the home. In Europe, the costs are higher, and more hazardous chemicals are banned outright. Currently, eighty-five pesticides approved for agricultural applications in the US are banned in the EU, or in the process of complete phase-out.[161] Pesticides banned in the EU account for more than a quarter of all agricultural pesticide use in the USA. There wasn't a breakout for residential or interior use. The EPA notes that insecticides and disinfectants are most commonly used indoors and suggest that 80 percent of most people's exposure to pesticides occurs indoors. Measurable levels of up to a dozen pesticides have been found in the air inside some homes.

True Cost, Better Health, Better Buildings

The goal of True Cost Accounting for buildings is to improve comfort and health of the built environment while maximizing use of renewable resources and minimizing life cycle costs. The life cycle savings are particularly important for retirees and for institutions that cannot count on increasing income in the future to offset large increases in the costs of energy, water, and other resources. True cost accounting should consider costs over the 30, 50, or 100+ year service life of a building from creation to deconstruction (not demolition).

Comfort and health, security and safety in power outages, energy and water use, waste, recyclability, and cost are key issues. Environmental and social considerations are critical in building siting, design, and operation, but are usually ignored.

True cost accounting will lead to dramatic changes in design and behavior. Increasing consideration of true costs will improve building design, operation, and maintenance, and will help us all stay healthier. With creative design and true cost accounting, we know that some of these external costs can be not only reduced but eliminated. Building sustainable buildings has never been easier. Improved sensors and control systems can markedly increase performance. These new sensors will also enable readily visible meters to monitor and manage energy and water use. More complete information is now available about materials, appliances, and equipment, enabling wiser decisions.

Integrated design solutions for both large and small buildings and homes have demonstrated that energy demand can often be cut 50-90 percent for a cost increase in construction of only zero to 15 percent.[162] Life cycle savings are outstanding, and the design choices we make today will affect climate change gas emissions for tens or hundreds of years. The cost of avoiding energy demand is often much less than the cost of energy generation. Solar-oriented design using thermal mass and careful window placement can reduce energy demand for heating and cooling by 50-90 percent. In a study of a more sustainable home design (validated by actually building the home) in Davis, California, the summer peak energy demand dropped from 3.6 kWh to 2 kWh, and annual energy use for heating and cooling dropped 67 percent. The improvements didn't cost anything—in fact, they reduced construction costs.

A synagogue in San Luis Obispo, California, using solar-oriented design, daylighting, and microclimate-based cooling and ventilation cut energy use for space conditioning more than 80 percent.[163] The 538,000 square foot NMB Bank in Amsterdam cost little more than conventional construction, but used only one-tenth as much energy.[164] NMB's former headquarters consumed 422,801 BTUs per square foot (4.8 GJs per square meter) per year, but the new one consumed less than one tenth as much: 35,246 BTUs per square foot (0.4 GJs per square meter). It was beloved by workers, and absenteeism dropped 15 percent. Unfortunately, it was redone to accommodate more workers, and some of its features were diminished. In another case, a sustainably designed factory complex doubled worker productivity! A very modest retrofit of a typical office building in San Diego reduced seasonal energy use 70 percent and improved comfort.

Better development design can minimize runoff and cut runoff pollution to near zero. Floodproofing and moving out of flood zones can minimize flood damage. Good design, material choices, and maintenance can minimize the risk of mold and sick building syndrome—increasing health and productivity. Sustainable design increases security and safety during power outages. A well-designed building will keep its occupants warm in winter and cool in summer even when the power goes off. A sustainably designed building will also be able to provide emergency water supplies from its rainwater harvesting system during a water main break or power outage. An integral solar hot water heater will provide hot water for showers and cleaning even when the electrical grid is disrupted.[165]

Developers, designers, and cities should develop accounting systems for the inflow and outflow of nitrogen, phosphorus and other elements and compounds. To be sustainable in the long term requires balance, yet as the study in Sweden revealed, even coping with a nontoxic element like phosphorus can be difficult. Developing nutrient balance will require local recycling, growing more food locally, using co-composted waste in town, and returning nutrients to farms to balance the phosphorus nutrient cycle. Local food production also reduces the energy cost and nitrogen pollution associated with fossil-fueled long-distance food transport.

Building materials can be environmentally friendly. Wood buildings sequester carbon for decades or hundreds of years. A wood home may use 25 tons of wood and sequester 12 tons of carbon. The renewed interest in large wood buildings is encouraging. The T3 wood high rise in Minnesota used 2.2 million board feet of wood and sequesters 700 tons of CO_2e. The managed forest that provided the wood also sequesters carbon. The shake table at the University of California, San Diego is conducting a test of a ten story mass wood building.[166] This is likely to confirm the benefit of mass wood buildings in seismic risk areas.

A straw bale house[167] can do even better, perhaps 40 tons for the straw and another four for wood used in framing and sheathing. These buildings are now recognized in the international building cods and are permitted in most areas. Super-insulated straw bale buildings also minimize energy use for heating and cooling. This could save another 900 tons of CO_2e over the building lifetime. The most important considerations in the calculation of the true costs of buildings are comfort, health, and productivity. These have not traditionally been considered when the goal has been to find the lowest cost per square foot or artistically stunning design. Regulations have favored bad design by focusing on just energy, and the sealed buildings that have answered this call save energy at the cost of bad air quality, resulting in human suffering. It is particularly important to get building designs right for high-occupancy buildings like schools, where carbon dioxide levels and moisture loads are elevated. Poor ventilation and air quality can increase the risk for the flu, COVID-19, and other lung diseases. Comfort and health demands good lighting with daylighting strategies and responsive electric lights.

What You Can Do!

Every local action must be made with consideration of the long-term global implications. Take a close look at your home (house, condo, apartment) and workplace energy use and environmental impact. What can you do, now? Do you need more insulation in the attic? Can you replace inefficient windows and doors? Can you install solar tubes for natural lighting? Would exterior shutters help reduce overheating in summer and cold in winter? Can you use a clothesline to dry laundry? Can you afford photovoltaic solar panels and backup batteries? Do you need HEPA air filtration?

If you can manage it, have your home (and workplace) analyzed by energy pros. Some utilities and extension services will help you figure this out for free. In other areas, you may have to pay for a careful review and recommendations for change. Over future years, this will pay for itself many times over. Encourage the company, school, or organization where you work to have an energy and comfort analysis done as well Ask them to consider upgrading your workplace with daylighting, improved ventilation and filtration, and as needed, better insulation and light-colored roofing. It is a win-win situation.

Examine your current water use. How much can be saved? Can more water-efficient appliances and fixtures be installed? Can the landscape be redone? Rethink how you irrigate your garden. Install a rainwater harvesting system and cistern if you can. Switch to less harmful cleaners and detergents. Use less toxic pest controls.

Support the groups that are working to calculate and reduce the true costs of constructing and operating buildings. Consider joining organizations like the Healthy Building Network that promote more healthy buildings. Help improve building materials and design with the Ecological Building Network, the Rocky Mountain Institute, the Healthy Building Program at Harvard, and the Green Building Councils.

True cost accounting will bring us all to better health and improved comfort at home and where we work.

CHAPTER 7

TRUE COST ACCOUNTING FOR HEALTH

Health is probably the most important element in true cost accounting, as ill health carries very large costs and emotional burdens for the individual, family, and society. Flawed accounting leads to erroneous policies and misunderstandings of what contributes to healthcare costs as well as what is essential for good health.[168] Most policies, programs, and economists neglect external social costs. Caring for a sick child or parent is not counted because nobody is being paid for the effort, yet the value of unpaid labor in the American economy has been estimated at $1.5 trillion.[169] True cost accounting looks at a wide range of social and environmental issues that are often ignored. The goal is always to improve

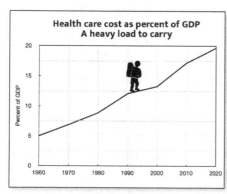

Markers of Cultural Failure

The Register's Annual Great Bicycle Ride Across Iowa, is more than just a 500 mile bike ride, it is an epic eight-day rolling festival of bicycles, music, food, camaraderie, and community. More than 10,000 bike riders take part— compare the health impact with that of a football stadium.

both the quality of life and the environment. The challenges are to reduce the disparity between men and women, people of color and whites.

Women do much more of this unpaid work than men. In the United States, women perform an average of four hours of unpaid work per day compared to men's two and a half hours. Time off work to care for ill children, partners, and parents costs women and families billions of dollars in lost wages. Workers are not productive if they are sick, exhausted, or worried about caring for a family member or friend.

Quality of life depends in part on access to healthcare and community support. Much needs to be done, because at least half of the world's population cannot obtain essential health services when they need them, according to the World Bank and World Health Organization. Even when people have access to healthcare, it may be compromised by lack of skilled medical personnel, hospitals, medicines, and diagnostic equipment. Each year, households are pushed into poverty because they must pay for healthcare, however limited it may be, out of their own pockets.

How much can we reduce true social costs if the elderly are treated better? If the mentally and physically disadvantaged are well treated? How can we ensure that people have time to participate in community-building activities and to volunteer? Do laws and law enforcement protect individuals from pollution, expropriation, crime, and government intervention? Is the population stable? Can children hope for a life as good as, or better than, their parents?

The True Costs of Obesity

The food system highlights many of the issues that can be addressed with true cost accounting. Subsidies favor less nutritious foods and are implicated in the obesity pandemic. Development policies that favor driving, not walking or cycling, harm health. Poor air quality and dangerous neighborhoods limit walking. Food deserts lead to harmful diets. Many other policies contribute to our obesity crises.[170] In 2017, the CDC reported 41.9 percent of Americans were obese, and in some subpopulations, the rate is much higher. Obesity is also a great concern for children. The CDC found 12.7 percent of two- to five-year-olds were obese. This rose to 20.7 percent for six- to eleven-year-olds, and 22.2 percent for twelve- to nineteen-year-olds.

More than 20 percent of the people in the Organization for Economic Cooperation and Development (OECD) countries are also obese.[171] On average, almost 10 percent of health expenditures in OECD countries are for obesity related disease. Just one in ten Italians is obese, significantly less than the OECD average. In Italy, the percentage of income spent on food is higher than in the US (14.4% vs. 8.6%) but the quality, taste, satisfaction, and health benefits are higher as well. In Japan only 4 percent of the people are obese, but the rates are growing. Japan has fewer overweight children than any other developed nation, in part due to healthy school lunches.[172]

Obesity increases the risk of hospitalization and death for many diseases, including COVID. It also increases the cost of care. America now spends $4 trillion[173] each year on health, while health continues to decline. Failure to count the true costs leads to health problems across all cultures. However, historical disenfranchisement through genocide and institutional racism has resulted in American Indians and Alaska Natives (AIAN) and African Americans experiencing the worst health outcomes. The COVID mortality rate for Native Americans and African Americans is higher than that for white people.[174] Tribal losses include many valued elders. The Navajo nation alone has lost almost 1,900 people.[175] At $10 million each, that represents a value of lost life of $19 billion.

Many obese people with low incomes will develop diabetes, which requires lifelong care and treatment. Many will die young. American Indians and Alaska Natives have the highest diabetes rates of all racial and ethnic groups. More than 16 percent of the native population has been diagnosed with diabetes, compared to 13 percent for non-Hispanic Black people and 8 percent in non-Hispanic whites. The Centers for Disease Control and Prevention (CDC) predict that soon, one in two AIAN children may develop type 2 diabetes in their lifetime. True cost accounting will help improve food quality and access, rediscovery of traditional foods, and promote exercise. All will help reduce the prevalence of diabetes.

Infant mortality is a good indicator of a nation's quality of life and sustainability. The OECD reports Estonia leads the way with only 1.4 deaths per 1,000 deliveries. The CDC notes the infant mortality rate in California is three times worse, but is still the best performing state. The average US rate is five times worse, and Mississippi is worst with more than 8 deaths per 1,000 births. In some African American and AIAN communities in the US, the rate is even worse.

The external cost of these deaths is high in terms of both healthcare, emotional suffering, and lost productivity. Total maternal morbidity costs for all US births in 2019 were estimated at $32.3 billion from conception through the child's fifth birthday.[176] For many preterm babies, the lifetime costs for compromised immune systems can be very high. The cost of care for preterm births was pegged at $13.6 billion. The overturn of *Roe v. Wade* will further increase the maternal death toll. Improving equity, returning jobs from off-shore, access to better food and healthcare, and hope will all help reduce maternal morbidity.

Suicide rates also reflect community health and sustainability. They are often related to lack of opportunity and hope from incomplete accounting. Suicides also have many external costs. The CDC suggests suicide and suicide attempts cost $70 billion a year. Things are not getting better. The overall suicide rate increased 30 percent between 2000 and 2020.[177] This is a sign of failure. Suicide was most common in AIAN men at 33.8 per 100,000, followed by White people at 28.2, Black people at 11.4, and Hispanics at 11.2. The suicide rate is lower for women, but follows a similar trend by race. The state with the highest rate of suicides in 2020 was Wyoming at 30.5, followed by Alaska at 27.5, Montana at 26.1, New Mexico 24.2, and Idaho 23.2. Seven states were 10 or below. Spain, Greece, Britain, Mexico and Italy were all below 10 and have the lowest rates in the OECD countries.

Lack of access to healthcare increases the cost to individuals, families and society. In 2020, the US Census found 28 million did not have health insurance at any point during the year. Before the pandemic, over half of the people working in the US had some kind of company health plan, but layoffs immediately left many uninsured. Workers without health insurance add to social costs in many ways. For example, many food and hospitality service workers earn very low wages and have no health insurance, so if they get sick, they still go to work. This exposes millions of people to colds and other illnesses each year, resulting in billions of dollars in lost work and treatment. These families often have no childcare alternatives, so a sick child may be sent to school lest the parents stay home and lose needed income.

One analysis suggests Emergency Department (ED) visits accounted for approximately $328.1 billion of overall national health expenditures in 2010. The costs of ED visits have grown in the US, with the rate of increase from 1996 to 2013 exceeding that for hospital inpatient care.[178] Lack of health insurance leads people to use emergency EDs for healthcare rather than seeing a physician. Costs are passed on to hospitals, taxpayers, and patients who do have health insurance. Even when people have private plans, healthcare can be expensive when policies have very high deductibles. Treatment for a broken leg may cost $2,500, an ambulance run can cost $1,000-$2,000, and an air ambulance $30,000 or more. Yet an examination of American savings found as many as four in ten Americans would have difficulty paying a $400 emergency expense.[179]

Inequity and Poverty

The failure of our current health system is revealed by the demand for Remote Area Medical (RAM) services. This remarkable nonprofit organization once provided medical relief missions only to developing nations, but today it focuses more than half of its attention on helping people in the US. It cannot meet the demand. RAM's corps of volunteers, including dental, vision, medical, and veterinary professionals, have treated more than 863,700 individuals, delivering more than $174 million worth of free care in the US and abroad. People in the US drive for many hours and camp in their cars at RAM clinics in the hopes of getting much-needed free medical, dental, and vision care.

The poor who need free care signal the growing inequality of the American economy driven by failure to count the true cost of our activities and markets. Inequity is approaching the extremes that prevailed prior to the Great Depression. Inequity places stress on society; to achieve a more stable society, we need to reduce the disparity in income and healthcare. The top 1 percent of Americans saw their wages grow by 179.3 percent from 1979-2020.[180] Wages for the top 0.1 percent grew more than twice as fast, up a spectacular 389.1 percent. In contrast, those in the bottom 90 percent had annual wages grow by 28.2 percent from 1979 to 2020. The differences are striking, and regional variation is high. In 2016, a study in Los Angeles found the average net worth of Japanese Americans was $592,000, followed by Asian Indians at $460,000, Chinese at $408,000, and whites at $355,000.[181] For African Americans, it fell to $72,000, and $42,000 for Latinos. Discrimination and institutional barriers of many kinds have made it worse in other areas where African American families' net worth is just a tenth of whites.

The Economic Policy Institute (EPI) estimates that CEO compensation has grown 1,322 percent since 1978, while typical worker compensation has risen just 18 percent. In 2020, CEOs of the top 350 firms in the US made $24.2 million on average—351 times more than a typical worker. In Germany, the CEO makes 136 times the average worker; in Japan, the CEO disparity is much lower, at just sixteen times higher.

Much of the inequity and disparity in social health costs has resulted from the "race to the bottom." The much-lauded search for "the lowest price at any cost" is considered only proper by some economists—who face little risk of seeing their own jobs outsourced. But this race is a major factor in transferring high external costs to people and the environment. This race to the bottom derails community stability and makes life much more difficult for people and communities as factories close and jobs evaporate. The result is despair, often leading to drug and alcohol abuse, suicide, and criminal activity.

Offshoring manufacturing has contributed to the increase in poverty in communities that once made products here. From the beginning of the twentieth century through the 1950s, shoe manufacturing companies were among the largest industrial employers in the US. Full-time employment in the sector fell by 94 percent from 233,400 in 1966 to 11,000 in 2021.[182] The US once made most of our own shoes, but today, as a result of offshoring, only about 1 percent of the shoes sold in the US are manufactured here.[183] The collapse of the industry impoverished many families and communities. In 2019, Vietnam accounted for more than a quarter of all shoe imports. Where will they go next? In 2020, the minimum monthly wages for garment workers were $26 in Ethiopia, $55 in Sri Lanka, $151 in Vietnam, $217 in China, $661 in Portugal, $1,160 in the US, $1,764 in Belgium, and $3,000 in Sweden.[184] When the true costs of transportation, materials, and energy are included, there will be dramatic shifts toward local production, and new factors will be considered in evaluating investing options.

Health and True Cost

Classical economics lacks empathy and has little interest in healthy people, families, communities, or social structures. In contrast, true cost accounting does value health and well-being. As John Ruskin put it back in 1860, "That country is the richest which nourishes the greatest number of noble and happy human beings."

A much more complex and integrated view of health must be developed that considers the external costs and benefits of health, happiness, and equity. We need to consider a broader range of issues—the value of a healthy child, a congenial village council, and a volunteer group that helps older adult shut-ins. The quality of life has value. Economists and policy-makers currently ignore a wide range of external uncounted costs and declines in the value of social capital. Today, health is counted only when it involves a financial transaction. If a person is healthy and needs no medical care—they are not counted. On the other hand, if they buy drugs or medical supplies, pay to see a doctor, go to the hospital, or die and need a funeral, the value of the transaction is noted. The sicker a person is, the better it is for the economy.

The external costs of health are compounded by lack of access to healthcare, the cost of healthcare, and limited capacity to deliver healthcare. These are serious and severe health problems in many areas of the US and the world. Food quality and nutrition are neglected. Low-wage workers find fast food and highly processed packaged foods convenient, cheap, and tasty. They are cheap because much of their production is subsidized by federal government policy that favors unhealthy foods rather than healthy alternatives. These fattening foods are more readily available in economically depressed communities and in food deserts. High-fructose corn syrup and corn oil are cheap because corn farmers are heavily subsidized. Feedlot cattle are fattened by policies that subsidize corn and other animal feed, and have eliminated most local slaughterhouses. They are also subsidized by uncompensated environmental impacts from overcrowding and pollution in feedlots and CAFOs. As you saw in Chapter 5, true cost accounting reveals the high price we really pay for cheap food.

Volunteer and unpaid labor is often ignored. A study in Norway revealed that more than 40 percent of work was unpaid even in an advanced egalitarian economy. In Norway, women still do 20 percent more unpaid work than men. The corresponding number is 60 percent in the US. In Japan, women do four times as much unpaid work as men.

In developing countries, the proportion of unpaid labor may reach 90 percent or more. If only paid labor is counted, almost every economic analysis will be wrong. Unpaid labor can involve care for family and friends, participation in the community, volunteering in schools, serving in rural fire departments, food banks, environmental restoration, and much more. Caregiving and raising children is not valued or counted unless it is paid for.

Tobacco, Alcohol, and Drugs

Tobacco, drugs (legal and illegal), and alcohol have some of the highest social costs, including cancer, allergies, heart attack, stroke, asthma, chronic pulmonary disease, and other injuries. The enormous costs involved have led to some true cost accounting. The personal costs are enormous and, as the example of Bulmers hard cider showed, may offset any profit the company appears to be making.

Cigarettes have exceptionally high external costs from health, suffering, and environmental impacts. Cigarettes are known to be both addictive and deadly, but are still sold in almost every community in the US and around the world. The worldwide annual death toll from cigarette smoking is estimated at between 4 million and 10 million people. In the US, the Centers for Disease Control (CDC) reports cigarettes kill 480,000 people a year. This is the equivalent of a passenger jet crashing every 5 hours. Imagine the news coverage that would make! Imagine if the corporate owners were not white . . .

The CDC estimates the external costs of smoking are $300+ billion a year. True costs are actually much higher because these estimates don't fully account for unpaid care, future costs, lost productivity, and suffering. Even if everyone stopped smoking today, health costs from smoking would continue for many decades. Cost estimates are incomplete when they fail to count the more subtle impacts of smoking and secondary exposure, including significant illness, lost work, and death. Suffering also entails the significant costs family members and friends of victims pay in time for care and worry as they watch their loved ones decline and die. New Zealand has taken these factors into account in a bold effort to end all smoking in the country.

Estimating the external costs of smoking has led to changes in government policy, but more needs to be done. This is personal for me. Like many others, my mother was influenced when she was young by the $119 million R. J. Reynolds spent in 1959 (valued in today's dollars) on ads with women promoting the benefits of smoking. She suffered from the ill effects of smoking Pall Mall cigarettes all her adult life. Like many women,[185] she found it impossible to break this addiction. Smoking leads to premature birth, and both my brother and I were very premature. Her smoking, and R. J. Reynolds, certainly contributed to my compromised immune system, lifelong asthma, and allergy challenges. I would charge them if I could.

In 2006, the R. J. Reynolds Tobacco Company produced about 28 percent of the cigarettes sold in the United States with a reported net income of $1.3 billion. A conventional economic analysis would show that this was a profitable company well worth investing in—and many pension systems, trust funds, and investors bought stock and profited from death. However, when the social costs of cigarettes are analyzed, the picture changes radically. These costs can be estimated by counting R. J. Reynold's share of the market against the estimated annual social costs of cigarette use in the United States. Their share works out to be $78 billion. If the tax revenue for cigarettes is counted as an offset, R. J. Reynold's share of taxes can be subtracted, about $6 billion. This leaves their share of the social cost at about $72 billion.

It gets even worse when we add the external environmental costs of tobacco farming and tobacco waste. In the US, about 200,000 acres are grown at an environmental cost of $500 per acre for a net cost of about $400 million a year. The cigarette butts left around the country also cause costly damage as toxic chemicals leach into the environment. Cigarette butts litter green spaces, sidewalks, roadsides, beaches, and waterways. They constitute an estimated 30 percent of the total litter (by count) on US shorelines, waterways, and on land. The chemicals that leach from butts contaminate water, poison fish, and harm other organisms and plants. In a clever twist, crows are being recruited to pick up discarded cigarette butts from the streets and squares of a Swedish city as part of a cost-cutting drive. The wild birds carry out the task as they receive a little food for every butt that they deposit in a bespoke machine designed by a startup in Södertälje, near Stockholm. The risk to the crows is uncertain, but should be considered.

Who should pay the external cost? You might say costs should be shared equally with customers and retailers, who also bear some responsibility for their choices. If the costs were split three ways, the net annual social cost for R. J. R. may drop to $25 billion. While profits that ignore true cost are considered adequate by Friedmanite economists, they clearly are not.

With a net annual loss of almost $23 billion (profit of $1.3 billion minus social cost of $25 billion), R. J. R. is no longer a profitable company. Investors will shun the tobacco companies when the enormous true costs are counted. The companies producing vaping products—often the same cigarette companies—would be equally unprofitable.

True Costs of Heavy Metals and Other Chemicals

There are high external health costs related to heavy metal exposure (cadmium, lead, mercury, arsenic) and other chemicals that permanently damage the brains of infants and children. This leads to declines in IQ and lower lifetime earnings. The true cost estimates range from $165-$233 billion a year in the US.[186] Associated tax revenue losses are estimated to cost another $25 to $35 billion per cohort of lead-poisoned children.

Studies have shown that changes in brain function contribute to crime and violence as well, so we can add a percentage of the 80 billion dollars spent on incarceration every year.[187] Reducing blood lead levels to less than 10 ppb among all US children between birth and age 6 years would reduce crime and increase on-time high school graduation rates later in life.[188] The net societal benefits arising from these improvements in high school graduation rates and reductions in crime would amount to $50,000 per child annually at a discount rate of 3 percent, resulting in overall savings of approximately $1.2 trillion.

The True Cost of Antimicrobial Resistance

Antibiotic misuse in medical practice (and agriculture) in the US has a high social capital cost. Antibiotics are a nonrenewable resource. Inappropriate use of antibiotics leads to a decline in effectiveness and rise in "super bugs" that are drug-resistant, meaning the antibiotics that once worked well will no longer help. In 2017, antibiotic-resistant pathogens (including methicillin-resistant *Staphylococcus aureus* [MRSA]) caused an estimated 4.9 million deaths around the world.[189] In the US, there were at least 26 deaths per 100,000 people. In Sweden, where at least some of the true costs are considered, the death rate dropped 90 percent.[190] Even nonfatal infections contribute to healthcare costs of almost $5 billion nationwide. Treatment for a typical case costs $60,000, and these often result in painful and frightening effects of lost tissue, muscle, and even limbs.

Farm workers are most at risk for infections with antibiotic-resistant bacteria because very large amounts of antibiotics are used. An estimated 9,000 tons of medically important antibiotics were fed to farm animals in the US in 2016.[191] Antibiotic use has been thoughtless in agricultural settings, where they are given to help healthy animals grow faster and to prevent them from getting sick in crowded and unsanitary facilities. A US study found that 20.9 percent of swine workers were colonized by MRSA.[192] People who had had MRSA were four times more likely to die than an infection-free group.[193]

Failure to fund research hides the impact. In 2015, reporting was required in only eleven US states. Federal research and reporting is hampered by statutes that protect "confidential information" and shield producers.

True Cost Accounting for People

The health, safety, and satisfaction of workers, families, communities, and customers should be a priority. These factors are related to Social Capital (comparable to Natural Capital), which considers the value of people, including their health, attitude, skills, abilities, and ethics. Are they healthy, happy, well-educated, engaged, and productive?

To understand these issues and account for these factors, we need a more integrated and comprehensive approach to evaluating our economies. We may want to consider following Bhutan's example of using Gross National Happiness (GNH) rather than Gross Domestic Product (GDP).[194] When Bhutan's prime minister first introduced GNH at a United Nations forum in 1998, it turned heads. But GNH is measurable and supports efforts to live in more sustainable ways. GNH considers the large-scale impacts of good governance, sustainable socioeconomic development, cultural preservation, and environmental conservation. It also includes psychological well-being, health, education, time use, cultural diversity, resilience, good governance, community vitality, ecological diversity, environmental resilience, and living standards. The US is failing by these measures. It ranked tenth in GNH in 2012, but fell to nineteenth in 2019 before rising to 16th in 2022.[195] Our goal should be to continue moving up toward first place. Finland ranked number 1, at 7.82 to the US 6.97.

We may also want to consider Gross Domestic Health (GDH). The Robert Wood Johnson Foundation has supported a "culture of health" initiative that places well-being at the center of every aspect of life, with the goal of enabling everyone in our diverse society to lead healthier lives, now and for generations to come. A culture of health also stresses health equity. Undoing the current system of medical services and payments will be challenging, but can reduce costs and result in healthier, happier, and safer people and workers. This would also improve the competitive position of US companies relative to companies in countries where universal health coverage exists and an individual's healthcare is not their employer's responsibility. At present, for too many, prospects for good health are limited by where we live, how much money we make, or the discrimination we face.

We can learn from successes elsewhere. Switzerland's health system has been described as the best in the world. The Swiss health care system ranks first overall out of 31 countries ranked in the World Index of Healthcare Innovation, with a score of 59.56, just ahead of second-ranked Germany and third-ranked Netherlands.[196] Switzerland scored well across the board, but especially in Quality (#1, 73.35), thanks to a high degree of patient-centered care and high-quality infrastructure; and Fiscal Sustainability (#5, 71.06), owing to its low debt-to-GDP ratio of 14.5 percent and its lower dependence on public financing. The US system is notable only for being the most expensive. Life expectancy is five years longer in Switzerland than in the US. Unlike many universal medical care systems in Europe, the Swiss system relies heavily but not exclusively on the private sector. Universal coverage in Switzerland is mandatory, but not socialized. Swiss private insurers are required to offer basic coverage to everyone, regardless of age or medical history, and all residents are obliged to purchase basic health insurance. The government shares the cost for the poorest people. Swiss health-related expenditures per person are 30 percent below those of the US. A remarkable 90 percent of users in Switzerland report moderate or complete satisfaction with the system. By comparison, 32 percent of those enrolled in the US Medicare Advantage insurance program had at least one problem with accessing care due to cost, as did 23 percent of those with traditional Medicare.

Before we achieve universal healthcare, larger companies that value healthy workers can provide on-site healthcare. Employees wouldn't need to take time off to go to a clinic or doctor. A large company can often negotiate with health providers for reduced costs, including on site services. Having convenient access to healthcare can improve workers' attitudes and productivity. In Oregon, the healthcare costs of Intel's Connected Care population were 17 percent less per member per month[197] with an annual saving of $21.6 million, compared to a risk-adjusted population of employees covered by the two traditional health plan offerings. This amount would factor into the true cost account calculation.

True cost accounting for health also addresses issues like a family's ability to stay together and meet basic needs. Do children have access to quality education, healthcare, nutritious food, and the internet? Should more doctors prescribe vegetable and fruits? Kids enrolled in an innovative program at Lincoln Medical and Mental Health Center in the Bronx meet with a doctor or nutritionist once a week to measure their blood pressure, insulin levels, and weight.

They leave with a prescription that can be swapped for "Health Bucks" accepted at 140 farmers' markets.

The true costs of health are also related to urban design, land use planning, and buildings. Where and how buildings are placed matters. If we count external costs and benefits, communities will be designed for people instead of for cars. We need to choose to make it safer and easier to walk, bike, and participate in calorie-burning activities that promote health. Companies can help by considering where facilities will be located and supporting more environmentally friendly and healthy commuting. More flexible work patterns created in response to the COVID pandemic make it even more important for walking and cycling to be easier and safer. Communities can help by developing and supporting community health initiatives. The Healthy Cities Movement[198] started in Toronto, Canada, in 1984 and has now been replicated in other cities around the world.

Community involvement is important for the health of a community and society, but is rarely measured.[199] A breakdown in community function can lead to the very high costs of despair, ill health, crime, and distrust. In many areas, minorities exist within a long and persistent culture of fear based on historical mistreatment by police, racism and risk of crime. This can limit exercise and quality of life.

Neighborhood designs that favor the automobile instead of people limit community interaction. Community participation and a feeling of security is best in communities with well-established neighborhoods where neighbors know and interact with each other. Many of the problems of community social isolation are designed into current development patterns by a perfect storm of perverse incentives, rules, and regulations involving city staff, planners, developers, engineers, architects, automakers, homebuilders, and financiers that ignore social and environmental costs. No one person is at fault, but everyone plays their part.

We can do so much better, at little to no added cost. The primary focus of the Village Homes solar subdivision I worked on in Davis, California, was community building—not solar energy or energy conservation.[200] The developers, Michael and Judy Corbett, included co-ownership of some common areas, shared laundry space for some units, shared garden space, public fruit trees and vineyards, and inviting paths for bicycling and walking. These were very successful in building a sense of community, and, unlike most developers, the Corbetts chose to live in the Village. Comparing their project to the surrounding standard suburbia was revelatory. The residents of Village Homes knew on average forty-two people in their neighborhood, compared to seventeen in other areas.[201] The average resident identified four of their best friends as people living in the Village, compared to 0.4 for people in conventional developments. This community spirit and people-first orientation contributed to a lower crime rate—only 10 percent of the city average at one point. That is the kind of social function we need to replicate.

Social Benefits

Reducing true costs and improving true value will take education, engagement, and hope. These are the most powerful tools to realize social benefits and fight depression, suicide, anxiety, drugs, gangs, and crime. Companies and organizations can help improve educational access for underserved and low-income workers and students by investing more in grants and scholarships—much more effective than the customary loans that add an overwhelming financial burden for students.

True social benefits can also be explored with true cost accounting. My *alma mater*, the University of California, San Diego, opened in 1963 and has grown steadily. It has a strong sustainability program, and in 2020, the university decreased its total greenhouse gas emissions by over 25 percent—over 70,000 MTCO$_2$e—from 2019. In their most recent review, the UCSD campus Scope 1 and 2 emissions were 191,000 tons of CO$_2$e. At Sweden's carbon impact fee of $137.50 per ton, the CCG cost would be $26 million—much less than 1 percent of the annual budget.

UCSD has also done very important work with COVID-19 on campus and in the community. The school has one of the best records in the nation for COVID management. Automated sewage monitoring allows thousands of tests to be done that can detect COVID, even from asymptomatic staff and students, and link infections to specific buildings and sites on campus. In the lab, robots concentrate the virus using magnetic nanoparticles and extract RNA for polymerase chain reaction testing. This automated high-throughput system can process twenty-four samples every 40 minutes. Data are added to a digital dashboard that maps new positive cases, building by building. Students and staff are notified of any infections in their area.

When investments are made in education, the value of Social Capital increases. This includes the value of knowledge, skills, satisfaction, and higher salaries for graduates; knowledge returns to the US and many other developed and developing countries around the world; and volunteer work by students, staff, and faculty. Much of the work done at UCSD involves pioneering research on biotechnology, engineering and health. Students and faculty have created, developed, and improved thousands of companies and organizations around the world. More than 30,000 jobs are directly attributable to UCSD-spawned companies. Almost 3,000 inventions are managed by the campus Office of Innovation and Commercialization.

What is the true value of universities like UCSD? The university claims spending of $5.8 billion and a net impact of $18.8 billion for the state of California. I believe this is a considerable undercount, as we could add $32.4 billion a year generated in companies using university technology. This would boost the return to almost $50 billion, a tenfold multiplier.

Politicians have not been intensely lobbied by university administrators, faculty, and students. As a result funding for the university system has declined, while California has spent more and more on state prisons. The prison budget is more than four times the support for the University of California. California wisely offered free tuition to in-state students until the 1970s. After State Proposition 13 limited tax collection in 1978, state support began to slip and has declined from 50 percent to less than 10 percent of the budget. As a result the university system has had to charge more and more for in state student tuition, and recruited more foreign and out-of-state students who pay three times as much in fees ($44,400). The UC system of nine campuses admitted 66,000 California residents. UCSD admitted 9,000. Fewer slots and higher costs have made it harder, yet again, for low-income students from California to get in and get ahead.

Employment that offers sufficient compensation to meet family needs is essential for community stability. If rents and home prices are too high in relation to wages, then more people end up living on the street. More than 8,000 people are homeless in San Diego, where they are at risk of being injured, sick, and spreaders of illness. San Diego had a nasty bout with hepatitis A in the homeless community in 2017 and is fighting shigellosis in 2022. The true costs of inequity and ill-health are not widely recognized and understood.

Many of the causes of ill health are elusive, and we need more research to improve our understanding of the hazards of chemical and pollution exposure. We know that we all carry a body load of hundreds of chemicals—and now, microplastics—but we don't know much about their impact. This should be a call to action, not indifference or despair. The expectation (and hope) is that most of the more than 300 chemicals in our blood are harmless or not very harmful. But it is likely that five or ten of these chemicals are very harmful and should be controlled with high true cost impact fees. The question at the moment is, which ones? The federal and state governments have done some work on this problem through biomonitoring efforts, but much more detail is needed. The CDC's Division of Laboratory Sciences (DLS) operates the National Biomonitoring Program (NBP), which looks at blood levels of more than 200 chemicals. It may make sense to do a full blood chemical screen for any person diagnosed with cancer. Companies that make or use those chemicals that routinely show up in these blood samples should be held accountable.

A Healthier, Happier Future

True social cost accounting will help us realize the importance of access to quality healthcare and education. Much of the funding can come from external cost savings from healthier and more productive communities, companies, families, and people. Money now flowing to harmful subsidies and fees recovered from external costs can make access to healthcare and quality education more equitable and effective. Gross Domestic Product should be relegated to the trash bin of history. With true cost accounting, our goal should be a top ranking in Gross National Happiness and Gross Domestic Health. Joyful and productive people in communities that care are the greatest wealth of all.

CHAPTER 8

ENERGY

W e all use energy every day and are responsible for the gases emitted when we generate electricity and use fossil fuels. These adversely impact the atmosphere, human health, and ecosystem in many ways with many costs that have traditionally gone uncounted. Carbon dioxide from fossil fuel burning may account for more than 80 percent of the increase in global warming. The US Energy Information Administration reports major energy use categories in the US are electricity 38 percent, transportation 28 percent, industrial 23 percent, residential 7 percent, and commercial 5 percent. In 2020, the CCG emissions for energy use in the US were more than 5.7 billion US tons. A CO_2e fee of $100 per ton would bring in $570 billion.

Life Cycle Energy Use

It is important to consider the energy use and impacts across the full life cycle of products and buildings. In a fifty-year comparison

True cost of electricity from coal adds 27 cents kwh.

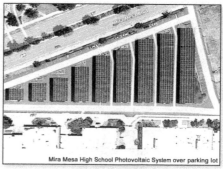

True cost of electricity from photovoltaic panels adds just 1.5 cents kwh

of a standard home to an energy-efficient home,[202] the total life-cycle energy was 15.1 billion BTU (16,000 Gj) for the standard home
and 6.1 billion BTU (6400 Gj) for the more energy-efficient home.
The use phase accounted for 91 percent and 74 percent of the total
life-cycle energy for the standard home and the more energy-efficient house, respectively. The energy for demolition or deconstruction is relatively insignificant compared to other life-cycle phases.
The CCG emissions for the standard home were 1010 tons ($101,000)
and 370 tons ($37,000) for the more energy-efficient home.

The True Cost of Electricity

The primary concern in studies has often been the CCGs of electricity. A wide range in estimated costs for energy generation suggests
how much we have yet to learn. There will be very large differences
between facilities' designs, age of factories and equipment, management skill, maintenance, and varied regulations and controls in
different regions and countries.

ENERGY GENERATION

	External costs cents per kwh[203]	
	Mean	Max
concentrated solar	18.3	39
coal	14.5	158
nuclear	5.6	54
biomass	5.9	104
oil	7.6	27
fuel cell	4	7
geothermal	0.09	0.1
hydro	1.8	21.2
natural gas	3.5	13.6
PV	5.3	75
wind	3	42.1
fuel cell	4.1	7
waste	14.6	31.7
solar thermal	1.5	8.0
passive solar	0	5

Other True Costs of Electricity

Billions of tons of CO_2e emissions every year are a significant problem, but energy generation and use also add many other external costs from emissions of nitrogen, mercury, and sulfur compounds as well as the adverse impact of dams and transmission lines. Methane and natural gas leakages from wells, pipelines, and refineries are important as well.

The true costs transferred to the environment, the poor, and future generations have been ignored and have made fossil-fuel-based electricity appear cheap. Fossil fuel energy has been, and still is, subsidized by government programs and taxpayers. The Inflation Reduction Act of 2022 supports green energy, but also provides millions of dollars for fossil fuels. Some fossil fueled plants could get up to $500 million a year.

Here are a few more details on the other external costs of energy: nitrogen, mercury, acidifying compounds, ecosystem disruption, and other energy impacts.

Nitrogen and Eutrophication

CCG impacts are important, but so is nitrogen pollution. Emission sources for bioreactive nitrogen in the US are primarily power plants, industry, and transportation. In Southern California, transportation is the major source. Before the Industrial Revolution, levels of nitrogen dioxide (N_2O) in the atmosphere were around 270 ppm. Human activity and developments in the last 200 years have thrown this system out of balance, and the nitrogen dioxide level in the atmosphere had risen to 335 ppm by 2021. The regional impacts of nitrogen pollution from fossil fuel combustion (power plants, automobiles, trucks, airplanes, ships, home heating systems, water heaters, stoves, and other urban sources) can be dramatic.

Nutrient pollution has serious adverse effects on both aquatic and terrestrial ecosystem function and structure. Most policy-makers remain unaware of the problem and are surprised when it is mentioned. This is perhaps understandable because nitrogen gas (N_2) is a major component of the atmosphere, and we eagerly apply nitrogen fertilizer to our gardens and farms. However, biologically available nitrogen is a limiting factor in most natural ecosystems, and increased inputs can wreak havoc on community structure and function. In many ecosystems, additional nitrogen is toxic.

When nutrients exceed historical levels there can be very rapid growth of algae in water and weeds on land. An algal bloom with the stink of dead fish in a pond is an understandable problem. Eutrophication on land is often harder to see. A field full of invasive weeds that grew fast with more nitrogen and crowded out the native species can be green and will not seem to be a problem to the average visitor. But biodiversity is diminished, and these annual weeds create more explosive conditions for wildfires in some ecosystems.

The long-term impacts of excess nutrients can be especially striking. At the Rothamsted long-term research plots in England, researchers added several levels of nitrogen over many decades. The higher levels reduced the number of plant species from thirty to three, a striking drop in biodiversity.[204] A twelve-year study of nitrogen application in Minnesota grasslands showed a reduction of species diversity and marked changes in community composition.[205] The number of native species was cut in half as native grasses were replaced by weedy invasive species. At Niwot Ridge, high in the mountains of Colorado, deposition rates as low as 1.3 lbs./acre disrupted alpine ecosystems.[206] In the deserts of the southwestern US, nitrogen deposition up to 28 pounds per acre has enabled invasive grasses and other weed species to thrive. When these die and dry out, they make an ideal fuel to carry wildfire, killing the fire-sensitive desert plant species that were once protected by bare ground between shrubs.[207] An estimated 1.3 million Joshua trees were killed when the 2020 Dome fire swept through a northern portion of the Mojave National Preserve.[208]

Damage from nitrogen compounds impacts hundreds of square miles and lasts for decades. The growing efforts to preserve local biodiversity through conservation plans and protected natural areas will be compromised unless we control nitrogen pollution. Invasive species favored by higher N levels need to be suppressed year after year on nature reserves, parks, and areas of special concern. This means costs year after year for manual labor with skilled field workers and, quite likely, repeated application of selective herbicides. The cost can run in the tens of thousands of dollars per acre with no guarantee of success. This work can sometimes be supported by spreading slow-to-decompose "recalcitrant" mulch with high lignin levels, which ties up some of the excess nitrogen as the mulch decomposes. More intensive treatment may need to be repeated, perhaps every ten years. Treating ecosystems that have been damaged is costly and may require replanting and maintenance for many years.

Mercury

Mercury emissions from US power production adversely affect both human health and ecosystems. Progress has been made, although the emissions data are not very clear or consistent. The Environmental Protection Agency (EPA) reports mercury emissions from power plants rose 13 percent from 2020-2021, but the total has dropped from 29 tons in 2010 to about 3 tons in 2021. The social cost may be $47 per gram.[209] Humans' predominant exposure to mercury used to be power plants, but now may be from the fish we eat. In some areas, mercury levels in waterways and lakes are high enough to recommend no swimming.

Mercury emissions from fossil fuel use (primarily coal) affect brain development in infants and can cause temporary as well as lifelong impacts, including lower IQ, abnormal muscle tone, and slowed motor functions. When compared to normal brains, mercury-affected brains weigh less, have fewer cells, and exhibit a less organized structure. Mercury compounds can also cause endocrine and heart problems in adults. The social cost of mercury emissions from power plants is estimated to be $1.3 billion a year.[210]

More critically, mercury from burning fossil fuels is converted to methylmercury (MeHg) and bioconcentrated up the food chain from insects, to fish and birds, to people who catch and eat fish. Every step increases the concentration ten times or more. Large predatory ocean fish may also have higher mercury levels. As much as 40 percent of American's mercury exposure may come from tuna.[211]

Fish exceeded the US EPA criterion for the protection of human health in about one in four streams in the US. High MeHg concentrations in fish are the primary cause of advisories in the US to not eat any or many fish. These advisories are needed. In 2010, the EPA advisories to limit or avoid fish consumption were issued for about 42 percent of the lake area and 36 percent of river length in the US. In the San Joaquin River basin in California, fish mercury levels were up to 0.7 ppm in several of the bass tested. This is 35 times higher than the EU's environmental quality standard of 0.02 ppm. Most of the concern in the US has been about the biomagnification of MeHg in food chains, but one study in China found that 79 percent of vegetable samples and 67 percent of grain samples from farms near a coal-fired power plant exceeded the WHO food safety standards for mercury.[212] Similar studies have not been done in the US. The annual benefit from preventing MeHg exposure to children within the EU was calculated at more than 600,000 IQ points per year, with a total economic benefit of between $9 and 10 billion a year.

Methylmercury also poses a significant threat to wildlife—including fish, amphibians, reptiles, birds, and mammals—because of its high bioavailability, its substantial bioaccumulation in food webs, and its extreme toxicity. Recent findings have shown that MeHg impairs the health and reproduction of fish and birds at much lower dietary or tissue concentrations than previously recognized. The median lethal dose was 0.12 ppm in the American kestrel (*Falco sparverius*), far below the allowable level for humans.[213]

Mercury emission reductions have been achieved by installing new pollution controls, enhancing existing pollution controls, and primarily by switching from coal to natural gas. Mercury reduction processes for power plants are costly, and some companies continue to resist change. By spending $8 billion on treatment costs, the Obama-era EPA estimated mercury health benefits would be $80 billion a year—well worth doing. The Trump-era EPA (perhaps

better termed the Enhanced Pollution Agency) reduced the estimated benefit to $4-6 billion—not worth doing. Ecosystem impact
costs were not included in either estimate. These probably exceed
the health costs.

Acidifying Compounds

Burning fossil fuels and biomass adds acidifying compounds to the
atmosphere. The main pollutants are sulfur oxides, sulfuric acid,
nitrogen oxides, hydrochloric acid, and ammonia. Power plant
emissions have led to forest death in the US, Canada, and Europe.
Forest death has been linked to the damage acid does to the soil bi-
ota and nutrient cycling. This acidification and rising temperatures
affect ecosystem function and change ecosystem structure. Acid
rain harms plants, animals and humans; and degrades materials
used in buildings. The acid rain increase the release of toxic ions
from copper and zinc roofing materials.

Damage from acid rain and mist may impact hundreds of square
miles and last for decades. Treatment became imperative in Sweden
after acid rains—much from English power plant emissions—devastated their forests and waterways. These acidic emissions led to the
decline (and in some cases, death) of lakes and river ecosystems.[214]
In Sweden 13,000 square kilometers were devoid of fish. Dead lakes
were common. Widespread application of lime with a price tag close
to a billion dollars helped neutralize the acidity. The results have
been encouraging.[215] The acidity of the River Atran in Sweden and
its tiny tributary, the Hogvadsan, had dropped to a pH level of 4.5.
This is unsuitable for most aquatic organisms. After applying more
than 10,000 tons of lime in the Atran River system over a decade,
the pH was neutral, at 7.1 in the Atran and 6.0 in the Hogvadsan.
In Germany, thousands of acres are treated with lime applications
by helicopter every year. A few projects with liming have also been
done in severely affected forest areas in the US. Treating acid-dam-
aged soil and then replanting and maintaining new forest seedlings
can be even more expensive.

Other Ecosystem Impacts

Ecosystem changes caused by CCG-induced heating from energy use are significant and will become much more important in an ever warmer world. The Climate Crisis Advisory Group (CCAG) has called for a "global state of emergency" as temperatures continue to climb in Siberia and other Arctic regions.[216] Permafrost is melting fast, and scientists have been shocked that the warm weather conducive to this thaw is occurring roughly seventy years ahead of model projections. This is a major concern because there are an estimated 1,400 gigatons of carbon frozen in permafrost—almost four times more than humans have emitted since the Industrial Revolution began, and nearly twice as much as is now in the atmosphere.

Energy production, delivery, and use involve many other external costs. Hydroelectric dams have completely disrupted the ecosystems of many rivers in America.[217] The failure to consider true costs has enabled dam builders to destroy valuable fisheries. Transmission lines commonly involve multiple access roads and road cuts. These are consistent, persistent sources of soil erosion. They introduce alien weed seeds and propagules carried on construction vehicles and equipment. They also serve as entry points for off-road vehicle activity and damage. Electrocution on US power lines is a significant cause of bird mortality, killing as many as 11.6 million a year.[218]

Impacts from Other Energy Uses

Electricity is not the only energy use we need to consider. Transportation energy use and the true costs of motor vehicles have been described in some detail by previous investigations,[219] and the transition to electric vehicles is underway. Energy use in the transportation sector can also be significantly reduced as we transition to renewable energy. Hybrid and electric cars have made great gains. In 2010, only 2,229 were sold, but by 2018, sales had risen to 253,678, and there were 100,000 recharge sites. Electric buses and trucks are also coming to market. Electric bikes may be more energy-efficient than even human-powered bikes and can bridge the gap between transit hub, home, and office. All can be improved—and will be, as costs rise. Efficiency will increase if there is a financial incentive for it.

The growing number of electric and hybrid cars are already reducing the external costs of CCGs, but for the best benefit, the electricity must come from clean energy sources. These vehicles are only as clean as the power plants used to charge their batteries. An electric car using coal-fired electricity is still typically cleaner than a comparably sized gas burner, but not by much. Electric vehicles also have supply chain problems as we mine and transport the cobalt, copper, and lithium for battery production. Questions also remain about battery recycling and recovery. Smartville Inc. is developing a very promising second life for used Tesla and Nissan batteries in utility storage systems.[220] Design and investment affect transportation energy use in other ways, too. Will density support transit? Can people walk or bike to work?

The industrial sector as defined by the US Energy Information Administration consists of manufacturing, agriculture (farming), construction, fishing, forestry, mining, and oil and gas drilling and pipelines. The industrial sector includes all facilities and equipment used for producing, processing, and assembling goods. In 2018, natural gas accounted for about 38 percent of total energy consumption as fuel and as feedstock for making products. The use of coal, coke, and fuel oils as feedstocks has declined since 2002. Some biomass is burned in heaters and stoves, but much is used to fuel power plants. Waste from wood and paper product industries is often burned to provide energy at the facility.

A growing concern has been the tremendous energy demand for cryptocurrency. Bitcoin, the world's largest cryptocurrency, currently consumes an estimated 150 terawatt-hours of electricity annually—more than the entire country of Argentina, population 45 million.[221] The US holds the lion's share of the global Bitcoin mining market, with nearly 38 percent of global hashrate[222] recovery. This leads to high energy demand for the large numbers of blockchain computations.[223]

Monetizing the True Cost of Energy

If we consider all the impacts of energy use, we can make better decisions. One of the most complete studies on the external cost of energy is worth reading.[224] Europeans have been studying the true cost of energy for almost twenty years.[225] These began with ExternE in Europe in 2005, the first effort to develop a systematic approach to estimating the external costs of energy over a wide range of uses and fuel cycles. This project computed external monetary damages associated with human health, crops, ecosystems, climate change, and materials. For ecosystem impacts, the project team also computed marginal and total restoration costs, where ecosystem costs were defined as the costs necessary to treat regions where critical pollutant loads were exceeded by 50 percent.

Studies of the external costs of energy have included many different boundaries, linkages, and impacts, and are not easily compared. However, I think it is likely that even the highest external cost estimates will still be low considering the enormous costs of long-term climate change, lifetime healthcare, and ecosystem damage. Many factors were not included in most studies because the data are limited. ExternE costs were estimated using a price of just $6.90-$27.80 per ton of CO_2e. This seemed appropriate at the time, but by 2017, the Carbon Pricing Leadership Coalition was suggesting the price needed to be set at between $50 and $100 per ton by 2030 to hold to the Paris Accord climate change targets. Sweden's fee per ton is already up to $137.50. Many suggest the true cost will be much higher.

Most external cost studies are very limited in scope and less helpful as a result. The US National Resource Council report in 2010 could have been much better.[226] Health and environmental costs are slighted. Many studies do not include a depletion cost for nonrenewable fuels. Consideration of catastrophic costs is also neglected, whether from billions of dollars in wildfire damage caused by utility lines or the potential for trillion-dollar nuclear meltdowns.

I feel comfortable using the cost estimates from a range of studies: 80 cents per kWh for coal, 54 for nuclear, 50 for biomass, 27 for oil, 21 for hydro, 14 for natural gas, 3 for wind, and 5.3 for photovoltaic solar. Direct use of the sun (passive solar) for heating, microclimate-based cooling, daylighting, and natural ventilation can often provide energy with zero true cost. The wide range in estimates reflects a range of systems and different boundaries and treatments of less well understood costs of ecosystem damage.

By comparison, the average retail price per kWh in the US was just 13 cents in 2020. In Hawaii it was 38 cents. San Diego residents paid 34¢ per kWh in 2022, with the price rising to 49¢ per kWh for tiers two and three (based on higher use). This would place external cost at about a third of retail cost. Much of our electricity is generated by fossil fuels, and rates may jump 20 percent or more due to the war in Ukraine.

Counting the true cost will help make central solar electric plants with concentrating mirrors a "future technology" whose time is past. Trying to remake an ideal dispersed energy source like solar energy into a conventional central power plant has always been a poor idea. This was highlighted by the Crescent Dunes tower power plant. This $1 billion project was to be the biggest solar plant of its kind. Citigroup Inc. and other financiers invested $140 million with its developer, Solar Reserve Inc. Steven Chu, the US Department of Energy secretary at the time, offered the company government loan guarantees; and Harry Reid, then the Senate majority leader and senior senator from Nevada, cleared the way for the company to build on public land. The energy from the plant cost about $135 per megawatt-hour, compared with less than $28 per mWh for wind, $32 for utility scale PV, and $44 for natural gas combined cycle.

Energy True Cost for a Project, Organization, or Building

We need to be responsible and calculate the true cost of our own energy use. Average costs are easier to work with, but a detailed workup for a specific site is the best way to do true cost accounting for energy as the external costs will vary by location, fuel, and equipment. An estimate of the external cost of energy for a particular power plant, home, or building begins with consideration of the site's climate (sun, temperatures, humidity, wind) and then looks at the site's technology, potential dispersion of pollutants (wind/water/microclimate), the response to the concentrations estimated (dose/response), and then finally the cost in dollars.

The cost analysis of a given energy source depends in part on the health impacts, which vary by population density near major users or power plants. This includes the poor and people of color who more often live near freeways, airports, harbors, and truck hubs. The true cost of energy can be estimated for the source of your electricity in some areas. For example, the coal-fired Martin Lake Power Plant in Texas emitted 44,000 tons of sulfur dioxide in 2021. At a social cost of $32,000 per ton, this totals $1.4 billion without even considering the full cost of environmental impacts. In the same year, the Allen James Power Plant in Alabama emitted 19 million tons of CO_2. Using the Swedish CO_2 fee of $137.50, this is a cost of $2.6 billion. The New Madrid Power Plant emitted 18,227 tons of NOx at a social cost of $7,700 per ton, or $140 million.

Natural gas is cleaner, but charging the true cost for natural gas generation will often double the price and encourage greater investment in conservation, efficiency, and renewable energy. Solar photovoltaics, hydro, wind, geothermal, tidal, and biofuels are becoming more cost-effective. Better building design, daylighting, process changes, and other improvements are already less costly than even wind power, but are neglected in the US and around the world. Doubling the price of energy with true cost recovery fees will stimulate innovation in building design and operation, manufacturing, and other energy applications.

Energy generation with fossil fuels has created millions of acres of acid-afflicted lakes, lands and forests. True cost recovery fees should help fund repair efforts for past damage. True cost accounting will ensure that new homes, offices, and institutional buildings will use renewable energy sources for temperature control, hot water, and ventilation. Work will also be done to retrofit existing buildings. Passive solar design using windows, thermal mass, and careful orientation will reduce energy demand for space conditioning.[227] The first modern 100 percent naturally heated and cooled house was built in California in 1974.[228] Microclimate resources can provide much or all of the cooling in many areas. Direct use of the sun for hot water heating can replace fossil fuels much of the year. Clothes drying costs Americans $9 billion each year. Solar clothes dryers can be bought for $50-200 and will last for decades. Our humble clothesline has saved us personally $100 a year for thirty years and cut our fossil fuel energy use by 30,000 kWh.

Daylighting and passive solar design can also reduce the energy use in commercial and industrial buildings, while lowering cooling energy requirements and reducing demand at peak prices.[229] New and retrofitted buildings have used 50-90 percent less energy for space conditioning, ventilation and lighting. A 4,500 square foot office building retrofit in Davis, California, was designed by Indigo Hammond and Playle Architects. It shows what can be done when the sun and climate resources are considered.[230] This office building is Zero Energy Certified by the International Living Future Institute based on at least twelve months of utility bills and energy production details. This was achieved while charging two electric vehicles.

Daylight retrofits with solar tubes and light pipes can be very effective and inexpensive, often cutting lighting costs by 25 percent or more.[231] Hydroelectric dams can be removed.[232] Transmission lines can be minimized when microgrids replace long transmission lines. This also reduces the risk of blackouts from costly failures of large power grids in storms, wildfires, ice storms, earthquakes or terrorism. More than two weeks after hurricane Ian thousands of residents were still without electricity. Many vulnerable elderly residents were without needed electricity.[233]

The Impact of Global Climate Change

With global warming, we expect more severe storms—more frequent and stronger hurricanes, ice storms, high winds, and tornados. These will leave thousands or millions of people without energy for days or weeks in freezing cold or blistering heat when the power grid is damaged. This leads to deaths from freezing and carbon monoxide poisoning in winter and heat stroke in summer.

Climate change has led to more intense heat waves in areas where buildings did not need air conditioning in the past. The Northwest heat wave in 2021 led to the death of 595 people in British Columbia and 112 people in Washington State. Without energy, people may also have no safe drinking water if their home well or water system pumps are silenced.

Climate change will increase the demand for energy for cooling while reducing the potential supply of hydroelectricity. In 2022, drought reduced hydropower in many areas. Sichuan province, China, for example, gets 80 percent of its energy from hydropower but lost 50 percent of capacity in the summer drought.[234] Drought may also affect power plants that use river (14%) or lake (15%) water for cooling. This is likely to lead to increased reliance on dirty coal fired plants.

Neglected but Essential to Consider: Nuclear Risk

Nuclear may look good as a stable, low environmental cost source of energy, but even today costs more (even without true cost considerations) than most renewable systems. It gets much worse when you count the cost of disasters. The 1986 Chernobyl catastrophe exposed more than 10 million people to nuclear radiation in the surrounding countries and has cost roughly $700 billion so far. It will require continued management for the next 320 years.

The Fukushima nuclear catastrophe in 2011 was caused by a large earthquake and tsunami. Cooling systems stopped working when electricity supplies failed and the cores melted down. More than 100,000 people were evacuated. Treatment will go on for decades. The ultimate cost may approach $1 trillion. More than 361 million gallons of contaminated water is currently stored in 1,000 tanks on site. These tanks will reach full capacity in mid to late-2023. After that, a million tons of low-level radioactive water will be released into the Pacific Ocean. The consequences will likely be very costly.

In 2022, the war in Ukraine exposed the Chernobyl nuclear disaster site to further disturbance and risk. Russian tanks and troops crossed the forested Chernobyl exclusion zone in the earliest hours of the invasion in February 2022. Fighting churned up highly contaminated soil from the site. For more than a month, some Russian soldiers bunked in the trenches within sight of the massive containment structure, and will pay the price. An even greater concern is fighting around Ukraine's nuclear facilities at Zaporizhzhia. This is the largest nuclear plant complex in Europe. In the fall of 2022, the plant's connection to the electrical grid was cut off. Generators have worked until the plant was reconnected, but this is very risky. The potential for a nuclear catastrophe remains high. If the cooling systems don't work, the disaster could be worse than Fukushima.

What You Can Do!

The world's electrical energy sources will change as true costs are phased in. Three fourths of the electricity used in the US is still from fossil fuels, but renewable sources are gaining ground. The energy savings from direct uses of the sun (winter heating through windows, crop drying, and daylighting) are never included but may equal a third of the total energy use. You can help the transition to renewable sources of lower true cost energy.

Many steps are included in other chapters on food, buildings, water, and more. Begin by starting an energy diary. How much energy do you use for these purposes? Home or apartment? Vehicle? Office? Job? It may help if you try some of the carbon footprint calculators that include transportation, housing, food, goods, services, and leisure. Then develop a plan to cut your energy use.

You can do a home energy evaluation with a professional audit, or do it yourself. A basic home energy audit will cost between $300 and $700 but can be well worth it. Some utility companies offer a rebate or a free energy audit. Many steps to cut energy use are simple and inexpensive.[235]

Develop a similar diary for your office, farm, or industrial space. The National Renewable Energy Lab has a nicely designed audit form.[236] Save energy with your transportation—ride a bike if it is safe. Take care of your vehicles.[237] Buy a more efficient car if you can. Check *Consumer Reports* for reliability and safety.

With true cost accounting for energy, you can see why and how you can reduce your impact on the planet. You can improve your health, comfort, security, and quality of life while protecting the environment. We know what to do and how to do it. True cost accounting can provide the impetus to get it done.

CHAPTER 9

TRUE COST ACCOUNTING FOR WATER

Water is our most critical resource. We can go for weeks without food, but only days without water. Water shortages are increasing around the world, often to critical levels. Climate change is contributing to these crises. UNESCO predicts that 1.6 billion people are experiencing water scarcity.[238] Half of the world may be living in water-stressed conditions by 2025. The causes of water shortages and water pollution vary, but most are

True cost considered water

New York City reduced the cost and improved water supply and quality by using forests instead of chemicals.

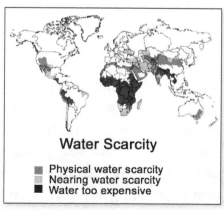

Water Scarcity

■ Physical water scarcity
▨ Nearing water scarcity
■ Water too expensive

The Global Crises in water have high social and environmental costs that are not being counted. Increasing numbers of refugees are people who lost access to water.

related to incomplete accounting. Water is misused because it is misvalued. True cost accounting can change the picture and lead to sustainable water use.

In the US, water is priced and supplied in a very complex and imperfect market. Subsidies and flawed government policy have facilitated a slow-rolling ecological and social catastrophe over the last 150 years. In most areas, the price of water has little to no relation to either the full cost (finance, installation, maintenance) or true cost (including all external costs). In many cases, users don't pay for the water, just for the delivery. In other areas, both are "free."

Water users and managers are generally unaware of the true costs of obtaining, treating, and delivering clean, safe water. Thousands of dams have been built to store water with no consideration of the adverse social and environmental impacts. Watersheds have been stripped of trees without considering the loss of water retention and storage.[239] Valuable fisheries, aquatic and riparian species, rich farmland, and cultural sites have been destroyed with rarely a thought. Despite this, more than two million Americans still live without running water and basic indoor plumbing, and many more without sanitation. Even when water is available it may not be safe to drink.

The external costs of water include energy used for water transfers, pumping, and treatment. The California State Water Project is the largest single user of energy in California, using 6-9.5 million MWh a year depending on the weather.[240] Delivering water from the San Francisco Bay Delta to Southern California uses 2 to 3 percent of all electricity consumed in the state. In San Diego, the energy cost of pumping water from the northern part of the state is 3,240 kWh/acre-foot.[241] If we look at true cost with CCG emissions of 0.5 lbs./kWh, the emissions would be about 1,625 pounds per acre foot with an external cost of $81. Water from the Colorado River costs less, but still uses 2,000 kWh/acre-foot. Energy costs per acre-foot were estimated at 3,236 kWh to the southern LA Basin, 1,165 to San Jose, and 2,826 to Santa Barbara. The energy cost for pumping local groundwater is about 600 kWh/acre-foot. The external costs for health and ecological damage will generally be larger than the current price.

Ninety percent of all electricity used on farms is devoted to pumping groundwater for irrigation; but energy for water transfers is also important. The energy subsidies for the Central Valley Project are enormous, with charges to irrigators as low as 1 cent per kWh. Many California farmers pay as little as 10 percent of the full cost of the water, perhaps as little as 1-5 percent of the true cost.[242] At 500 kWh/acre-foot a crop using 3 acre-feet a year would use 1,500 kWh per acre. This much water costs a San Diego resident more than $600, but the farmer may pay only $15. The ongoing drought is likely to change this.

If we look at true cost with CCG emissions of 0.5 lbs./kWh, the emissions for 1,500 kWh would be about 750 pounds of CO_2e per acre. With a $100 per ton CCG fee, the charge would be $37.50 per acre. For a farm of 2,000 acres, the emissions fee could be $75,000. That would be enough to change behavior.

True cost accounting for water involves many of the same issues as energy—including historical misuse. These problems are compounded by complex ownership and rights (which vary by nation, state, and region as well as by surface versus groundwater). In the US, water supply involves thousands of government agencies, quasi-private utility companies, private companies, and special districts. Other countries may have a mix of privatized water systems with government agencies and special districts. Many if not most water suppliers have problems with maintenance deficits and repair backlogs.

Full Costs Not Paid

Full costs (traditional internal costs such as labor and finance) are rarely covered. Veolia Water Technologies, a French water company with over 130 business units around the world, has developed a tool called the "True Cost of Water" to help businesses and municipalities assess the financial implications of water supply and use. They call it true cost, but this is really just the Full Cost of water without environmental and social costs. This tool combines traditional calculations of capital and operating expenditures with analysis of water risks and their financial implications for businesses and organizations, but it needs to be expanded to include true cost.

Studies in many areas have shown that water utilities often fail to do even basic full cost accounting. One Canadian study[243] found that the cost of water supply and sewage treatment in Ontario was understated by a factor of 16-55 percent. Failure to do accounting for existing costs and maintenance has contributed to the city of San Diego's $5 billion infrastructure debt.

In 1989, the government in England privatized the water supply system to avoid paying for needed upgrades to deteriorating infrastructure. It has not been a success—the private companies were also unable to meet the full cost of fixing the systems and continued to ignore the true costs. These companies have failed to upgrade sewer systems despite price increases of 40 percent above inflation since privatization. In 2021, Southern Water pleaded guilty to knowingly allowing "poisonous, noxious or polluting matter and/or waste matter and/or sewage effluent"—or raw sewage—to enter coastal waters.[244] The company was fined £90 million for discharging 4-5 billion gallons of raw sewage into some of the most "precious and delicate ecosystems and coastlines" with a disregard "for human health, and for fisheries and other legitimate businesses that operate in the coastal waters."

It is no different in the agricultural sector. Full costs are not paid, and true costs are ignored. Farmers usually pay only a fraction of their full cost of water. Full cost payment was mandated in many government water projects, but the costs were cut or eliminated when farmers were unable to pay.

Outrageous Subsidies

The Columbia Basin Project managed to achieve a subsidy of 96.7-98.5 percent of full cost. Most other projects across the country have been subsidized as well. If we add true costs, the picture is even worse: users often pay less than 1 percent of the true cost of water.

There is also great inequity in who gets the subsidies. The Environmental Working Group found that water subsidies in the Central Valley Project of California were overwhelmingly collected by the largest farms. In 2002, the largest 10 percent of farms got 67 percent of the water, for an average subsidy worth up to $349,000 each, at market rates, for replacement water. Twenty-seven large farms received subsidies worth $1 million or more.

Over the years, the price for water in the Central Valley of California has crept up, but remains a fraction of its true cost. The water supply networks of dams, recharge basins, pumps, and canals have been heavily subsidized by the state and federal governments, and the water itself has always been considered to be free—prices were set to cover part of the cost of infrastructure with no consideration for depletion of nonrenewable groundwater extraction.

Water Footprints

For mega-farms, the external costs and subsidies add up. Water use is high, and so is the water-related energy cost. A water footprint for California pistachios and almonds offers a good example. When the Shah of Iran was deposed in 1979, exports of pistachios from Iran collapsed. Growers in the San Joaquin Valley in California saw the opportunity and now grow half the world's pistachios and 80 percent of the world's almonds. Nut production was only possible because streams had been dammed and canals, pumps, and power plants built. Today, the farmers pay only a fraction of the cost of developing and maintaining this infrastructure.

Pistachio and almond production has been dominated by two families. The Resnicks' 121,000 acres of nut crops require 20-50 inches of irrigation water a year in an area where the rainfall is less than 10 inches a year.[245] The Resnicks' tree crops consume an estimated 130 billion gallons (400,000 acre-feet) of water per year. The Assemis family grows 30 million pounds of pistachios a year.[246] Water for both families' orchards and farms comes from a variety of sources, but much is drawn from groundwater and is not sustainable.

Water Exports

Arizona has problems with groundwater supply as serious as California's. After using up their desert aquifers in 2014, Saudi Arabia began purchasing and leasing large areas of American farmland, most in Arizona, to grow alfalfa to be exported and consumed by Saudi cattle. The largest dairy company in the Middle East is Al Kharj Farms, just outside Riyadh. Their herd of more than 93,000 milk cows needs a lot of feed. By 2015, they held more than 10,000 acres of US farmland. The amount of water they use is not known, but worth millions of dollars. For alfalfa, the water use may be 5 feet per year. If all the Saudi land was in alfalfa, the water use could be more than 50,000 acre-feet worth $50 million. But they pay very little for it. For example, the Saudis lease land from the state of Arizona State Land Department, including farms in Vicksburg and Butler Valley.[247] They pay about $86 thousand a year for water worth three to four million dollars a year. This subsidy adds more long-term costs to the residents of Arizona and more damage to the desert ecosystem.

The Saudis are exporting almost free water. This is possible because groundwater in rural Arizona is unregulated and most falls under a "reasonable use" designation. This means it is considered a private resource without government interference. It is free! Except for pumping costs. A few years from now, when people ask what happened to Arizona's water, the answer will be, "The Saudi cows ate it." But the UAE and American firms are also taking advantage of this water bargain.[248] Equity investors have realized the potential value of almost free water. International Farming Corporation was seeking to raise $1.5 billion in capital to buy and then lease land. Integrated Ag was created in 2012 and headquartered in Scottsdale Arizona. In 2015, they were planning to use $450 million to invest in real estate in Arizona and Nevada.

More than a tenth of the global nonrenewable groundwater used for irrigation goes to produce crops that are traded on the international market. Two thirds of exported crops that depend on nonrenewable groundwater are produced by Pakistan (29 percent), the United States (27 percent), and India (12 percent). The crops they produce are effectively exporting water at tremendous future costs to farms, residents, and communities when the wells run dry. The social and environmental costs are staggering, in the trillions of dollars globally.

Inefficient Water Use

Water use in agriculture around the world is often very inefficient and wasteful, while the low cost of water discourages investment in more efficient systems. Here in the US and around the world, much irrigation is still done using the very inefficient flood or furrow method. "Use it or lose it" water rights laws have also encouraged inefficient use of water to grow high water demand crops. Drip irrigation systems with demand controllers can reduce water use by 50 percent or more. More sophisticated sprinklers deliver more water to the crops with less evaporation. Soil surface treatment, mulches, crop rotations, soil health, different crops and improved management can also reduce water demand. Plant breeding can create more water-efficient cultivars to maintain yield with climate change. Where we grow our crops must also change.

For small landholders and gardeners in the US and around the world, even more efficient systems can be used. The Chinese agronomist Fan Shengzhi described buried clay pot irrigation in texts more than 2,000 years old, for use by farmers with too little land and too little water.[249] I have studied these systems for years and never fail to be impressed. A recent study in Kenya found that using the buried clay pot system instead of furrow irrigation used only 3 percent as much water for corn and 2 percent for tomatoes.[250] The buried clay pot system also increased corn yield by 32 percent and tomato yields by 44 percent. So we can get the same yield for about 1 percent of the water. Hard to beat!

As the groundwater level drops, wells run dry and have to be drilled deeper, or water has to be trucked in or siphoned off other systems. The Resnicks have been very determined and aggressive in sourcing water and have crafted a plan that benefits from a new water banking system. As Char Miller, the director of environmental analysis at Pomona College, describes it, "They have been banking water by using public and private dollars to corral a public resource. Because of their water rights and their wealth, they are insulating themselves from the drought. Private capital has no problem with the drought. . . . That's one of the deep social divides." As the saying goes, "Water flows uphill to money."

Water Crises

Although it is essential for life, water is running out in other areas of the world as well. Mismanagement and incomplete accounting caused problems before the deeper droughts caused by climate change began. As many as four billion people, representing nearly half of the global population, experience serious drinking water scarcity during at least one month of the year.

The supply of water for agriculture is also failing. Surface waters in many parts of the world are over-committed, and farmers respond by drilling deeper wells and pumping more groundwater— if they can afford it. Crops are dying from drought and heat. Livestock die from lack of water and food. Many rivers have simply run dry. Diversion for irrigation has had catastrophic effects on soils, streams, lakes, and riparian ecosystems.

Much of what was once the 26,000 square mile Aral Sea is now desert, but efforts to save the northern section of 300 square miles have been effective. The Salton Sea in California is drying up as well; treatment will cost billions of dollars. More and more exposed lake bottom is drying out and leading to dust storms laced with selenium and other harmful pollutants. Asthma rates are high and climbing.

Groundwater Mining

Groundwater depletion is common as use exceeds recharge. Groundwater depletion is not obvious because groundwater declines go unseen and changes can be difficult to measure and monitor. When groundwater is overused, it can be replenished in some geologic settings, but more often, the storage capacity is lost forever. In coastal areas, groundwater pumping can create a pressure gradient that leads to seawater intrusion into the groundwater. This has occurred in many coastal aquifers around the world. The extent of seawater intrusion varies widely among localities and hydrogeological settings, but can render water unusable for drinking or irrigation. Wells may have to be shut down or require costly desalinization treatment facilities, with water costs rising up to $2,000 per acre-foot. The intrusion of saline water will get worse and worse on coastlines as sea level rises.

When the groundwater drops, plant roots are left high and dry. Shallow-rooted plants die first, and finally mesquite and other deeply rooted trees are killed. Trees that started growing when there was water at the surface can follow the water down, but once the groundwater drops below 30 feet, there are few survivors. Even if the water table is only at 10 or 20 feet, it is very hard to replant trees. Pole planting and wick irrigation may sometimes succeed.

In California, the groundwater overdraft has averaged about 1.8 million acre-feet per year in the San Joaquin Valley. But the region-wide overdraft from 2003–2017 rose to 2.4 MAF/year.[251] This has led to widespread decline in water tables and land subsidence over 5,000 square miles. Over-pumping has caused the ground surface to drop by as much as 27 feet in some areas, with costly damage to infrastructure.[252] A 33-mile stretch of the 153-mile Friant-Kern canal that delivers water to more than one million acres and 250,000 people has lost roughly 60 percent of its original capacity due to subsidence.

In California, groundwater over-pumping finally got so bad that a state law was passed to require sustainable groundwater use. Once again, it was too little, too late, but at least the problem was acknowledged. The passage of California's Sustainable Groundwater Management Act in 2014 established a statewide framework to protect groundwater resources over the long term. The act, its amendments, and subsequent regulations require local agencies to form groundwater sustainability agencies (GSAs) for high- and medium-priority groundwater basins.

GSAs must develop and implement groundwater sustainability plans (GSPs) to avoid undesirable impacts and mitigate overdrafts within twenty years. Implementation will not be easy, and early reviews of the first basin reports have not been promising. In some areas, it will mean cutting long-term water use by 30 to 50 percent. Even where cuts are less severe, considerable investment will be needed to improve management practices and replenish groundwater supplies. As many as 500,000 to one million acres of farmland in the San Joaquin Valley will fall out of production.

In a new report on the current drought's economic effects in California, researchers estimated that irrigated farmland shrank by 752,000 acres in 2022 compared with 2019.[253] Nearly all the farmland that was left unplanted and dry is in the Central Valley, and a large portion of it was in the valley's northern half. This is expected to cost $1.7 billion dollars in losses and have large adverse impacts on wildlife, fish and waterfowl. The total area of fallowed land in California is likely to exceed a million acres in the future. California water agencies will start 2023 with as little as 5% of the requested supplies.[254]

The dust that will blow after these farmlands are fallowed and no longer irrigated will cause health problems throughout the valley, including a resurgence of the fungal disease Valley Fever (*Coccidioidomycosis*). This can be fatal. Treatment for health issues related to dust and efforts to reduce dust generation will cost millions of dollars.

In the south central US, groundwater pumping of the High Plains (Ogallala) aquifer for irrigation over more than eighty years has resulted in water table declines exceeding 240 feet in places, as well as loss of groundwater storage. The total cumulative groundwater depletion from 1950 through the end of 2000 was estimated to be 267 million acre-feet.[255] Today, the total depletion is probably more than 300 million acre-feet. Valued at $2,000 per acre-foot, that represents a loss of $600 billion. Problems with groundwater depletion at a smaller scale exist in the Midwest, Northwest, South, and Southeast.

Groundwater accounts for as much as one-third of total water withdrawals, and its overuse and depletion is almost universal around the world because the true costs of water aren't counted. More than two billion people rely on groundwater as their primary water source. Serious problems are being seen in Australia, Libya, Tunisia, Jordan, Sudan, Yemen, Kuwait, China, India, Iran, Pakistan, Saudi Arabia, and across Africa and South America. Some countries, including India, have subsidized electricity costs for pumping to encourage greater agricultural production while ignoring falling aquifer levels.

External Costs from Inadequate Maintenance

When water mains, canals, and dams fail, many external costs result from damage to farms, roads, buildings, cars, and infrastructure. Water system maintenance has declined as federal subsidies fell to just 9 percent of capital spending in 2017. State and local governments and the water districts have paid the rest. The maintenance backlog for the US water and wastewater treatment was estimated to reach $1 trillion by 2021.[256] Nationwide, there is a water main break every two minutes, and an estimated six billion gallons of treated water are lost each day in the US. The US Environmental Protection Agency estimates that about a half of 1 percent of this infrastructure is being replaced in any given year. At that rate, it may take 140 years to replace them all.

The external costs add up. The city of San Diego, for example, had thirty-three water main breaks in 2020. Over the years, the city has paid millions of dollars to victims of flooding caused by water main failures. Some of the cast-iron water mains in the city are now 100 years old—way past their life expectancy. In 2021, two major lines broke on the same day. The resulting floods lost tens of millions of gallons of fresh water, damaged buildings and cars, and shut down two lanes of Interstate 5 for many hours.

Health Costs

The quality of water is important for human health. Most water systems in the US are adequate, but smaller cities and towns and individuals with limited budgets have problems as private systems range from exceptional to hazardous. There was surprisingly little concern or accountability for poisoning from lead water pipes until the Flint crisis hit the headlines. Flint, Michigan, is not the only city with lead pipes, but an error in water source and treatment chemicals released more lead into the flow and created a catastrophe. Washington DC, Newark, Philadelphia, and many other older cities also have many lead supply pipes. Up to 10 million American households connect to water through lead pipes and service lines.

Lead water pipes in the US cause billions of dollars of external health costs with diseases and brain damage, primarily to the poor and people of color.[257] The $192 to 270 billion in costs per birth cohort related to lead exposure fall broadly into six categories: healthcare, IQ loss, increased special education needs, lower earnings, behavior problems and crime. Replacing lead pipes is also expected to dramatically reduce the risk of cardiovascular disease, saving $22,000 in medical costs for each lead service line replaced.[258] The Biden-Harris Lead Pipe and Paint Action Plan directs the EPA to allocate $3 billion in Bipartisan Infrastructure Law funding to states, tribes, and territories for lead service line replacement in 2022, and calls on states to prioritize underserved communities. The plan also allows federal funds to be used to replace lead service lines as well as faucets and fixtures inside schools and child care facilities. This will help if the funding is actually made available and put to work. Even then, lead pipes will remain a global problem.

Water resources are degraded by the attendant health costs from a wide range of pollutants including nitrate, hexavalent chromium, perchlorate, TCP, jet fuel, gasoline, radioactive minerals, and a witch's brew of pesticides. Groundwater contamination has shut down wells around the country. Hawaii in particular has been hard hit. One aquifer impacted by leaking jet fuel supplied about 20 percent of urban Honolulu's drinking water. In recent tests, the petroleum level was 350 times what is considered safe in drinking water, and three thousand people were displaced. Levels of the carcinogenic chromium 6 found in the water of twenty-five cities tested by the Environmental Working Group were higher than California's proposed public health goal. Tap water from Norman, Oklahoma, had more than 200 times California's proposed safe limit.

Surface water is also at risk. A new USGS study of pesticides in US rivers and streams reports that at least one pesticide was detected at 71 of the 74 sites, on average 17 unique pesticides were detected at every site, and 105 of the 221 study pesticides were detected at least once. Seventy-five percent of the detected pesticides had not been measured in previous studies.[259] An Environmental Protection Agency (EPA) chronic aquatic-life benchmark was exceeded at least once at more than half of the stream sites in every region—Midwest, South, Northeast, West, and Pacific.

In 2021 2,662 wells were tested for 221 pesticides or degradates (breakdown products). More than 300 wells tested positive for one or more pesticides or degradates. Sampling detected 41 pesticides or degradates, nine not registered for use in California.[260] In the San Joaquin Valley, nitrates were detected in 97 percent of the wells sampled.[261] Nitrates can cause many health problems, including "blue baby syndrome" and even death. In Tulare County, where 65 percent of residents identify as Latino or Hispanic, one in five small public water systems was delivering water with nitrate levels far in excess of federal health limits.[262] Levels below 5 ppm have been implicated in colorectal cancer, thyroid disease, and neural tube birth defects. Some water supplies tested had over 20 ppm.

Ecological Costs

Ecological costs can be as large or larger than social costs. Lead, nitrate, pesticides, and other compounds disrupt and damage aquatic ecosystems at very low concentrations. Damage reduces the value of ecosystem services. True cost accounting is needed to improve management and reduce ecological damage and true costs.

Habitat loss is a key issue. Healthy ecosystems of the lower Colorado River declined from 400,000 acres in 1894 to just 6,000 acres today.[263] Changes in the river flow have contributed to the invasion of non-native salt cedar (*Tamarix spp.*)[264] and Russian olive (*Elaeagnus angustifolia*) trees. So much Colorado River water has been diverted for human use that the river's delta no longer works the way it used to and is often dry, with no water reaching the Gulf of California. The loss of benefits society could gain from the natural function of a healthy Colorado River Delta are estimated to exceed $2 billion per year.[265] Assuming that the Colorado River supplies 13 million acre-feet of water per year, the ecosystem service value of water is $208 per acre-foot. Current US agricultural water prices for Colorado River water ranged from $16 to $32 per acre-foot (in 2004). The loss in ecosystem value is a subsidy to the regional water users.

This below-cost water has also opened up areas that should never have been farmed. Irrigation in the desert can lead to toxic agricultural drain water. In 1982, ducks and other waterfowl began dying mysteriously at the Kesterson National Wildlife Refuge, and by the spring of 1983, record numbers of migratory birds were emerging from their eggs with massive deformities, including misshapen beaks, twisted legs, missing wings, and incompletely formed skulls. Investigations showed this had been caused by the high levels of selenium from the highly saline soils of the San Luis unit of the Central Valley Project.[266] Ecological solutions were suggested, but not pursued.[267]

Salt and alkali buildup (salinization) is a major environmental problem that develops from irrigation in dry lands. It affects drinking water, agriculture, and natural ecosystems. Salinity is a global challenge, but worst in arid and semi-arid areas. Secondary salinity can develop when rising water levels from over-irrigation bring salt to the surface, or when clearing vegetation causes the accumulation of salt and alkali in the soil and groundwater. Irrigation may also lead to high concentrations of sodium, sulphate, boron, fluoride, selenium, arsenic, and radioactive minerals in the water and in soil.

Removing water from streams and wetlands and adding toxic pollutants has hit fish populations hard in California. Of the twenty-nine fish species native to the Sacramento and San Joaquin Rivers and the Bay Delta, two are extinct, six are endangered, five are rare, and nine others are declining. Many streams and rivers simply run dry in late summer as withdrawals increase. This affects all the species that were once found in healthy riparian ecosystems.

True Cost Accounting for Water

As with other materials, we need to know where our water comes from, what is in it, where it goes, and what it costs. Unrecovered external costs for the misuse of water can include:

- Loss of drinking water to small landholders and cities as groundwater levels fall and salt water intrudes
- Decline in river and stream flows affecting water supplies for people and ecosystems
- Decreased water quality (increased alkalinity and turbidity)
- Loss of the natural cycle of floods that replenish soil nutrients
- Loss of habitats
- Reduction in river and floodplain biodiversity
- Floodplain and river salinization
- Climate change gases from pumping, water treatment, and desalinization
- Invasion by exotic fish and plant species
- Agricultural waste water drainage and storage ponds
- Waterfowl and wildlife killed by agricultural drain water
- Barriers to fish migrations
- Increased incidence of blue-green algal blooms
- Cold, nutrient-poor water releases from reservoirs
- Loss of estuarine habitats—nursery areas for fish
- Increased vulnerability for flooding
- Increased risk of erosion during flood events

- Excess evaporation from reservoirs and transport canals
- Rising groundwater with formation of alkali and salt scabs
- Damage to infrastructure from subsidence

In California, heavily subsidized water prices and dysfunctional water rights have encouraged inefficient water use. This has led to the planting of low-value, high-water-intensive crops such as alfalfa in the desert. It takes 5-7 acre-feet of water to grow 7 tons of alfalfa per acre, worth $1,750. The open market water cost is about $1,000 acre-foot, so alfalfa uses $7,000 of water to grow $1,750 worth of crop. Growing $5 billion of nuts with water worth more than $300 billion (at $1,000 an acre-foot, the recent market price paid by a water agency to supply tree crop growers) is even worse. The true cost would be billions more for the widespread health costs, ecosystem damages, social disruption, damage from subsidence, and most critically, often irreversible depletion of groundwater reserves.

As water is pumped, water tables can drop, and some wells may run dry a high cost to local communities and families. Natural Capital is being squandered and destroyed. In many areas, water was once found flowing at the surface in artesian wells. Over time, overuse has seen the groundwater levels drop deeper and deeper. In the Antelope Valley of California, once dotted by artesian wells, the water table has dropped to more than 200 feet in some areas.[268] In Tucson, Arizona, the water level has dropped rapidly.[269] Predictions for future well depths suggest wells may have to be drilled to 800 or 1100 feet. The water being used is often 7-8000 years old and we will not likely have another ice age to recharge it. In most cases the groundwater cannot recover even if the effort is made.

Once the surface water is gone, so is the riparian habitat and the very biodiverse wetlands, called *ciénagas*. As the groundwater drops plants and trees are stranded and die from the lack of water. Tree skeletons are all that is left.

Legislative Roadblocks to Recovering the External Costs of Water

California state law today only allows water agencies to collect the cost of operation specifically linked to the services for each property.

This jeopardizes the implementation of conservation-oriented programs and the development of nontraditional sources of water. It also limits water utilities' ability to provide "lifeline" discounts to low-income households, an important equity-oriented feature of many billing systems. Voter approval is required for fees and assessments for "property-related" flood protection and stormwater management costs. Anything not qualifying as a fee is a tax, and taxes require a two-thirds super-majority of local voters. Proposition 26, a constitutional reform passed in 2010, further restricts the definition of other non-property-related fees. These legal strictures make it hard to support more integrated water management systems—a necessary approach for effectively meeting the state's water goals during times of water scarcity and climate change. These restrictions have led to a funding gap on the order of $400 million to $700 million just for ecosystem support for endangered species.[270] To cover all the costs, a recent study suggested Californians would need to pay $150 to $230 more per household annually.

California is not the only state to go off the rails at times. Colorado banned all rainwater collection until 2016, when House Bill 16-1005 was passed, allowing Colorado residents to collect rainwater from a catchment system on their roofs into two rain barrels with a combined capacity of no more than 110 gallons. The collected rainwater must be used on the property where it is collected and may only be used for outdoor purposes such as lawn irrigation and gardening. This is still absurd, but better than a total ban.

Our Water Future with True Cost Accounting

There is actually enough water in most areas if we use it wisely. If our picture of the water market is made more complete, the necessary adjustments will be made to where and how crops are grown and how consumers value and use water. Agriculture will get much less water, and urban areas won't face water crises as often. Climate change will still pose challenges as drought and high temperatures reduce snow pack and stream flow, increase water demand, and require further water allocation to protect fisheries and restore

riparian ecosystems. Revisions in legal codes are required, and that
will take legislation. A key step is diminishing the impact of the
"right of prior appropriation," which holds that the first beneficial
use of water from a stream has the highest priority, but if all the
water is not used, the excess may revert to the public. This encourages waste and growing low-value crops in places they should not
be grown. A small but important step is reducing the active disin-
centives against using less water. Adding more options to the definition of "beneficial use" or exempting more activities from forfeiture
and abandonment if not all the water is used will help. The lack of
enforcement of forfeiture and abandonment in some instances is
beginning to achieve this end. However, it will be better to amend
the law to provide some assurance to water right holders that they
will not lose their rights if they use less water. This will require the
states to select activities for exemption that they view as beneficial
for the purposes of sustainable water management. In Arizona, water exchange arrangements under Section 45 141(E) of the Arizona
Revised Statutes are exempted. California's sustainable groundwater regulations and water basin planning are also notable, though
slow-acting. Similar approaches could be effective in other states
with critical groundwater supply problems.

It will be helpful if the USGS or an NGO would develop a comprehensive report on best management practices and precedent/docu-
mentation from other states, countries, and organizations. What are
the true costs? What rules have worked? What have the economic
costs and benefits been? Who are the experts and potential support
groups? When something has been done before, officials are more
likely to consider the possibilities.[271]

In 1996, for example, Pliny Fisk and Gail Vittori prepared the
first report on rainwater harvesting potential in Texas.[272] This led
to changes in local and state policy, and their clear statement on the
value of rainwater harvesting inspired and enabled many others to
adopt similar policies. Talking about water means talking to engineers and policy-makers who are likely to pay attention if the facts
are clear and proposed changes are straightforward.

Changes in forest and rangeland management can also improve the stability of the water supply. Selective cutting instead of clear-cutting can reduce peak flows and flooding. Minimizing grazing in riparian areas can improve stream bed stability and water quality. In some cases, restored riparian areas can support the reintroduction of beaver. The complex networks of beaver dams and canals can hold more water in the watershed and prolong stream flow. Changes to water storage facilitated by beaver dams can be partitioned into two categories, water that is impounded and stored above ground in beaver ponds, and water added to groundwater bring the water table up closer to the surface.[273] Groundwater base levels in a California stream were highest in years when the beaver dams were actively maintained.[274]

True cost accounting will result in many changes in the way water is used. Families, communities, states and the nation will respond to reduce the misuse of water. Water budgets will be developed and maintained. Progress can be dramatic and relatively quick when there is a commitment to change and funding. At UCSD, the campus water conservation projects reached their goal of a 25 percent cut in just six years, and they are well on the way to their next goal of a 36 percent cut. Automatic metering allows near real-time data acquisition and analysis that enables the Campus Utilities and Sustainability Team to identify irregular water use patterns. This has saved millions of gallons of water. Monitoring information is also available for energy and water use by individual buildings and campus groups.

What You Can Do!

You can help protect the water resources you use today and the water your grandchildren will need by valuing water appropriately. In most areas, the price consumers currently pay for water doesn't even come close to the current cost of operations—let alone the social and environmental costs. As water shortages hit the Southwest in 2021, the price paid for water went up as high as $2,000 per acre-foot, or about a penny per gallon. Fully covering operating costs could double the cost, and adding the true cost could double it again. It is not surprising that Trucost estimates the true cost of water could be up to 4¢ per gallon in areas of scarcity. In contrast, consumers in the US willingly pay up to $10 per gallon for bottled water.

True cost accounting for water has received surprisingly little attention. Urge your water supplier, city, company, or organization to improve water efficiency by calculating the True Cost of Water.[275] Once the costs are clear, the need for change will be clear. True cost prices will play a critical role in our efforts to develop a sustainable water future. It can and must be done.

Until then, there is much you can do. First, take a close look at water use in your home and landscape.[276] What is your water footprint?[277] The EPA reports the average American uses about 90 gallons of water every day. In San Diego County, water use fell from 220 gallons per day to 140 gallons in just 15 years. This water is drinking-water quality brought from hundreds of miles away. Valuable clean water is used to flush toilets, water lawns, and wash dishes, clothes, and cars. This happens only because we don't count the true cost of water.

In most single-family homes, the easiest place to conserve water is in the landscape. Replace the lawn with landscape plants and use irrigation systems that require little water.[278] Landscape changes and improved irrigation systems can cut use by 90 percent. In many areas, cities or water districts will help you pay for this.

Take a close look at rainwater harvesting from your roof and hardscapes. It is relatively easy to put in collection pipes and a cistern, but a professional installation will often prove worthwhile and provide more reliable, cleaner water. Rainwater use for drinking and bathing is still the norm in rural Hawaii.[279] Check local codes as some areas still ban or restrict rainwater harvesting.

Consider replumbing so you can save and use gray water (if allowed in your city)[280] for flushing toilets and irrigation. Australia has done a good job of supporting gray water use. My parents diverted laundry water to the garden for more than 40 years. Growing water shortages and improved understanding of the best "gray water" practices are stimulating many jurisdictions and states to encourage gray water use and to support personal initiatives to reduce the environmental impacts of living. Some areas even allow it for commercial buildings.

The water flow out of a home also includes clean water that is run while warming water before a shower or cleaning dishes. It's not unusual for 50 feet of piping--or more--to extend from the water heater to the most distant fixtures. It can take a long time for hot water to reach the tap; while waiting all the water goes down the drain. An on-demand circulation systems can prevent this loss but these are rarely considered because they are expensive. Water from a shower or bath can be fairly clean if safe soaps and shampoos are used. A prewash, following Japanese practice before entering the *furo* (tub), can help keep the water clean.[281] The condensate from the air conditioner is essentially distilled water. Gray water from a kitchen sink can be kept relatively clean if most waste goes to the compost heap or is picked up by the garbage collectors instead of being run through the garbage grinder. Vermicomposting with worms to treat organic waste can also be effective.

Only about a quarter of the water leaving the home is from the toilet. Replace old toilets (3-7 gallon) with low-flow models (1.28-1.6 gallons). A dual flush feature can help save water. It is senseless to transport water hundreds of miles, clean it at high cost, and then contaminate it with human waste. Flushing should be done with gray water or rainwater. Composting toilets can work well, but they require management and are not for everyone.

Leaks may account for 15 percent of the water leaving the water main to the house. These could be from leaky faucets, shower heads, sprinklers, or pipes. Have a skilled plumber help tighten up your house and replace inefficient fixtures. Energy Star certified washing machines use an average of 14 gallons of water per load, 33 percent less than regular washers. Some models only use 7 gallons. Even if you are a renter you can use less water. Capture the preheat water in the shower (5 gallon bucket) and kitchen sink. Reduce shower time.

Flush for solids but not just urine. Advocate for better fixtures and water conservation in the complex and community.

How much water do you really need? Many families in the world have to get by with only 1.5 to 3 gallons a day. This water may have to be carried miles from a well and is very precious. The Minimum Cost Housing Group shows how to cut water use for bathing from 10-30 gallons to just 2 quarts.[282]

True cost accounting will play a critical role in our efforts to develop a sustainable water future. It can and must be done. True costs will help provide secure water supplies with safe and sufficient drinking water. Agricultural water use can be cut while still growing plentiful food. Working to change water law and long-established policy is essential and will take planning and commitment, but if we act now, true cost accounting can ensure we don't run dry.

CHAPTER 10

PRODUCTS AND CONSUMPTION

Every day, with every purchase, we cast a vote about our future, but it can be hard to know what we are voting for. The impact of our choices depends on the products we buy and use and how they are made. Unfortunately, there is very little accessible information about the impacts and external costs of manufacturing, using, maintaining, and getting rid of the things we buy. The EPA reports the total generation of municipal waste in 2018 was 292.4 million tons, up from 208.3 million tons in 1990. The US produces more than 30 percent of the planet's total waste, even though it is home to only 4 percent of the world's population. The typical American throws out five pounds of materials every day, for a staggering total of 1,855 pounds a year. This is as much as a small car. Imagine it all on a cart you have to pull!

The true costs of our choice of products are not counted, so waste and pollution continue almost unabated. People get sick and die from exposure to chemicals, but the producers are not punished because the cause of a particular fatal cancer is often unclear. The

True cost ignored and plastic waste covers the earth.

Buy less, waste less - cut true cost

difficulty in distinguishing between correlation and causation in human health allows manufacturers and polluters to evade responsibility for the damage, death, suffering, and disruption they cause. Materials aren't recycled, reused, or returned to nature—but landfilled as waste or burned.

True Cost Accounting for Products

True Cost Accounting will make more complete product labels possible so that consumers can understand a product's health, social, and environmental costs. This might be linked with a QR code so a consumer can quickly check online for more detailed information. External cost recovery will also become easier with better information. Companies can be held responsible for control and cleanup as well as payments for medical costs, lifetime costs of diminished mental capacity, and ecosystem disruption. Developing a better understanding of human and ecosystem responses to ecotoxic materials is key to understanding these true costs.

We need to develop and apply true cost accounting tools to assess products and services over their lifetime of use. Where do things come from? Where do they go? As William McDonough and Michael Braungart (2002) put it in their pioneering work *Cradle to Cradle: Remaking the Way We Make Things*, "Think about it: you may be referred to as a consumer, but there is very little that you actually consume—some food, some liquids. Everything else is designed for you to throw away when you are finished with it. But where is 'away'? Of course, 'away' does not exist. 'Away' has gone away."

The ecological footprint of a material helps us understand the total quantity (in kg) of natural material (M) that is disturbed in its natural setting and is thus considered the total input (I) in order to generate a product—counted from the cradle to the point when the product is ready for use—minus the weight (in kg) of the product itself.[283] This can be extended to the environmental and health impacts and costs spread over the lifetime of a product. Material Intensity (MI) tables can be used to estimate the true costs of materials, which is the first step in product life cycle analysis (more in Appendix 1). Natural and recycled materials and materials made from waste have much more favorable MI rankings. Here is a comparison of some aggregated MIs for commonly used materials from Schmidt-Bleek. Like in golf, a lower number is better.

MATERIAL INTENSITY RANKING

wood	1.2
glass	2
plastics	2 to 7
steel	7
paper	15
aluminum	85
platinum	500,000

If we calculate the abiotic (nonliving) material costs for a specific design strength, we find that wood is eighteen times better than steel. Based on specific strength per weight, wood is also ten times better at reducing adverse water impacts and 30,000 times better at reducing air impacts. The energy cost of wood is also only 2 percent of the energy cost of steel and 1 percent that of aluminum. Wood would get used for many purposes if we had more quality wood available at reasonable prices (more in Chapter 11 and also www. truecostalways.com).

Material Intensity (MI) analysis can be done for a family, product, service, industry, sector of the economy, or nation. Material intensity studies help identify physical flows of hazardous materials throughout a product's lifetime. These studies can be revealing. Electricity generated in Germany by burning coal was found to be fifty times as material (and energy) intensive as wind or natural gas and eight times worse than photovoltaic cells. This hints at the true cost. Material flow analysis can help manufacturers design products that are safer and more durable, repairable, and recyclable.

Too often, we do not know where materials go or what harm they do to humans or ecosystems. To date, most research efforts have been focused on better understanding the human health risks of the most toxic materials. The available information, however, covers only a few of the potential risks, and research has been limited by lack of funding. Even when they have been studied, the risks have rarely been linked to costs. Research usually starts after a cluster of deaths occur or an accident garners national attention—but after the publicity dies down, the funding often fades away.

Material Intensity per Service

Material Intensity Per Service (MIPS) takes the next step and examines MI over the full life cycle. A product's service life may be short, single-use, or long, depending on the skill of designers and engineers, the quality of materials, manufacturing precision, and care in operation and maintenance. Many products have remarkable life cycles if they are well maintained. I bought my steel-frame Peugeot UO8 bicycle in 1972 and expect it will be in use long after I am gone. A cast-iron skillet, like the one our family uses, will still be functional after 100 years.

Companies, industries, and governments can help develop and maintain MI and MIPS databases. This will help them improve their products and service while identifying problem areas. It will also make it easier to calculate true cost. Consumer organizations can help maintain databases that identify better than, worse than, and average performance and reliability. *Consumer Reports* does this very well in the United States. Improved understanding will enable companies and consumers to better predict the MIPS for a product or service they make, use, or are considering using. Designers and manufacturers will benefit from determining MIPS while they are evaluating the potential value of new products and services.

Calculating MIPS requires some care because a product built with material X can be good or bad depending on the source and treatment of X. Chain of custody information is needed, just as in organic foods. Is the clothesline frame made with virgin aluminum or recycled aluminum? Was the cotton shirt made with naturally colored cotton planted on an organic farm by well-paid labor and sewn by a women's cooperative that provides a living wage and benefits? Or was it made in a forced labor camp with cotton grown on a chemical-intensive farm with no pollution controls, bleached with chlorine and colored with toxic dyes?

The next step is determining or estimating the true cost. A life cycle outline for true cost accounting includes:

	Pollution			CCG		Social	
	Air	Water	Land	Toxics	Energy	Health	Equity
Resource extraction							
Material gathering							
Material processing							
Manufacturing							
Assembly							
Distribution							
Sales							
Use							
Maintenance							
Disposal (reuse, recycle, return to nature, landfill, burn)							

The production of denim jeans has been examined by the Impact Institute. They considered the negative externalities that making jeans have on people and the planet in great detail. They found the uncounted social and environmental costs of typical jean production in India and Bangladesh for sale in Amsterdam were almost $33. With a current retail price of about $80, the added cost is about 40 percent to make the true cost of the jeans $113.[284]

To understand true costs, we need to know where the resources came from, how much of the material there is now, and where the rest went (more in Appendix 1). Do they move in air, water, food, dust? Is it local or global? Is it concentrated or diffused? What are the personal exposure and load factors for humans (blood tests and monitoring)? Is the material biomagnified (search in medical, ecological publications)? Are effects cumulative or instantaneous (medical and toxicological reports)? Are the effects lethal (medical research articles and product safety sheets)? Does the material affect reproduction? Are the effects mutagenic or teratogenic? Even if the material is nontoxic to humans, will it cause ecosystem damage or catastrophe? Can humans or ecosystems shed the material if exposures are infrequent, or does the material build up over time?

What secondary effects or pathways exist? Biomonitoring is often much more revealing than individual chemical analysis. Biomonitoring may measure chemicals in human body fluids and tissues or in other organisms and ecosystems. Biomonitoring tests can also examine the response of organisms to different levels of exposure. This information makes it possible to choose marker species for surveys evaluating ecosystem condition. One freshwater crustacean, *Daphnia sp.*, is often used to measure the health status of aquatic ecosystems.[285] Are they present or absent? Lab tests might also be done.

Are metabolites or breakdown products more hazardous? How do they interact? How persistent is the material in the environment? Does it break down in hours, days, years, millennia? Can it be collected? Can it be reused or repurposed? Can it be used by another industry as a basic supply? Can it be recycled for the same use? Can it be recycled for lower uses?

True cost accounting and material flow analysis require commitment and funding, but can provide many benefits to businesses. It can reduce waste, reduce costs, and increase profits. It can reduce risk and liability. It can improve health, worker satisfaction, and productivity by limiting exposures to harmful materials. This will be a great field for future work as many trained investigators, TCA accountants and auditors will be needed. Universities need to start programs to meet this demand. They may start with short courses and certification within an environmental studies, sustainability, or accounting program. As soon as possible TCA undergraduate and graduate programs should be created. Most large companies now have a sustainability officer or program manager, but they should begin hiring environmental accountants ensure that social and environmental costs are identified and charged to products, services, or activities—not to overhead.

Extended Product Responsibility

A good company should track the impact of the materials it uses, and be willing and able to take them back at the end of a product's life. This is called Extended Producer Responsibility (EPR) or Product Stewardship.[286] This strategy places shared responsibility for end-of-life product management on producers and other entities involved in the product chain, instead of the public. Several options have been explored, including product take-back requirements.[287] Take-back policies require the producer or retailer to collect the product at the post-consumer stage. Economic and market-based instruments include deposit-refund, advanced disposal fees (ADF), material taxes, and upstream combination tax/subsidies (UCTS) that reward the producer for complying with EPR. In South Korea, for example, ADFs are imposed on importers and producers of products that are hazardous and more difficult to recycle. Regulations and performance standards such as minimum recycled content can also help encourage EPR. Standards can be government mandates or programs developed by industries.

Some of the first EPR requirements have been for packaging. Germany was one of the first countries to set up an Extended Producer Responsibility (EPR) system for packaging, back in the 1990s, and it has developed significantly since.[288] In Germany, all expenses associated with the collection, sorting, and recycling of packaging waste are to be paid by covered companies. Rather than having each company working alone, most industries set up and join a central register and pay fees to a waste management operator of their choice. The recycling targets for most forms of packaging was 90 percent for most materials by 2022. The most difficult materials have less strict requirements—but still more than 50 percent. By comparison, the US recycles only half as much, and much of the waste recovered from recycling bins is rejected because it is contaminated. It then goes to be landfilled or burned.

EPR is well suited for managing electronic waste and other potentially harmful products and materials. Although the estimated value of recoverable e-waste materials exceeds $65 billion annually, only about 20 percent of global e-waste is recycled.[289] EPR policies and programs for e-waste have been established in Europe, Canada, Japan, and South Korea. Several US states have developed some EPR requirements as well. The best state, Vermont, recovered 7.7 pounds per person; the worst, Missouri, only 0.3 pounds.[290]

The challenge keeps growing. From 2011 to 2019, the amount of electronics put on the market in the EU increased from 7.6 million tons to 11.2 million tons. In the same period, the total e-waste collected increased from 3.0 to 4.5 million tons.[291] This is still less than half recovered. Seventeen countries were above 50 percent.

In the US, more than seventy EPR laws have been adopted in thirty-two states to cover ten categories of consumer products such as automobile batteries, mobile phones, paint, pesticide containers, carpet, electronics, thermostats, and fluorescent lamps. In California, rules cover mercury thermostats, pesticide containers, paint, carpets, mattresses, and medical waste/sharps.

The Oregon paint EPR began as a pilot program in July 2010; during the first two years, they collected nearly one million gallons of leftover paint. Paintcare California now collects and processes more than four million gallons of post-consumer paint a year.[292] About 96 percent is reused, recycled back into paint or another product, or used for another purpose. Two thousand tons of metal and plastic cans have been collected as well. Taking such an approach to leftover paint is important because this difficult-to-manage waste makes up the largest volume of materials collected by local household hazardous waste treatment programs.

Design for Disassembly

Good design and good maintenance are required to reduce true costs and MIPS. Designs that allow owners to repair products help reduce true cost. Design for Disassembly helps reduce cost to consumers, but also makes it easier to recycle or reuse components at the end of life.[293] The strategies are straightforward but demand care in choosing materials, fasteners, and assembly steps.[294] When I was teaching environmental design, one of the most popular class activities was "taking things apart night." I would bring in a full range of tools, and students would bring in failed or broken products. They would then take them apart and sort the fasteners, electronic components, and materials into categories. It often took a saw or hammer to get things apart.

Dell Computer has been a leader in design for disassembly.[295] Their Inspiron laptop received the top score of 10 from iFixit[296] for the way its design supports easy repair and upgrades. Apple had resisted, but in mid-November 2021, they announced they would launch a self-service repair program that would allow their customers to purchase some parts and provide access to repair manuals.

Right to repair laws and rules are gaining ground.[297] Many companies resist the right to repair approach by threatening to void warranties if customers don't use the companies' authorized facilities for repairs, maintenance, or upgrades, or install unapproved parts. This can be against the law unless a manufacturer foots the bill for repairs. Warranty limitations like this are illegal unless a waiver is first obtained from the FTC—and it has never granted one.

Health and Environmental Impacts of Materials

We also have to choose the materials we use more carefully. The environment is contaminated, and people as well as many other species are getting sick, failing to reproduce, and dying. As many as 1,000 chemicals are endocrine disruptors with varying proposed mechanisms of action that have potential impacts on fertility. These are implicated in the global decline in male fertility.[298] Sperm counts in countries with better control of toxic substances showed little change in fertility, while in others, the sperm quality declined.

Continued use of harmful chemicals is made possible by willful ignorance. Growing concerns about the potential liability that would arise from a better understanding of health and ecosystem impacts have helped polluters "encourage" Congress to cut research funding. Industries have often closed the door, cut off data, and even sued researchers whose findings might hurt their sales.

The EPA should have been doing health and ecosystem research on wastes for the last fifty years. Always reluctant to confront industry, the EPA became an enemy of regulation and research during the Trump presidency. He appointed an industry lobbyist to implement the new mission of the "Environmental Pollution Agency." Many of the best staff left in disgust. Around 700 scientists and a total of more than 1,600 employees quit. EPA enforcement officers suffered large losses, and the staffing level fell below their legislative mandate.

With little long-term government-funded research, the task of risk assessment has fallen to small NGOs with limited funding, little access to company data, and less sophisticated testing equipment needed for sophisticated field or health studies. These heroic NGOs, like the Environmental Working Group and the American Academy of Pediatrics, also face many challenges in trying to maintain research projects and lobbying efforts over the years.

There is still considerable uncertainty about the health and environmental impacts of even the more dangerous chemicals. Data on material flows and impacts are missing or weak even for hazardous materials in the US. It is much worse in developing countries, where very little information on flow may be available even for the most toxic and hazardous materials. Improved tracking of hazardous and toxic materials should be a priority for international funding and NGO intervention.

Many countries try to track the most toxic materials, but it is not easy. Details are limited for heavy metals (cadmium, lead, chromium, arsenic), nuclear materials, and the more than 100,000 chemical compounds in use that are known to pose health and environmental risks. Several European countries and Japan have been pioneers in developing and applying material flow analysis to better manage these materials.

Hazardous materials are of particular concern because they can have impacts on people and the environment for decades. Children are particularly vulnerable. Heavy metal poisoning has life-long impacts on brain development and IQ.[299] There may also be generational effects from exposure to pesticides and other pollut-ant. This was not expected, but research suggests the effects from the pesticide DDT are intergenerational.[300] Banned in the US nearly fifty years ago, DDT appears to contribute to the falling age of first periods and increased obesity in young women today. The risk of obesity in young adult granddaughters was two to three times greater when their grandmothers (who were not overweight) had higher levels of o,p'-DDT (a contaminant of commercial DDT) in their blood during or just after pregnancy. Granddaughters were twice as likely to have earlier first menstrual periods when their grandmothers had higher o,p'-DDT blood levels. DDT and its related chemicals are known to be endocrine disrupting compounds that can alter and interfere with natural hormones' essential function-ing. As many as half a million drums of DDT waste were dumped in the Pacific Ocean near Los Angeles from 1947-1982.[301]

Lead

Several recent studies have found that relative to control groups, children affected by lead and cadmium, even at low levels, exhib-ited more learning problems and antisocial behaviors, including those resulting in suspensions, absences, school crimes, and violent crime arrests.[302]

The problems of lead in water are discussed in Chapter 9, but wa-ter is not the only place where lead poses risks. By the early 2000s, the total demand for lead in all types of lead-acid storage batter-ies represented 88 percent of apparent US lead consumption. Other significant uses included ammunition, oxides in glass and ceram-ics, casting metals, and sheet lead. In the US, an estimated 3,000 tons are spread through the environment from lead shot and bullets every year. Another 4,000 tons are released from fishing weights. And perhaps 2,000 tons are distributed as older lead wheel weights that fall off of car wheels.

Before it was banned, leaded gasoline contaminated soils around the country and world. Lead-based paints have been implicated in children's poisonings since 1904, when this was first diagnosed in

Australia. The lead paint companies worked effectively to protect their profits. Lead paint worked well and was cheap, so it continued to be used extensively for more than seventy years. At one time, up to 70 percent of the paint in a can could be lead. A voluntary standard for the US limited lead in interior paints starting in 1955. In 1977, the allowable lead concentration for households and toy paints dropped to 600 ppm, and in 2009, that limit dropped to 90 ppm. An exception was made for industrial uses.[303] Old lead paint is a threat to children in older homes and apartments and to remodelers and home repair contractors. Lead-based paint is still legal in many countries. Lead and cadmium from pottery glazes can also be a problem.

Lead is still used in some aviation gas. The most commonly used fuel for piston-driven aircraft in the United States is Avgas 100LL. The LL stands for low lead, but it contains up to 0.56 grams of lead per liter. Avgas 100 contains even more lead and is still in widespread use. The Federal Aviation Administration is working to remove lead from aviation gas by 2030.

Toys may be made of (or include) lead, and the paint on a toy may contain lead or cadmium. Whether the toy is safe or poisonous, it will look the same. Plastic toys carry their own risks.[304] Studies at the Danish Technical University found 419 chemicals in hard, soft, and foam plastic materials used in children's toys. Of these, 126 can harm children's health, including thirty-one plasticizers, eighteen flame retardants, and eight fragrances. Hormone mimics are a special concern for long-term health. Even low doses of endocrine-disrupting chemicals may be unsafe. The body's normal endocrine functioning involves very small changes in hormone levels that we have learned can cause significant developmental and biological effects.

Topics of Special Concern

In addition to heavy metals and hazardous materials, there are many other materials of concern that pose threats to people and the environment. These include cancer causing chemicals or materials, teratogenic chemicals or materials that affect infant development, and mutagenic chemicals or materials that damage DNA. These can lead to permanent changes (mutations) in the DNA sequence.

It is estimated that about 1,000 chemicals may have endocrine-acting properties (for more information, see Chapter 7 and endocrine.org). For an early warning alarm, see the book *Our Stolen Future*. Hormone mimics can cause all kinds of havoc.[305]

Fire retardants are used in a wide range of products and are a special concern in contact situations such as bedding, clothing, and furniture. The goal of fire safety was notable, but failure to consider the true cost and impacts of these chemicals was catastrophic. Today, polybrominated diphenyl ethers (PBDEs) are found in our bodies and the environment. Flame retardants have overtaken heavy metals as the biggest contributors to chemically induced IQ loss. PBDE exposure was found to be the greatest contributor to intellectual disability burden, resulting in a total of 162 million IQ points lost and over 738,000 cases of intellectual disability.[306] Research has suggested the fire retardants disrupt hormone signaling and neurodevelopment, a particular problem when they are used in baby pajamas and infant bedding. These uses were eventually restricted, but led to a switch to different yet similar chemicals.

The Environmental Working Group and scientists at Duke University found the urine in every mother and child tested showed they had been exposed to TDCIPP, a cancer-causing fire retardant.[307] In the children, the average concentration of the chemical biomarker left when TDCIPP breaks down was nearly five times the average in the mothers. One child had twenty-three times the level measured in the mother. Widespread exposure to fire-retardant chemicals was driven by a flawed California regulation that triggered widespread use of fire retardants in furniture without adequate research about health and environmental risks and costs.

The use of poly- and perfluoroalkyl substances (PFAS) is now restricted in several states. In August 2022, the EPA reclassified these as Hazardous Materials. PFAS have been used as stain-blockers on carpets, upholstery, and clothing. The defense department and some fire departments used a firefighting foam with PFAS for decades, leading to widespread contamination of ground and drinking water at military bases and other wells nationwide.[308] A recent study detected PFAS in half of all carpet samples tested. It is expected that 95 percent of Americans have traces of these chemicals in their blood. One carpet tested, sold by the largest US carpet manufacturer, contained high levels of six different types of PFAS.

The related PFOS (Scotchguard) and its chemical cousin, PFOA, were phased out under pressure after secret studies by their manufacturers revealed they caused cancer and birth defects in lab animals, built up in people's bodies, and did not break down in the environment. New short-chain relatives may prove equally risky.

Plastics

More than 300 million tons of new plastic are now produced annually with less than 10 percent recycled. The worldwide plastic problem has gained attention following the revelation of five floating garbage patches in the world's oceans.[309] The central Pacific gyre, also known as the Pacific garbage patch, is the size of a continent and may have 80,000 tons of floating plastic waste in an estimated two trillion pieces. Over the past fifty years, plastics from the US and other countries have flowed into the ocean. Plastic items, fragments, and films are building up in beach sands, rivers, and lake sediments and soils. Even the most remote islands are affected. Future health and ecosystem problems from these plastic wastes can be anticipated.

While fees are being charged for single-use bags and other minor products, they are far too weak. The EU tax on plastic packaging waste, $0.80 per kilogram, is part of the pandemic recovery package agreement. It took effect in January 2021 and was to go directly to the EU to fund coronavirus control efforts.[310] A global tax on 300 million tons of new plastic produced annually could start at about 10 percent, around $100 per ton, increasing 5 percent a year. This would raise $30 billion for research on "sustainable plastics," plastics impacts, and alternatives to plastic. This fee would fund healthcare, cleanup, and restoration of damaged areas and species adversely impacted by plastics.

Microplastics

Particles or fibers smaller than 5 mm are called microplastics. They can come from the breakdown of larger plastic items, or they may have been made intentionally small for inclusion in cosmetic or hygiene products. Together with industry partners, the outdoor clothing retailer Patagonia commissioned the Ocean Wise Plastics Lab to investigate the tiny textile particles that are shed from synthetic fabric garments over their lifetime. Researchers found that the garments shed between 31,000 and 3,500,000 fibers per load during normal laundering in household washing machines. Some shed fewer particles after the initial wash.

Microplastics are now found in most fish and seafood. A recent study by OrbMedia analyzed 159 water samples sourced from both tap water and bottled water in fourteen countries and found that over 93 percent of all samples contained tiny plastic particles.[311] The US led the way, with 94 percent of water samples containing microplastics. Beaches sampled at Point Reyes National Seashore and the Golden Gate National Recreation Area near San Francisco had an average of fifty plastic pieces per cup of sand.

We are all exposed, but impacts on human health have not been well studied.[312] Lab studies suggest that interactions of micro- and nano-plastics with the immune system may potentially lead to immuno-suppression (decreased host resistance to infectious agents and tumors), immune activation (increased risk of developing allergic and autoimmune diseases), and abnormal inflammatory responses (chronic inflammation, tissue or organ damage and dysfunction). The human experiment is ongoing.

E-Waste

Electronic waste involves many potentially harmful materials and is, as noted, a good candidate for Extended Product Responsibility, but more waste is still thrown out. In 2021, the world discarded 63 million tons of computers, phones, and other e-waste.[313] Only 17.4

percent were recycled. E-waste is difficult to process and is often sent to developing countries for manual processing despite rules and regulations intended to control their dispersal. Much once went to China, but in 2018, they limited imports of e-waste; this has slowed the flow. Now e-waste flows to India, Pakistan, Vietnam, Ghana, Nigeria, Chile, Uruguay, Colombia, Peru, Ecuador, and the Philippines for processing and disposal. Often, much of the waste just ends up in fields or streams. Workers and communities are exposed to very high levels of contamination. Communities of recyclers often live in toxic piles of e-waste.

True Cost Accounting of Materials and Consumption

Health studies on material risks have been improving, but the more complex and challenging task of understanding the financial costs these materials cause to people and ecosystems is less advanced. For most ecosystems and species, there are very few answers to the most basic questions about the effects of exposure and chemical buildup, as well as little understanding of the impacts on mammals, birds, insects, and fish health, including birth defects and infertility. Ongoing studies of the honeybee decline show how complex these problems can be. Sixty-one factors were examined in one study with no clear answer.[314]

Runoff from algae-resistant composite shingles as well as copper, galvanized, and lead roofing releases sufficient metal ions to be ecotoxic. Runoff from streets and parking lots may contain antifreeze, oils, copper, lead, and other ecotoxic materials. Other types of material in everyday use can also cause ecosystem damage.

Europe has been far ahead of the US in controlling the use of hazardous materials. Products sold into the European Union are required to be free of many of the worst offenders. Inspections have caught some problem products before they could reach the market. California's legislature modeled the California Restriction of Hazard Substances (RoHS) law after EU Directive 2002/95/EC. This bans certain hazardous substances from electrical and electronic equipment. The California RoHS law required the state's Department of

Toxic Substances Control to adopt regulations that would prevent electronic devices from being sold or offered for sale in California if that device is prohibited from being sold or offered for sale in the EU.

Austria passed a law more than 30 years ago that required batteries to be recycled, and many other nations have followed suit. The US has favored industry-sponsored battery recycling efforts, which have been weak. Nickel-cadmium, mercury, and lithium batteries were uncontrolled for many years. Lithium batteries are a growing concern with electric vehicle adoption. Currently, many of the massive car batteries—the Tesla version weighs about 900 pounds—appear to be stockpiled in hopes of greater reuse and recycling markets in the future. A new lithium battery recycling company[315] is opening in California, but the systems to deal with the coming flood of batteries are probably inadequate.

Hurricane Ian revealed another challenge with lithium batteries. When soaked in salt water from storm surge the batteries can short circuit and burst into flames. This may take place days or weeks after the soaking. Houses have been burned down by these car fires. Lithium burns very hot and it can take 10,000-30,000 gallons of water for a fire truck to cool them off below the ignition point. This is ten to thirty times more than the water required for a conventional car fire.

California passed a battery recycling law 15 years ago that requires almost all batteries to be recycled, but there is little oversight of consumer behavior. Lead acid auto battery recovery is very good, near 100 percent in some areas. In 2020, California also recovered 408,823 pounds of lithium-ion batteries (Li-ion) and 252,969 pounds of nickel-cadmium batteries (Ni-Cd). Nationwide sales were estimated at 6 million pounds for NiCads, so California's share would be expected to be at least 600,000 pounds, suggesting the recovery rate may only be 50 percent. True cost accounting would make this figure clearer and encourage greater compliance.

Batteries have other environmental and social costs. The cobalt used in many batteries has high external costs since half of the world's production of cobalt comes from the People's Democratic Republic of the Congo and is tied to armed conflict, illegal mining, child labor, abuse of human rights, and harmful environmental practices. Lithium mines in South America are facing increasing conflict with local communities over water use. Limited sources of lithium may also lead to national vulnerability. China is currently home to 73 percent of the global lithium battery cell manufacturing capacity, with the US lagging far behind at 12 percent. Production is expected to double by 2021, with Germany moving past the US to number two in the world.[316]

Major carmakers have plans for electric vehicles to cut greenhouse gas emissions, but some of their lithium-ion batteries are being made in places with some of the most polluting power grids in the world. Calculations suggest the average German car owner could drive a gasoline-powered vehicle for three and a half years, or more than 30,000 miles, before a Nissan Leaf with a 30-kWh battery would beat it on carbon-dioxide emissions. Just building each car battery, weighing almost half a ton for a sport utility vehicle, can emit up to 74% more CO_2 than producing an efficient conventional car if the battery is made in a factory operating with electricity generated from coal. Solar and renewable energy-based factories will be coming soon.

Over the last three years, 70 percent of battery cells in plug-in electric cars have been produced domestically in the US, and this number is expected to increase significantly with multiple very large investments in new battery gigafactories. Tesla leads the way, but GM-LG Chem and Ford-SK Innovation joint ventures are in the works.[317] Total battery capacity for EVs has reached 76,000 MWh.[318]

Developing accurate and monetized impact assessments for our manufacturing and consumption will require research and policy development. How can the needed material flow analyses and impact assessments be funded? A fee of $1 per kWh would bring in $76 million today.

Any potentially harmful contaminant found in the environment should pay an external cost impact fee, starting with the most problematic ones. For mercury, the estimated external cost is $15,000 per pound. The cost of not doing material flow analysis far exceeds the cost of performing this research and providing educational support and incentives for more complete material flow accounting. Many of the costs of not doing material flow analyses are long term and, in many cases, will reach into the billions of dollars.

A use fee of $1 per pound for pesticides would bring in $1 billion to $2 billion each year for the United States. A use fee of $0.50 per prescription of an antibiotic would help fund health and environmental impact studies of antibiotics. State paint recycling programs have fees ranging from $0.75 to $0.99 per gallon container, which have been sufficient to run the programs.

The government also has a role to play, and innovation can be encouraged. In January 2019, the US Department of Energy announced the creation of a lithium-ion battery recycling research and development center and launched the Battery Recycling Prize. This is a $5.5 million phased prize competition designed to encourage inventors and entrepreneurs to develop and demonstrate processes that can profitably capture 90 percent of all discarded or spent lithium-based batteries in the US and close the life cycle loop. In August 2022, California's Air Resources Board committed to allowing only electric or hydrogen powered vehicles to be sold in the state in 2035.

Every country, region, watershed, industrial sector, and business should maintain an accounting of materials that are imported, created, used, exported, escape, or are disposed of appropriately. Thanks to the internet and vastly improved computing capabilities, this type of accounting is no longer overwhelming. It will, however, require increased investment to better understand impacts and to monitor human health, ecosystems, and opportunities for more sustainable materials and products. This would be an excellent opportunity for university programs training tomorrow's accountants, biologists, med students, engineers, and ecologists.

A more complete understanding of impacts will help material users and waste generators link up in local, regional, national and global webs. Better information on material flows will make it possible to redesign and rethink industrial systems and food systems so they mimic natural ecosystems. Individual companies, like organisms in an ecosystem, can work for their own survival and prosperity while benefiting the environment. One company's waste can be another company's raw material.[319] Individual companies can work for their own survival and prosperity while also benefiting the environment. Industrial ecologies will be designed to fit into the landscape without harming the environment or human health, and while using only sustainable or fully recyclable resources.

The challenge is to create a culture of sustainability, because the impact of consumption is cumulative and systemic. Lifestyle choices, diet, water use, and energy use of every person in every country determines that society's overall ecological impact. While much is shaped by economic and environmental policies, social norms are also important. What is culturally accepted and financially feasible? Is the health risk more serious for refugees, the poor, immigrants, and people from other disadvantaged groups? How can costs be covered by those most able to pay? Is the environmental damage irreparable?

What You Can Do!

As noted in Chapter 4, the Global Reporting Initiative and the B-Corporation certification have encouraged many companies to start doing more comprehensive reviews of the impact and true cost of their products. You can do this for your family, neighborhood or community. Keep a record of your purchases for a week, month or year. How much energy? How much water? How many dollars? How many pounds of plastic? If you have the time, sort the plastic. How little will actually be recyclable in your town? How many pounds of packaging? Paper?

What changes can you make to reduce your consumption's true cost? Celebrate Buy Nothing Day on November 25. Can you grow, sew, make, or buy used or recycled products instead of buying new ones in boxes and unrecyclable plastic blister packs?

Get in touch with your colleges and schools and get them involved. Keeping track of the types of plastic in the waste stream is a good project. For older students studies might include tests of water toxicity. Students can also explore the fate of electronics (phones, computers, etc.) at their school or at home. Are they diverted to e-waste recovery or dumped in the trash?

How much green and food waste do you or your local school or college cafeteria compost or send to the landfill? How many pounds of recyclables are generated in a week? Does the waste hauler provide any assurance that it will be recycled? How many pounds of trash?

True cost accounting will help us close resource loops and eliminate waste. To create these more sustainable systems, we need to better understand the life cycle costs and benefits of products from the cradle to the grave (made, used, disposed)—or the cradle to the cradle (made, used, recycled, reused, or returned to nature). Join and support the groups that are working for a more sustainable economy with lower true costs. Encourage your local leaders, state representatives, and national Congress members to push for true cost accounting.

With true cost accounting, consumers will be able to live reasonably well without compromising their children's future.

CHAPTER 11

TCA FORESTRY

Trees and forests have many values besides wood. They help fight climate change, emit oxygen, support biodiversity, filter and store water, reduce flooding, minimize erosion, and control landslides. They also provide many other services including recreation, grazing, and additional products like ginseng and mushrooms. The value of individual trees or a whole forest can be calculated. Growing understanding is helping us calculate the true value of trees.

Failed accounting is leading to the destruction and mismanagement of forests around the world. The Amazon rain forest in Brazil, sometimes called the "lungs of the planet," lost more than 4 million acres in 2021.[320] Valuable trees and forests are being removed, often with subsidies, to grow soybeans, corn, and pastures for cattle. High

Failure to count true costs led to "dog hair" stands of worthless wood primed for explosive wildfires.

True cost accounting can provide open forests kept healthy with controlled low intensity fires

rates of loss are occurring in other forests as well. We can't really look down on these ecological and social catastrophes because they are simply doing what American forest managers have done.

Recent studies have documented the loss and decline of forests around the world.[321] The drivers of forest mismanagement include incomplete accounting, ignorance, and greed. Most forestry management has focused solely on timber yield. Theorists would measure tree growth and plan harvest timing for maximum economic timber yield. Without considering the wide range of true costs and benefits of the forest, the most profitable rotation is always shorter than the most ecological or productive rotation. The very valuable ecosystem services of the forest—flood control, water, oxygen, biodiversity—have been ignored. The minor products and uses such as mushrooms, firewood, berries, and grazing have been deliberately excluded from management reports and policy, and in doing so, have sparked conflicts with local communities.

Climate change is highlighting past errors in management, increasing the vulnerability of forests to drought, wildfire, disease, and pests. In North America, climate change has brought both drought and disease. In California, the lessons are particularly clear, with severe diebacks fueling massive wildfires sweeping through dead and dying forestlands. Between 2010 and 2019, approximately 147 million trees worth perhaps $20 billion died from drought and disease. More have died since, and even more were lost in the catastrophic wildfires that have burned across California in recent years. In 2021, a total of 8,619 fires burned 2.5 million acres. The incredible number of dead trees fueled the 2021 Caldor and Dixie fires in California. They burned 1,800 square miles, an area much larger than Rhode Island. The Forest Service estimates that more than 100 million trees died in the northern Sierras' Dixie Fire alone—at $100 per tree, that represents the loss of another $10 billion.

These massive high intensity fires can have catastrophic effects on aquatic ecosystems. Without trees and forest litter to retain water, flash floods full of debris and ash can be devastating to fish.[322] Sediment pulses also damage infrastructure and reduce reservoir capacity. This adds to the loss of billions of dollars of Natural Capital. Recreation and tourism businesses will be affected for many years.

Tree mortality has increased rapidly across the Western United States in recent decades and represents a CCG emission to the atmosphere of 7-25 Tg CO_2e per year.[323] This pulse needs to be considered in the projections of future carbon emissions. If pine forests have not been thinned to encourage vigorous trees that better fend off beetles, they become predisposed to bark beetle attack. Major forest disease problems are also exacerbated by climate change. Many insect pests and fungi have benefited from warmer temperatures.

A recent outbreak of the mountain pine beetle has affected more than 40 million acres in British Columbia and 4 million acres in the US.[324] At a timber value of perhaps $10,000 per acre, that represents a loss of $440 billion to the pine beetle, even considering the salvage logging that was able to be done. Of the five states with the highest percentage of mortality losses, four had volume losses greater than 24 billion board feet (Colorado, Idaho, Montana, and Wyoming). Of six states with high salvageable volumes, only Idaho, Oregon, and Montana have sufficient processing capacity to deal with large quantities of salvage logs.[325] The die-offs have left many private land owners stuck with standing dead trees they cannot harvest and sell, or simply fields of ashes. Their hopes of paying for their children's college or their own retirement have been crushed.

Sudden oak death has reached epidemic proportions in California and Oregon since it first arrived in the San Francisco Bay area in about 1990. In California, infestations in natural settings have been found in 15 central and northern coastal counties.[326] Since the mid-1990s, *Phytophthora ramorum*, the exotic plant pathogen that causes sudden oak death, has killed millions of oak and tanoak trees. Douglas fir, grand fir, coast redwood, Pacific madrone, Pacific rhododendron, evergreen huckleberry, and other tree and shrub species are also affected.[327] The US nursery industry and forests were not widely impacted by the pathogen until 2004, when a few large West Coast nurseries inadvertently shipped over a million potentially infected rhododendron and camellia plants throughout the US.

The ash borer, native to Asia and Russia, was first discovered in Michigan in 2002. Failure to consider true cost led to inadequate inspection of packing crates and the arrival of the borer. International trade often has unintended and costly consequences. As a result, it now appears likely that ash trees will be lost across most of North America.[328] The ash trees were an important part of North American forest landscapes for millennia, but now almost all green (*Fraxinus pennsylvanica*), white (*F. americana*), and black (*F. nigra*) ash are expected to die from ash borer damage. A parasitic wasp that kills borers may help, but the odds are long.[329] These three species of ash total eight billion trees and saplings, and represent an estimated value of $280 billion.[330] Throughout their range, ash trees account for nearly 14 percent of all woody species. Emerald ash borers have killed tens of millions of landscape trees with an estimated replacement cost of $10-25 billion. The ash timber industry had produced over 100 million board feet annually, valued at over $25 billion.

Their decline is happening so fast that scientists expect ash will be compared to other "lost" species[331] (elm, chestnut, butternut) that were wiped out during the twentieth century. Cold winter temperatures had helped control the borer, and it is possible some of the northernmost ash trees will survive. However, climate change could eliminate these refuges.

In North America, one of the little recognized forest management problems is cutting northern boreal forest and southeastern pine forest to make paper towels, tissues, and toilet paper.[332] The three companies with the largest market shares in the tissue sector, Procter & Gamble, Kimberly-Clark, and Georgia-Pacific, still rely almost exclusively on virgin pulp for their at-home tissue brands. This creates a "tree-to-toilet pipeline," with centuries-old trees cut, converted into tissue pulp, rolled into perforated sheets or stuffed into boxes, and flushed or thrown away. The consequences for First Nations, treasured wildlife, biodiversity, and the global climate are devastating.

Forest Ecosystem Services

Narrowly defined and simplistic goals of maximum timber yield are no longer sufficient for forest managers. The value of Nature's Services (water retention, filtration, flood control) and Natural Capital (standing timber, water) are changing management decisions. The value of Nature's Services is often greater than all the benefits for timber, recreation, minerals, and grazing combined. The forest manager or urban forester today may consider the most important functions to be carbon sequestration, habitat protection and restoration, microclimate modification, or water supply. Wood yield may be a minor element of their planning and operations.

Nature's Services

- Provisioning services—oxygen; water; market products including timber, poles, firewood, food (mushrooms, berries, nuts, etc.); medicinal herbs like ginseng; ornamental products like wreaths and Christmas trees; grazing land for livestock; mined items like minerals, sand and gravel, oil and gas; etc.
- Regulating services—climate balancing, air and water pollution amelioration, flood reduction, wind erosion control, waste treatment, carbon sequestration.
- Cultural services—tourism, recreation, relaxation, wellness, sports, fishing, hunting, bird-watching, beauty, photography, art
- Legacy, and historical values for future generations.

Preparing a True Cost Account for a Forest

- Assessment of ecosystem structure and function
- Determination of the economic value of products and services
- Evaluation of the health and well-being of workers
- Estimation of Natural Capital (standing timber, water supply, biodiversity, etc.)

- Determination of the damage cost avoided by reducing floods, nitrogen leaking, and wind
- Estimation of the damage to adjacent crops and livestock related to protected species
- Determination of cultural value by contingent valuation (asking people what they would be willing to pay)
- Detailed management costs including pruning, prescribed fire, weed control, etc.
- Enumeration of replanting or restoration costs
- Determination of the benefit transfer based on existing studies conducted elsewhere
- Other factors . . .

The services a forest provides have not been priced carefully, but a few studies have hinted at their true value.[333] Forests and trees release oxygen and sequester carbon. An acre of woodlot can sequester carbon and counter the global change gas emissions of about 2.7 cars. A fifty-year-old oak forest can sequester more than 15 tons of carbon dioxide per acre every year and emit 11 tons of oxygen.[334] The 15 tons of CCG storage would be worth $1,500. At 5¢ per pound, the oxygen from the oak forest would be worth $1,100.

US forests stored 72 billion tons of carbon in 2020,[335] worth at least $7.2 trillion at a fee of $100 per ton of CO_2e. Forests continue to sequester more carbon than they release each year, as trees reclaim abandoned farmland in the Northeast. Combined with urban forests and harvested wood products (that lock carbon away in buildings), trees offset nearly 15 percent of total greenhouse US gas emissions in 2012.

Permanently protected forests can be set aside for carbon sequestration, but even after trees are cut, much carbon remains sequestered in roots and glomalin, a protein made by mycorrhizal fungi. Carbon sequestration has become an income source for some forest managers; however, the costs of registration and compliance can be substantial, which makes this option more attractive for large landholders. Options for carbon payments for sequestration in the US have grown. IndigoAg (a subsidiary of Ecometrx LLC) is offering about $20 for each ton of carbon a farmer sequesters.[336] For a forest sequestering 15 tons per acre, this would provide a welcome $300 an acre. The actual value is probably closer to the Swedish CCG fee of $137.50 per ton. At this level, each acre would be worth more than $2,000 a year. As concern over climate change mounts, carbon sequestration payments will rise, and more simplified methods of enrolling and certification will be implemented.

It is essential to monetize at least some of these services so a landowner can realize a profit for some of economic benefits the forest provides for society. As one Swedish forest owner put it, "One could utilize the forest for wellness of course, but somehow you need to get paid because otherwise it must be harvested." This is where payment for ecosystem services becomes important, even though calculating the more indirect values of a forest can be challenging.

The ecosystem service value of forests has been estimated at $542 per acre per year.[337] Wetland forests were much more valuable at $10,397 per acre. More subtle benefits may also be important. For example, the Northwest forests have added value because the perceived environmental quality of the area makes it easier to recruit qualified high-tech workers for companies in Seattle and Portland. This value may be comparable to the recreation value, yet has rarely been considered. Environmental quality has very real economic benefits.

Forest Management Considering True Cost

Improving forest management is not easy. Tradition and culture may still downplay climate change and may also resist ecosystem-based forest management. But improved true cost accounting for forests is being done. A detailed study of forestland in New Zealand found the timber was worth $541 per acre, carbon storage $253, avoided nitrogen damage $310, and avoided erosion $390.[338] Total value of the factors considered was $1,159 per acre. Timber accounted for just 16 percent of the forest ecosystem value. The recreational value of mountain biking alone for Whakarewarewa Forest was five times the timber revenue.[339]

In other areas, the value of water management by forests has been set as high as $2,500 per acre per year, while air pollution reduction from trees in cities has been estimated at $750 per acre per year. The value of the forest to water supply and water quality in New York was described in Chapter 9. A broader look at the value of forest wetlands suggests the potential value if all services are counted. For Georgia, the value of forest wetlands was estimated at $67 billion.[340] The greatest values were aesthetics, water supply, water flow regulation, protection from extreme events, food, waste treatment, and recreation.

Several states and many nations have developed forest regulations that support better forest management. Most were too little too late. Management is complicated by differing regulations and rules affecting the many types of ownership, Private lands, which make up almost 40 percent of California forests, have provided the majority of California's timber since the 1940s. The state's Z'Berg-Nejedly Forest Practice Act (FPA) of 1973 governs management of California's privately owned forestlands. The FPA authorizes the state Board of Forestry and Fire Protection to develop regulations related to most commercial and noncommercial timber harvesting activities. These are known as the Forest Practice Rules (FPR).[341]

California's FPR and Timber Harvest Plans (THP) for private forest holdings are now very comprehensive. The THP, which may be 100-500 pages long, must be prepared by a registered professional forester, who also has to oversee the harvest. About a thousand THPs are prepared each year with costs that can reach $10,000. The state's Natural Resources Agency oversees the Timber Regulation and Forest Restoration Program, including coordinating multi-department reviews of Timber Harvest Plans and developing performance measures for how timber harvest policies are meeting the state's ecological goals. The strict rules and cost have led to unintended consequences as some industrial forest companies have sold out of California and moved to states with minimal forest rules.

California added the option of a Nonindustrial Timber Management Plan (NTMP) for smaller forest holders in 1991. NTMPs involve a long-term management plan better suited to the intended land uses than a THP. The Working Forest Management Plan program of 2013 enacted through Chapter 648 (AB 904, Chesbro) allows for long-term forest management plans for nonindustrial forest owners who wish to harvest and sell some of their trees but own less than 15,000 acres of timberlands.

The long time it takes trees to grow requires careful evaluation of cumulative effects over larger areas and many holdings. What is desirable locally now, such as jobs today from cutting old-growth timber, may be very harmful in the future. A Douglas fir tree cut in 1936 measured in at 48,669 board feet.[342] With a value of perhaps $10 per board foot today, that would have been a half-million-dollar tree. But trees were cut with little concern for the future.

Forest plantings and forest rotations are driven by discount rates and alternative investment opportunities. A change from a 1 per cent to a 3 percent discount rate reduced the preferred forest rotation length in one case from ninety years to sixty years—in a system where optimal biological growth was 100 years. It also cut the optimal thinning before harvest from three times to two. Higher discount rates keep forests from being planted or restored when only timber value is counted. A conservative discount rate of near zero will improve forest management.

Recent timber harvests in the US have shifted from over-cut and poorly managed public lands in the West to private lands in the East and South. In the three states on the West Coast, only a little more than a third of the forestland is privately held. In the South, it is almost all privately held. In South Carolina, for example, 88 percent is private. In Europe, about half the forestland is in private hands, and almost all of their old-growth forest is gone.

Hardwood and softwood forests in the US and around the world have suffered from high grading, another failure to consider the true cost. Only the best, tallest, straightest trees are cut, and low-value deformed and diseased trees that are harder to cut and more difficult to mill are left. These less desirable trees then seed the next forest. Over time, this can degrade the timber resource, resulting in slower-growing trees with poorer forms that are diseased or more susceptible to disease, drought, or insect pests. Avoiding this result can be a challenge for family forest owners when they try to find a contract logger. A professional forester or certified master logger can help set up harvest contracts to ensure the best value now and in the future.

Trees have become so valuable that they are being stolen. In 1996, it was estimated that timber rustlers were taking as much as $1 million worth of wood products from state and federal lands in Washington every month. Large cedar trees are particularly valuable. Some timber has even been stolen using helicopters. Timber theft has also been a problem in Canada. In many developing countries, almost all the timber is illegally cut. Other high-value forest products[343] may also be stolen on public and private land. The more valuable ones, like matsutake mushrooms worth $60 a pound and ginseng root at $600 per pound, have led to fights and even murder.

Forest Work and Safety

If you plan to cut trees or do other work in the forest: take classes, get advice, and use the best equipment possible. If you hire contractors or workers, make sure they are well-trained and insured. Logging is inherently dangerous. Work conditions can be harsh and the environment can be challenging. The pressure to get the cut out at the lowest price "at any cost" attitude often encountered in the industry increases the risk of injury and death for forest workers.

Training historically has been done on the job and in a very uneven manner. Today, workshops, courses, and master logger certification are helping to reduce risk. Some sustainable forest initiatives are requiring or recommending master logger certification for cutting on certified sustainable lands. Certified master loggers can often get a break on workers' compensation insurance to offset training costs. In some certification programs, field verifiers visit harvest sites to determine whether candidates for master logger certification are meeting or exceeding the standards.

Better training and improved equipment do make a difference in woods work. The accident rate for nonprofessional forest workers is higher than for the pros. More than 20,000 chain saw injuries occur every year.[344] In 2016, the Bureau of Labor Statistics reported the nationwide fatality rate for loggers was 100.1 per 100,000 full-time equivalent workers. The Oregon fatality rate per 100,000 professional forest workers was 220 in 1983 but dropped to 212 in 2018. This is higher than the national average because Oregon loggers face more dangerous working conditions, steep slopes, rain, and wind. In Sweden, an average of only one professional logger dies per year, or 35 in 100,000 equivalent workers.[345] Sweden has a much stronger educational system for forest workers. You can learn a lot from videos and books—but hands-on training is best.

Forest Management for Sustainable Value

Forest owners are often unaware of the many values of the forest so one of the first important steps is education. This will encourage greater participation on the part of public and private forest owners. As payment for ecosystem services increase, it will be easier to make converts. There are about 275.7 million acres of forest in private hands.[346] Family forest owners include an estimated 9.7 million owners with more than 10 acres of forest, but only one in five gets any annual income from that land. Only 8 percent of the families and individuals who own US forestland have a written management plan. Even so, plans for larger holdings include only 24 percent of the total forestland. Active forest management with planting, pruning, thinning, weed management, integrated pest management, and fire risk reduction can improve short- and long-term value, but these practices have not been widely adopted in the US.

Calculating the value of carbon sequestration and other ecosystem services can potentially increase income if an organization interested in paying for Ecosystem Services can be found. For the majority of forest landowners to get more involved, they will need to be able to realize some of the value from nature's services, wood, minor products, recreation, and biodiversity. Improving management will take both private and public investment.

Trees in urban and suburban areas also provide ecosystem services that should be considered in true cost accounting. You can count the trees around your home as a carbon sink in your carbon calculations. Native species support biodiversity. Douglas Tallamy makes an excellent case for planting native trees and taking steps to make every yard part of the "Homegrown National Park." The oaks in North America support more than 900 species of caterpillars, while the alien eucalyptus supports only one species in California.[347] This has impacts all across the food web: birds need hundreds of caterpillars a day to feed their nestlings, and a pair of birds may need more than 4,000 caterpillars to fledge their young. And oaks may live 1,000 years or more and are ideal for carbon sequestration, with deep and wide-ranging root systems and mycorrhizal root symbionts adding glomalin to the soil. Glomalin is a sticky protein produced by root-dwelling fungi and sloughed into soil as roots grow. By gluing soil particles and organic matter together, it stabilizes soil and keeps carbon from escaping into the atmosphere.[348]

Management studies and recommendations for private forest landowners should include measurements of cost effectiveness, environmental effectiveness, distributional impacts, funding requirements, and the potential for new markets. Using external cost fees to improve accounting and payment for ecosystem services makes sense. Payments for flood control, oxygen, and carbon sequestration may also be important.

Forest planning once seemed simple—just cut less than the annual growth with some planning for uncertainty as well as disease, drought, wildfire, and market volatility. Today, the forest or urban tree manager should be considering the full range of possible benefits and external costs, regulations, and risk.

Even greater diversity is needed as we face climate change. Typical forest cutting cycles (known as rotations) are long enough to reach through many political administrations and sometimes generations. In the Southeast US and New Zealand, a thirty-five-year rotation is not unusual (almost a forester's whole career). For a California mixed conifer forest, it might be sixty-five years on a productive site. For redwood trees, it may be better to think of 100-150-year cycles. In the UK and France, some oaks are still being grown on a 100+ year cycle.

Old growth forest may have three times the biodiversity of a young plantation.[349] For the benefits of old-growth forest and maximum ecological diversity, a 200-year rotation may be a good start, but is hard to even imagine in our time of rapid climate change. This might be done on only 5-10 percent of a forest so as not to unduly limit productivity and short-term income. In Europe, coppices (smaller trees that resprout readily) planted together with standards (scattered tall trees) allow for the harvest of the coppices every thirty years or so. This benefits the standard trees by releasing resources and allowing them more sun so they can grow to their full size faster and produce very high-value wood.

Careful processing can also increase timber value. Thoughtful sawing and drying are important for maximum value. Solar kilns can reduce the energy cost of drying. Value can be added to timber by resawing and gluing smaller pieces to make clear stock. Laminated woods can make strong straight beams and rafters for even major buildings. Value-added mills are expensive to build, but are more resistant to changes in demand or the price of raw materials.

The forest can also provide valuable products like mushrooms. Shiitakes make a good starter for forest farmers.[350] The market is strong, chefs like them, and they are well understood. Logs are prepared and inoculated with commercial spawn. A beginner might start with 300 logs producing 10 pounds of mushrooms a week. Wild harvest of berries, herbs, medicinal plants, fruits, nuts, and acorns can also provide food and income.

Harvesting with horses, mules, and oxen will be more common with true cost accounting. They are much easier on the forest and there is little damage from skidding (dragging) trees.[351] Trees growing close to animal skid trails have higher growth rates than those growing near tractor skidder trails. Soil compaction from animal skidders is much lower than that with tractor skidders—sometimes as low as zero.

Research has shown the use of horses instead of tractors in high-volume industrial community forestry in Mexico to be successful.[352] Studies from China, Africa, Iran, and the Missouri Ozarks have also shown the many ecological benefits this can provide.

Horse logging is good for parks and watersheds. It is more people-friendly and can reduce complaints of noise and limit erosion. After a storm blew down dozens of trees on a hillside in north Georgia, the Chattooga Watershed Coalition brought in horse loggers to minimize pollution risks to the water supply.

Animal-powered logging won't replace conventional equipment in industrial logging, but in areas where preserving the landscape is important, horse loggers can pull their weight. Horses are more economical ($25,000 for two Percherons or a Tigercat skidder for $95,000). They are more maneuverable and flexible in handling varying timber dimensions. Fossil fuel consumption and CCG emissions are also minimized.

New and improved mechanical harvesting equipment can also reduce impact. Harvesters with a boom can reach 30 feet to the side. More expensive models can lay the tree down in the least damaging location, cut off the branches, cut the log to length, and maintain a running tally of the cut. In some areas, loggers have found that they can minimize soil damage by laying the slash (cut branches) in the harvester's path.

Mini-mills also offer new potential for processing logs in the forest, which can make hauling with animals more practical. Milling wood in the forest provides several benefits. As mills break down logs to smaller dimensions, the milling debris is returned to the forest floor. On-site milling near the cut can minimize skidding and hauling damage. When old, large trees fall or fail, some should be left in place as nurse logs to help the next generation of trees get started. For high-value trees, like cedar, even old logs found on the forest floor or on the beach may be of value. Mini-mills can also help with the timber harvest in urban areas. Many trees have very high-quality wood, and some cities and companies now make good use of these trees. Epilogue LLC in Charbonneau, Oregon, is a good example of a timber salvage company that produces high-value kiln-dried wood from urban trees and trees from rural property and farms.

TCA and Sustainable Forests

The key issues are not technical questions about harvesting systems but those dealing with the true value of the forest and all its products and services, risks, and opportunities. A key step will be more inclusive goal-setting that considers the full range of Natural Capital and Nature's Services to include tourism, recreation, hunting, fishing, water sports, wildlife viewing, and quiet solitude. We need a broad range of people, both men and women, from diverse cultural backgrounds working together to guide the transition. Women need to be included in planning and management for long-term sustainability. A survey in Sweden found there were clear differences between the priorities of the men (who traditionally have made all the rules and done most of the forest work) and women who lived in the forest.[353] Women felt health, wellness, and a good living environment were twice as important as the men did.

Forest management has been driven by short-term economics and government policy; we now need the wisdom to develop incentives to do things well and to manage for the long term. Consumer-driven efforts to improve forest and landscape management have led to certifying organizations that encourage forest companies to adopt more sustainable practices and then to ensure that they are following the rules. Programs for better landscape management include the National Wildlife Federation's certified habitat program, with 2.5 million acres enrolled; the Audubon Society's Bring Conservation Home; and many others. The Old Growth Forest Network has adopted a bold goal for reforestation. They are campaigning for one forest in every county in the US (that has or had forests) to be set aside to grow without cutting. This is important because you can never imagine the old-growth forest to be as remarkably beautiful and engaging as it really is and how important these old trees are for thousands of species.

Two major forest organizations certify good practices. The Forest Stewardship Council (FSC) was founded in 1994 with fairly demanding requirements and now has members in 90 countries, with 155 million acres enrolled in the US and Canada. The FSC program has had a tremendous impact, even when it was not the certification process selected by the forest manager. FSC certificate holders can also join together to create a group certification program. They can share efforts for forest management planning, harvesting, monitoring and marketing their products. Group certification makes it easier, particularly for smallholders, to become FSC certified, as it enables group members to share costs and workload for applying and maintaining an FSC certificate. Small or low-intensity managed forests (SLIMF) are eligible for streamlined requirements and auditing procedures that reduce the costs and efforts of the certification.[354]

The strictness of this process led the forest industry and paper companies to develop an alternative, the Sustainable Forestry Initiative (SFI), which started with relatively low standards and no outside monitoring and has grown to include 285 million acres in the US and Canada. The SFI Forest Management Standard[355] now considers a broader range of forest values, including protection of biodiversity, species at risk, and wildlife habitat; sustainable harvest levels; protection of water quality; and prompt regeneration. SFI certifications now require independent, third-party audits by internationally accredited certification bodies. The National Tree Farm Association's "Green Tag" and the American Tree Farm System Certification may be more appropriate for owners of small forests.

Many producers here and abroad cannot call on the skilled consultants needed to support certification. Costs for consultants and required research can be prohibitive unless a group of smaller producers join together. The Forest Certification Resources Center can help with up-to-date information, including the latest from the Canadian Standards Association and the Programme for the Endorsement of Forest Certification. The European Forest Institute deserves credit for setting up a Certification Information Service. Active NGO engagement and support are likely to remain critical in the effort to develop and maintain strong and effective certification programs outside the US and Europe.

Alternative policy options for conserving forest biodiversity include the following:

- Educating forest owners
- Improving accounting along the harvest supply chain
- Developing policy and programs to monetize forest benefits
- Paying for ecosystem services—watershed protection, carbon sequestration, biodiversity
- Ensuring the provision of a healthy and good living environment, silence, solitude, privacy
- Improving understanding of pruning and thinning for high-value timber
- Creating better timber harvest plan guides and review
- Formulating land use and land management regulations
- Expanding protected areas
- Issuing carbon sequestration credits
- Using biodiversity credits
- Supporting and regulating ecotourism
- Generating non-timber forest product rules—for berries, mushrooms, firewood
- Certifying forests by FSC, SFI, etc.
- Developing regulations for prospecting and bioprospecting
- Regulating lumber imports (to ensure a level playing field)
- Use local lumber for pallets and use native landscape plants to reduce the risk of importing pests
- Strengthening rules for grazing
- Managing road construction to minimize erosion, landslides
- Managing off-road vehicle use to reduce damage
- Promoting bird-watching, wildlife viewing, biking, paddling, rafting
- Managing hunting and fishing to minimize ecosystem damage

True Cost Accounting and Payment for Ecosystem Services

True cost accounting will help forest managers consider the full value of Natures Services and Natural Capital. It can help ensure that the value of ecosystem services is recognized and included. This will also develop new income streams to landowners and managers. Sequestering 600 million tons of carbon per year with forests would offset a third of the current annual US carbon emissions at a cost of only $27 to $105 per ton.[356] It could bring $25 billion in revenue to forest and landscape owners.

True cost accounting will change timber harvesting. When true costs are counted, the trees may be cut and placed on the landing by a master logger in the owner's employ, using the least harmful harvesting system and utmost care. Logs would then be sold as a known commodity. Some of the timber harvest in Japan is done this way. The bidders at the auction know exactly what they will get. In areas with many small private holdings, a regional or cooperative THP might be able to reduce costs per participant.

Forest accounting varies by state and nation and may take some effort to understand. Taxation policy that neglects true costs can lead to forest mismanagement. Annual property taxes can easily exceed the value of sustainable forest harvests. Alaska, Delaware, and Iowa avoid this problem by not taxing forestland. In some places, the value of the standing timber is taxed; in other areas, the value of the timber is only taxed when the trees are cut. This requires calculation of the timber basis and depletion allowance. Some governments offer other types of timber tax incentives. Careful accounting for investments, operations, and forest value is needed. This may require the help of both a professional forester (registered in some states) and an accountant familiar with forest taxes. They can also help plan the best way to deal with estate taxes when inherited forests can lead to significant tax burdens. A forest may be very valuable, even if it is not providing any annual income. Inheritors often end up cutting trees to pay taxes.

Payments for ecosystem services (PESs) are being used to improve forest management in the US and around the world. As many as twenty federal programs provide some support for private forest owners to protect ecosystem services. PESs by the federal government may exceed $500 million a year, but they are very hard to tease out of the complex federal budget and overlapping programs from forest, agriculture, and environmental agencies. The US Forest Service budget for 2021 included $217 million for state and private forestry programs to support the agency's Shared Stewardship initiative. Forty percent will address emerging threats to forest health on and off Forest Service lands. The budget also commits $21 million to the Working Forest Lands program to focus on priority areas identified in state forest action plans. Reviews are needed to determine what the value of these programs has been. What has changed?

The states also fund and do some work. In response to poor forest conditions and clear needs, the 2017-18 state budget for California included providing $195 million in greenhouse gas reduction funds to CalFire (the state forestry agency) for forest health and fire prevention activities. Many states have active forest stewardship programs (in cooperation with the USFS), but I could not find any studies on the effectiveness of these programs. The fact that only 10-20 percent of family forests have active management plans[357] suggests these programs have not been able to reach many people.

Privately funded PES programs are also in place in the US and around the world. Conservation organizations have been paying forest landowners conservation easements for decades to protect ecosystem services. A 2011 study by the Ecosystem Marketplace found that payments for forest-based ecosystem services to US forest owners from private funding sources may have been $1.5 billion.[358] Key payments were for sales of forest wetland mitigation credits at $727 million, conservation bank credits of $34 million, sales of carbon offsets for $1.7 million, conservation easements of $315 million, hunting leases and entrance fees of $410 million, and wildlife viewing entrance fees of $33 million. Wetland mitigation accounted for the largest percentage of forest-based ecosystem service payments, but funds went to less than 200 private forest mitigation banks, representing just 0.00002 percent of all private forest landowners in the US. Carbon offsets accounted for only 0.001 percent of all forest PESs. These figures do not include payments for water services due to a lack of data on payments made to forest landowners.

Costa Rica's Payments for Environmental Services program began in 1997 after the country experienced one of the highest deforestation rates in Latin America. Their PES and other policies managed to turn that around in a relatively short period of time. Costa Rica has paired its ban on deforestation with the introduction of PES, which pays farmers to protect watersheds, conserve biodiversity, or capture carbon dioxide.[359] The PES program has helped Costa Rica's forest cover recover from 24 percent to more than 60 percent by promoting forest ecosystem conservation and combating land degradation. Landowners receive direct payments for the environmental services from their lands when they adopt sustainable land-use and forest-management techniques. A tax on fossil fuels is the main source of funding (80%), while the other 20 percent comes from international sale of carbon credits in public protected areas.[360] More than 18,000 families have benefited from the program, with an investment of $524 million in the PES projects and more than 1.3 million hectares under contracts.[361] Costa Rica's reforestation has been such a success that it was recently awarded the Earthshot Prize.

The United States and countries around the world will participate in reforestation, forest protection, and tree planting in urban and suburban areas once true costs and true benefits are counted. These efforts can be supported with external cost recovery fees for CCGs. The Swiss Federal Institute of Technology calculated that there was room on the planet to plant an additional one trillion trees.[362] Some 2.2 billion acres of land could store 205 gigatons of carbon when the trees mature in 50-100 years.

What You Can Do!

When you buy wood, ask for certified sustainable sources. Use fewer paper towels. Consider adding a bidet to your bathroom. A bidet seat or bidet attachment can lower toilet paper use by 75 percent or more—saving almost 300 trees that would be cut down to make your lifetime toilet-paper supply. If you own land with a few trees or a forest, calculate their true value and the services they provide. How much of a carbon offset can you count? Support organizations that work to improve forest accounting and taxation, payment for environmental services, and improved management both here and abroad. Donations to groups like Trees for the Future will provide important benefits for the land holders around the world. Their programs provide hands-on agroforestry training and resources for farming communities. These can help people meet the challenge of climate change and generational poverty.

Contact your representatives and tell them you want true cost accounting done for state and federal forests. Press for government funding for restoration work on the millions of acres of fire-prone, degraded, burned, and eroded lands.

If you are one of the 11 million private forest owners in the US, you can find some excellent guidance in *Wild Logging: A Guide to Environmentally and Economically Sustainable Forestry, Restoration Forestry, The Once and Future Forest, Farming the Woods*, and *A Landowner's Guide to Managing Your Woods*. Although many forest farmers traditionally planted a single species over thousands of acres, wiser forest managers have always appreciated the value of diversity. Market changes affect the value of different species, and this can be hard to predict. Insect pests may arrive and decimate one species. How will you manage your woods for the lowest true cost and best returns?

Develop a master plan for long-term management in the face of climate change. In a recent survey in the US, family forest owners[363] were not adapting to climate change because they were not engaged in what foresters consider healthy active forest management practices. Even in states where a plan is not required, hiring a professional forester or certified master logger (CML) can help ensure better logging practices that will protect future value. The CML certification was first developed in Maine but is now available in many states and other countries. The certification process includes education and, in some cases, field verification of best practices.

Healthy forests and urban trees are good for everyone. They support biodiversity and wildlife, protect and provide water, and generate oxygen. They are good for people's health, attitude, and enjoyment. Restoration is underway in many areas, and people are taking steps to make forests healthier and more resilient. Volunteer to help with reforestation both locally and internationally. Take part!

CHAPTER 12

TCA FISHERIES

T rue cost accounting could have protected the world's fish, but failure to count costs has doomed the fish and, in many cases, the fishermen. Overfishing, habitat damage, and pollution have led to collapse and extinction of important fish species.[364] Enormous runs of salmon, shad, eels, alewives, steelhead, and more once filled the rivers and streams of North America. In the West, spring and fall runs of multiple species of salmon provided food for native people and wildlife while fertilizing watersheds.[365] Offshore fishing was equally productive after the Europeans arrived, but these bountiful fish stocks would eventually be over-harvested and collapse. The Grand Banks cod is the most notable, but is just one of far too many examples of the high price of not counting the true cost. Many other Atlantic species have already become

Cod fishing was sustainable for 400 years

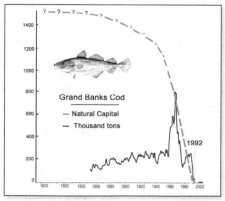

Failure to count the true cost led to the collapse of the cod fishery. 40,000 people lost their jobs.

commercially extinct, including the Atlantic halibut and redfish. In the 1980s, two other commercially important Georges Bank species, haddock and yellowtail flounder, appeared to be headed to a similar fate, but the measures that were put in place to protect the remaining Atlantic cod have resulted in their partial recovery.

The Collapse of the Cod Fishery

In 1497, John Cabot's crew reported that "... the sea there is full of fish that can be taken not only with nets but with fishing-baskets."[366] By 1600, English fishing captains still reported cod shoals, "So thick by the shore that we hardly have been able to row a boat through them." Even within memory, there were many cod. One old salt recalled hauling in 25 tons in 20 minutes at one of his favorite fishing spots, filling his net so full that it could not be brought on board and had to be dragged behind him into port.

The Grand Bank cod fishery off Nova Scotia was first exploited by Europeans in the 1400s and was heavily fished by the 1500s. Fish were caught for 700 years with simple hooks and lines with only a gradual decline in the harvest and the fish stocks (Natural Capital). But by the 1800s, a careful study of fishing intensity and catches on the Scotian Shelf found that even hand-lining was decreasing the cod stocks.[367] Between 1852 and 1857, the Beverly Company vessels fished the Scotian Shelf almost 90 percent of the time. This declined to 60 percent in 1859 as the captains searched for more profitable concentrations of cod. Catch per unit of fishing effort (CPUE in fish per day per ton of vessel) had declined by over 50 percent in just seven years. In 1852, the cod biomass was estimated to be 1.39 million tons, and today it is down to 55,000 tons, with only 3,300 tons reaching maturity—at a smaller size.

The fishery provided stable jobs that kept families and communities together. This would all change beginning in 1906 with the arrival of steam-powered trawlers from France.[368] A trawler dragging its scraper and nets across the sea floor causes severe damage that can't be fixed. This was known to some—the US Commissioner of

Fisheries sounded the first warning about the danger of trawlers to cod populations in 1914—but was not fully appreciated.

Beginning in 1950, the technology changed even more dramatically with the arrival of 400-foot-long trawlers with onboard fish processing. Sonar also helped locate schools of cod. In one hour, these massive ships could catch the same tonnage as a traditional ship might catch in a season. The damage that bottom trawlers do to habitats depends on the design and weight of the gear on the seabed, the towing speed, the nature of the bottom sediments, and the strength of the tides and currents. The greater the frequency of impact on an area, the greater the likelihood of permanent change. After the ocean bottom is trawled, it can look as though it has been bulldozed. If cod territories are damaged by trawling, the cod may not reproduce as well or at all. Recovery of the cod remains impeded because the ocean floor on the banks is now repeatedly raked by crab and shrimp boats. Shelter for the young cod and their food is also lost, so survival may be limited.

The switch to trawling was significant. It cost less to catch the fish—but the true cost was high. Demand and prices for cod remained high, and pressure on the Grand Banks fishery increased from local and international fleets. By the early 1960s, an estimated two billion cod remained. Fishing intensity and profits increased dramatically until the cod harvest peaked in 1968 at 810,000 tons— roughly four times the typical historic catch, representing 40 percent of the world's total fishery harvests that year.

A seventy-six-year-old Newfoundland resident describes the rush of foreign trawlers that came to the area at its peak, "I remember going out onto the cape in the night, and all you could see were dragger [trawler] lights as far as the eye could see, just like a city in the sea. We all knew it was wrong. They were taking the mother fish which had been out there spawning over the years."[369]

The looming catastrophe represented a perfect storm of failure in science, regulation, and politics.[370] The Canadian Department of Fisheries and Oceans (DFO) was the manager of the fishery and tried to apply scientific rigor by formulating a mathematical model of the cod population to calculate the maximum sustainable yield (MSY). The US government has used a comparable concept called "optimal yield." Both models are single-species models that fail to consider the complexity of the fish ecosystem and fishery operations. By the 1970s, concern about overfishing was growing, and the Canadian total allowable catch was lowered. A 200-mile limit to restrict foreign trawlers was enacted, but they were soon replaced with local trawlers.

In the course of DFO management, the catch limit was set by negotiation between the scientists at the DFO, the fishing industry, and politicians. In 1989, the DFO advised that the total allowable catch of codfish should be 125,000 tons. The Canadian Minister of Fisheries arbitrarily increased this to 235,000 tons. The DFO had already set the catch much too high, but the politicians raised it still further. With more effective and deadly equipment, inappropriate management, and flawed limits, the catch in the last years of cod fishing on the Grand Banks may have been 60 percent of the total cod population instead of the 16 percent the models suggested as appropriate. Errors by the government fishery scientists in using inappropriate statistical methods were compounded by the actions of politicians and fishermen. Some fishermen had raised the alarm about overfishing but were overruled by the technocrats. They all failed to consider not only the cod, but the ecosystem that supported the cod, the value of the cod stock, and the economic dependence of the community of fishermen.

The destruction of the ocean floor ecosystem by trawlers for decades has probably played an important role in limiting recovery. Research has shown that cod may have very local breeding grounds. While spawning, cod are extremely vulnerable to fishing activity because they are intent on mating.[371] The males are unwilling to leave their hard-won display areas (leks), so both sexes are less likely to try to evade oncoming nets. Physical disturbance during mating will disrupt the activity and potentially destroy the lek areas and limit reproduction. Trawlers may also disrupt the breeding patterns of cod as the trawlers' nets damage and disperse the fertilized cod eggs, further reducing survival. The shellfish and seaweed beds that support crustaceans, mollusks, and small fish are destroyed. Without them, there is less food for the cod. Gone too are the smaller fish the cod ate, the types of food those smaller fish ate, and the complex ocean-bottom ecosystem that provides safe haven for small fish to grow in. The managers and fishermen have neglected ecosystem structure and function. Incomplete accounting has failed to protect the cod and the ecosystem they need to survive. By 1991, the population of some cod stocks had dropped to less than 1 percent of their original size. The spawning biomass of northern cod dropped from an estimated 1.6 million tons in 1962 to less than 100,000 tons in 1992.[372] This is an asset value decline of 1.5 million tons and loss of Natural Capital of 10-20 billion dollars!

The Closure of the Cod Fishery

In 1992, the cod fishery was closed indefinitely, putting 35,000 people out of work—12 percent of the area's workforce. Ten percent of the people left the area. The collapse of the fishery led to very costly government support for the out-of-work fishermen and their families. The income loss to families over thirty years may be more than $26 billion.[373] The Canadian government has spent more than $8 billion to offset some of this loss. The remaining fishermen and -women were making about $15,000 a year in 2008 and getting another $10,000 from unemployment insurance. The personal cost of the loss of careers, often after multiple generations, led to depression, alcohol and drug use, anger, and violence. In addition, many secondary businesses failed. The multiplier effect may be 2-3 times the direct loss, perhaps reaching 40-60 billion dollars.

Today, some thirty years after the moratorium that halted fishing, northern cod stocks continue to languish.[374] The explanation for the slow recovery is likely to include subtle ecosystem structure changes that may be irreparable. Targeting larger individual fish with large mesh size allows smaller individuals to escape, so the fish gradually get smaller. Fish mortality is heavily skewed toward larger individuals, so decades of strong selection favor smaller, faster-maturing, slower-growing fish. This is another economic loss.

In 2000, the World Wildlife Fund placed cod on the endangered species list. The cod population has not recovered, but some cod can be found, and a small commercial cod fishery, known as the "stewardship" fishery, is operating. The Canadian Fisheries Department's latest stock assessment, released in early 2021, recommends a maximum catch of 12,999 tons for the year This is about 6 percent of the once sustainable harvest, and many feel even this level of fishing pressure will prevent the cod population from ever recovering.

Norwegian Success

The Norwegian cod stocks were plunging as well until harvest restrictions were put in place. The catch had been about 800,000 tons per year until the late 1970s.[375] The Norwegian government slashed the cod quota in 1989, cutting the allowable catch in 1990 to just 200,000 tons. In addition, a rights-based management scheme was implemented, setting individual vessel quotas. The Norwegian government also put a moratorium on catching caplin, the main prey of the cod, and banned fishing on the spawning grounds. At the time, no studies had proved that dragging huge nets through schools of spawning cod interfered with reproduction, but the Norwegians were determined to leave reproducing fish alone. If they had waited another two years, as the Canadian DFO did, it might have been a different, very sad story. But for once, the change came in time, and the allowable catch soon rose to 740,000 tons. These stocks vary from year to year but appear to be stable. The Norwegian fishery managers acknowledge that human-induced climate change is affecting the oceans and argue there is an urgent need to find the best solutions for robust and sustainable fishery management.

Natural Capital

The mismanagement and collapse of the cod fishery in the Grand Bank has had enormous financial, social, and environmental costs. The Natural Capital value of the intact fishery can be estimated by looking at the harvest levels when they were stable. The size of the

Grand Bank cod fish stock in 1700 is impossible to know, but may have been twenty times the typical harvest over the centuries. This would be ten times 200,000 tons, or about two million tons, with a Natural Capital value of $16 billion at $4 per pound. This value, however, neglects other ecosystem services that the Grand Bank and the cod provided before they were wiped out. A more realistic estimate of asset value might be $30 billion.

As classic open-access resources with incomplete accounting, 70 percent of the major world fisheries are in decline—often severe. Only 7 percent of the ocean is under some form of protection, and much of that may not be effective. As a result, most of the world's fresh and saltwater fisheries are in deep trouble. As the most profitable big fish are cleared out, the fisheries shift to smaller fish; when those are gone, they shift to deeper water or to shrimp and crabs. Some of the fish species living at depths greater than 1,500 feet that are now being harvested take decades to reach breeding maturity. Catches logged by trawlers operating in the North Atlantic from 1978 to 1994 show that at least five species of deep-sea fish are at such low levels that they qualify for the World Conservation Union's critically endangered list.

Along with the fish, the shellfish, including oysters, clams, abalone, and other species, are gone from many coastlines. Commercial fishing of abalone in California peaked at 2,750 tons in 1957.[376] Commercial abalone landings and abalone abundance continued to decline after 1969 and by 1994 had dropped to approximately 150 tons—a decline of 95 percent. Two of California's abalone species are now federally listed as endangered, and none are currently open to fishing. The ban on abalone fishing will be reconsidered in 2026.

The tragedies are equally great for species after species of shellfish. Found, over-exploited, and then gone. Giant clams once grew so thickly on the shallow coasts of the Indo-Pacific ocean that a 19th century British conchologist reported drifting over a bank of them a mile long.[377] Today they are extinct in many areas where they were once so common. The sad history of oysters is well told by Mark Kurlansky.[378] More recently, the increase in seaweed harvests and aquaculture farms is raising new concerns as damage extends to new areas every year.

In Tasmania, a similar pattern of overharvesting developed for rock lobsters. Fortunately, managers had learned from earlier failures around the world, and the allowable take was cut significantly. Reductions were made in 2008, 2009, and 2010, dropping from 1,524 to just 1,163 tons in 2010. The precipitous decline of the lobster was halted just in time. One or two more years might have meant the end. Instead, lobster populations have recovered, and harvests have stabilized for the time being. Climate change and increasing acidity in the ocean may cause new problems going forward.

The external costs of fishing can be very large but often go unseen. Bottom trawlers bulldoze the sea floor and destroy complex ecosystems in a single pass. Trawls damage both ecosystem structure and function. The decline in one species may trigger a change in the ecosystem that ripples up and down the food chain. These changes can limit recovery as fewer eggs are produced, fertility is limited, and predation of eggs and young fish increases. This can cause damage that lasts decades or centuries.

The mismanagement—sometimes collapse—of most fisheries is a direct outcome of incomplete accounting for Natural Capital and Nature's Services driven by ignorance and flawed regulatory policy. Incredibly valuable Natural Capital can be squandered in just a matter of years. The collapse of different cod fisheries in the North Atlantic has demonstrated how costly these mistakes can be to people and marine ecosystems.

In 2021, excessive heat on the Canadian west coast led to a die-off of marine organisms unable to cope with air temperatures of 120°F.[379] One scientist estimated there were 600,000 dead mussels on just one 164-foot stretch of beach. Overall, the death toll was in the billions. The death of so many sea creatures at once not only affected ocean life but harmed the birds that feed on sea life, people running fisheries, and tourism-based businesses. Beachgoers who headed to the water to cool off were greeted with the putrid stench of rotting shellfish.

The decline of five Pacific salmon species has been linked to climate changes.[380] This makes efforts to restore these fisheries more problematic. If the conditions are no longer suitable for the salmon, it is likely they are also harming other species that aren't being studied. Ripple effects can be expected as salmon disappear. New research has demonstrated unexpected external costs from the Pacific Coast-wide decline in salmon populations. Their removal has resulted in adverse ecological impacts to terrestrial food webs and the health of the forest. Researchers in Washington State[381] found that salmon provided food for many species of microbes, stream invertebrates, mammals, and birds. These "salmon-derived" nutrients from decaying fish are important to the health of stream and riparian ecosystems and especially to the growth and development of young fish. Nitrogen and other nutrients are spread away from the creeks and rivers by the bears and other animals and birds that eat salmon. Trees on the banks of salmon-stocked rivers were found to be growing more than three times faster than their counterparts on salmon-free rivers. Sitka spruce on salmon rivers take eighty-six years, rather than 300 years, to reach a 50 cm diameter at breast height.[382] The loss of salmon costs money in terms of tree growth and harvest revenue, tourism earnings, and declines in biodiversity and resilience.

Ignorance

Our understanding of ocean and river ecosystems is not very good, but is improving. This can cause problems because the social–ecological linkages between each fish stock and natural and human ecosystems need to be understood to manage the fishery and determine the true costs. Ecosystem-based restoration and management also demand better understanding, and this has to include the fishing community. Historical data is very limited, and most studies that have been done only occurred after severe declines in fish populations and the deterioration of ecosystems. Pollution and changes in rivers and waterways from dams, drainage, and development have all harmed fisheries. In California, the Gold Rush added

400 million cubic meters of sediment to San Francisco Bay. Miners also added 20,000 tons of mercury to rivers and streams.

Fishers, scientists, and the general public are often hampered by their "feel" for the situation. This is understandable because we are most familiar with the conditions that exist during our lifetime. Past abundance is not easy to comprehend, even if we read about it or see pictures. Our bias for the contemporary leads to what is now called "shifting baselines." We accept the degraded state as being normal or natural. Each generation sees a worse and worse environment, but may not see the change as serious because it is incremental. Sure the fish are harder to catch and smaller this year, but not by much, and "next year" will be better.

True Cost Accounting for Fish and Fisheries

True cost accounting for fisheries will require new research on human behavior as well as the structure and function of marine and river ecosystems. External costs for lost or damaged fish stocks can be far-ranging, affecting the fishing community, fish processing, markets, and restaurants. Declining fisheries also hurt tourism. Ecosystem impacts can be dramatic and extend far inland for anadromous fish, like salmon, that spawn in fresh water.

An estimate of the loss can be made by looking at the value of what could have been, or what it would cost to recover the fishery. The Grand Banks cod might have sustainably produced 200,000 tons a year. At $4 per pound, that represents an annual loss of $2 billion. Over the last fifty years, the lost value may have reached $100 billion.

The global impacts of rising temperatures, changes in currents, and increasing ocean acidity will play a more important role in the future of the world's fisheries and ocean ecosystems and losses are likely to increase. The decline of the Great Barrier Reef is a worrisome example as it has suffered a number of mass bleaching events from high ocean temperatures. Indeed, a majority of Great Barrier Reef coral studied in 2022 was bleached.[383]

Fixing broken fisheries is difficult and costly. Funding is usually too little, too late. Efforts to restore salmon populations in the Northwest have cost $7 billion so far, with limited success. Watershed restoration is costly, but some studies have suggested a return of $2.50-$3.00 for every dollar spent.[384]

Dam removal is gaining more supporters and will be critical for salmon. After the removal of the Elwha dams, fish recovery was proceeding apace once fish were granted renewed access to miles of pristine riverbeds that had been denied to them for a century.[385] Rainbow trout counts increased from 3,218 in 2008 to 25,000 in 2019. The 2019 survey counted more than 340 summer steelhead, nonexistent before the dam removal. Full salmon recovery could take at least twenty to thirty years, although climate change may make it more difficult.

Fishing boat operations generate CCGs. Older diesel engines are big emitters. In 2016, total CO_2 emissions of the global industrial fishing sector were estimated to be more than 200 million tons. The smaller fishing boats emitted 53 million tons in 2016, compared to only 8.8 million tons in 1950.

The California Air Resources Board has proposed amendments to reduce diesel particulate matter from boats by 1,560 tons between 2023-2038. This is equal to the emissions generated by 246,000 heavy-duty diesel trucks traveling from Los Angeles to Sacramento every day for a year. These benefits are predicted to include avoiding 531 premature deaths, 161 hospital admissions, and 236 emergency room visits, providing $5.25 billion in benefits versus $1.98 billion in costs. Even though the projected benefits outweigh the costs, upgrading engines will be very costly and is being fought in court by small fishing boat owners. Retrofitting or rebuilding diesels to reduce emissions will be offset with some savings from increased efficiency. A new diesel may also require other changes in the engine room. The Tier 4 standards require that emissions of PM and NOx be reduced by about 90 percent. This applies to trucks as well as boats. The Tier 4 improvements reduce emissions using catalytic after-treatment technology, including selective catalytic reduction

(SCR). These engines can be difficult to retrofit in boats. Replacing engines in an excursion boat can cost more than half a million dollars. A new sport fishing charter boat with a Tier 4 engine can cost $1.3 million.[386]

Boats have other true costs. Modern biocidal antifouling paints, used to slow the growth of unwanted subaquatic organisms on the hull, adversely affect the health of marine ecosystems. These paints often contain copper, zinc, or tin. Marinas and other areas can build up high concentrations as the paint slowly wears away or flakes off. When boats are abandoned, the paints peel and chip off, and poisonous particles make their way into the environment. These particles and ions can also be released during hull cleaning, sanding, and repainting. The fate, characteristics, and effects of sloughed off paint particles have not been well studied or publicized. One Swedish study used a snail as a biomarker to compare toxic effects. They found that snail reproduction in marinas with antifouling paint contamination was cut more than 95 percent.[387] The snail test suggests there is likely very extensive ecosystem disruption.

Refrigeration systems used on boats and in processing facilities leak potent CCGs including HFCs and CFCs. In 2019, Seattle-based fisheries giant Trident Seafoods Corporation agreed to reduce emissions of ozone-depleting substances from refrigeration equipment on its vessels. The proposed settlement with the US Environmental Protection Agency and US Department of Justice would resolve alleged violations of the Clean Air Act.[388] The company was slated to spend up to $23 million to reduce coolant leaks from refrigerators and other equipment, use alternative refrigerants, and improve company-wide compliance. They also had to pay a $900,000 civil penalty.

The benefits and external costs of fish farming and other forms of aquaculture need to be understood more clearly. External costs can be high when fish are harvested to feed other fish, or when pests or diseases are spread from farmed fish to wild fish. Sea lice (*Lepeophtheirus salmonis* and *Caligus* species) are a challenge for many aquaculture programs; their economic damage has been estimated at between 400 and 600 million dollars a year.[389] The capture of young wild tuna to grow them out in pens is problematic, to say the least. The spread of farm-fish genetics is also a problem, reducing the odds of survival for fish stocks that were once co-evolved and highly adapted to the local conditions.

Ecosystem impacts from trawlers contribute to global climate change gases. Marine sediments may well be the largest pool of carbon storage in the world, and as trawlers drag across and disturb the ocean floor, they release carbon dioxide. The annual release may exceed that of the entire aviation industry, adding a billion tons of carbon to the atmosphere every year. With external CCG cost recovery set at $100 per ton, that is a cost of $100 billion. The carbon dioxide released from the seabed sediment will also increase ocean acidification and adversely affect productivity and biodiversity.

Regulatory Failure from Failed Accounting

With a lack of true cost accounting information, it is easy for politicians to make mistakes. They can respond to pressure from fishermen and local communities because they "don't know" what will happen. When harvest restrictions are put in place to "save" a fish stock, the reduction may be just half or even a tenth of what is needed.

Natural Capital research on fisheries and other potentially renewable resources must explore the often perverse effects of government actions and policies. Once a problem in a fishery is realized, regulations are developed, but they tend to trail science by several years or decades. There are many changes in ecosystem structure and function when a key predator is removed. The decline of cod has probably had impacts that ripple throughout the ecosystem in a trophic cascade, with species interactions spreading like a line of dominos falling down. Just some of the species intertwined with cod include seals, crabs, small pelagic fish, and zooplankton.

There can be winners as well as losers. The removal of the cod led to booming shrimp populations and the rise of a shrimp fishery in Newfoundland. Unfortunately, shrimp trawlers cause extensive sea floor damage that is likely to limit cod recovery and cause other ecosystem damage. When the Atlantic cod populations collapsed, fishermen turned to other species, including capelin, a small forage fish that is an important food source for the Atlantic cod. The ensuing reduction in capelin may also be hampering cod recovery. In the Barents Sea, capelin were being eaten by herring, and it became clear that the three large fish stocks (capelin, cod, and herring) had to be managed at a multispecies/community level.

Government interference, particularly subsidies, distorts the market and disrupts management in many ways. Today, the worldwide subsidy from governments paid to fishermen, often for improved fishing vessels, is estimated to provide $1.50-worth of subsidy for every $1.00 of fish harvested. By helping build bigger, faster, and more destructive fishery gear, subsidies have driven fish stocks in many parts of the world to extinction at steep environmental and social costs. They also played a role in the cod fish collapse.[390]

Subsidizing faster and bigger fishing boats simply accelerates the destruction. Subsidies are not a new problem; they began for fishermen in the 1700s in England. As Adam Smith noted in 1776, subsidies often go awry: "The bounty [subsidy] to the white-herring fishery is a tonnage bounty, and is proportioned to the burden [capacity] of the ship, not to her diligence or success in the fishery; and it has, I am afraid, been too common for vessels to fit out for the sole purpose of catching not the fish, but the bounty." Europe's deep-sea trawlers operate at a financial loss with $279 million in government subsidies making up the difference.[391] China spends even more, with $629 million supporting 4,615 vessels. Without the subsidy, most would stop immediately.

Subsidies help support deep-sea trawling that damages millions of acres every year.[392] Sediment from chronically trawled areas had 80 percent fewer tiny benthic organisms, called "meiofauna," and 50 percent less biodiversity than areas that were not trawled. Trawling was also linked to a 52 percent reduction in organic matter, and a 37 percent reduction in organic carbon consumption.

When the true cost is counted, the damage to the deep sea[393] could be minimized or halted.

Natural Capital

If the Natural Capital asset values of most global fisheries are plotted, they would resemble the cod fishery in the Grand Bank. For most, action will once again come too little, too late. Fishing pressure, politics, pollution, and climate change are compounded by continuing government subsidies. Fishery fleet registration is growing fastest in the poorest countries with lax laws and little or no enforcement. Many fishing boats from developed nations are being reregistered in these "lowest price at any cost" havens, with a nominal local captain.

A healthy fish stock should have a spawning biomass significantly above any precautionary levels, and a good variety in age and stock structure to weather natural climate variation. A healthy fishery should be based on the principles of true cost accounting and ecosystem-based management to ensure that ecosystem functions and integrity are sustained.

In some cases, providing some type of ownership rights or tenure for the fish or fisher may help. This can encourage more intensive and careful management. Some of the most sustainable fisheries in the world work because they are collectively managed with individual "ownership" of specific areas that may hold over generations. This matters when fish are local and linked to a specific area. Research has found that New England's cod did not belong to one big breeding population but rather consisted of many smaller populations that returned to the same areas each year to breed. Spawning grounds can perhaps be protected with long-term leases. But these need to be carefully structured to provide incentives for sustainable management and the ability to transfer leases to children or new owners.

We might also consider territorial fishing rights with long-term leases, 50+ years, instead of annual licenses or permits for harvesting fish. For example, a Klamath River Yurok-Karuk salmon co-op could be set up and empowered to manage the salmon and represent the river in management deliberations. Ownership could also be linked to the offshore harvest of the Klamath River salmon. A group like this would have more political power and better resources to combat damage from dams and unsustainable management of farms and forests than individual fishermen or the current complex mix of state and federal agencies, tribes, and NGOs.

More detailed research and long-term monitoring will help improve our understanding of aquatic ecosystems. True cost accounting will make the world safer for fish and fishermen while helping to ensure sustainable harvests that benefit the fishing community as well as the supporting ecosystem. Manager's reports will need to include Natural Capital value, annual cost/benefit, and trends. This will also help drive efforts to restore damaged or lost fisheries.[394] Ending subsidies is essential. Integrating biological, ecosystem, and social information in fisheries' management planning will help.

What You Can Do!

Choose more sustainable fish at the market. Fish wild-caught by hand lines from a stable population can be found. Take a look at Patagonia Provisions new products. The best resource on fish sustainability is the Seafood Watch program, owned and operated by the Monterey Bay Aquarium (www.seafoodwatch.org). The detailed studies they provide evaluate the individual source areas. Albacore, for example, is sustainably sourced from nine fisheries, and unsustainably from eleven. The best of these sources rates a score of 4.27, the worst 1.65.

Support the organizations[395] that are working to understand the true cost and benefits of protecting fisheries, restoring damaged watersheds, and limiting global climate change. You may find a local group to work with, or start a group.

Local communities have risen to the challenge of protecting and restoring the ocean where they live. Howard Wood and a friend used their own personal savings to found the Community of Arran Seabed Trust (COAST) in 1995, a citizen group of volunteer activists committed to protecting the local marine environment. Wood had no formal training as an environmental activist but felt a responsibility to the tight-knit community in Arran, Scotland. Their mission was to do all they could to restore and protect the marine resources that had been a source of cultural identity and economic sustainability for the islanders for generations. The South Arran Marine Protected Area was established in 2014—the first community-developed MPA in the country.

In Madagascar the local communities have also risen to the challenge. Temporary closure of one area for one species of octopus led to surprising recovery of other species as well. This led many other communties to consider similar controls and this management technique has now been replicated hundreds of times along the coast north of Toliara, South West Madagascar.[396] Fishing catch improved.

Natural Capital can be recovered and will grow in value with good management. As one old salt said, "We can do it. It can be done. I know it can be done. If we can send somebody to the moon, we sure as hell can fix this fishery."[397]

CHAPTER 13

SEEKING BALANCE

Out in the rural West, where I was raised, the determination and perseverance of the people was exemplified by the saying "Get 'er done." Despite bad weather, illness, injury, cantankerous tractors, difficult horses, and stubborn mules, the work just had to be done. That is the attitude we need now on climate change and true cost accounting. If we don't get it done soon, it will be too late, and we can expect catastrophes of all kinds.

The Paani Foundation water saving contest was a great success.

Boomerang Bags have used fabric scraps to build community and make a half million shopping bags around the world

Middle school children and farmers saved the majestic Hokkaido red crowned crane

Floods, infernos, droughts, flooding from sea level rise, temperature extremes, and ever stronger hurricanes and storms will create millions of environmental refugees, economic dislocations, and country collapses. These are already being seen, and they will get worse. Lytton, British Columbia, experienced a taste in 2021. First it set a temperature record for Canada at 121 °F, then it burned to the ground in a wildfire, and soon after that, severe flooding destroyed the major highway after torrential rains.

The big challenge remains making these changes quickly enough. For this we will need the energy of youth, greater participation from women, engagement with communities of color, the skill and expertise of accountants and scientists, and a renewed spirit of community. Greta Thunberg, Autumn Peltier, and other young climate advocates understand this and are committed to change. Most of the rich old generation in charge doesn't, yet, or may see change as a threat to their power and privilege.

We can do so much better. We can have wonderful communities with healthier and happier people if we count the external costs, make changes, and enable families to thrive. This chapter looks at the larger issue of what society needs to do, and then, what we each can do.

Without Pressure, There Is No Change

How do we effect change? The young climate advocates along with their mothers and grandmothers may need to take a day off worldwide to press for action on climate change and true cost accounting. This tactic worked when the women of Iceland took a day off on October 24, 1975. More than 90 percent of women in the country took part. Instead of going to the office, doing housework, or caring for children, they took to the streets to rally for equal rights. It completely paralyzed the country and was a watershed moment. Banks, factories, schools, nurseries, and shops had to close. It was a baptism by fire for many fathers, who sometimes call it the "Long Friday." Iceland went on to elect the first woman president in the world. Perhaps a "Millennials' Day Off" will help, making the case for the

1.8 billion people in this generation who will be slammed by climate change if nothing is done.

We can also learn from the Estonian people who confronted the occupying Soviet administration in the 1980s with peaceful protests. One of their first efforts was an environmental struggle against proposed phosphate mines in 1986. At the Tartu Pop Music Festival in May 1988, the feelings grew stronger, and on September 11, the song festival in Tallinn brought in 300,000 people, nearly a fourth of the population. You cannot help being moved by the sound of 300,000 voices joined together (http://singingrevolution.com). On August 23, 1989, 700,000 Estonians joined half a million Latvians and a million Lithuanians in linking hands the length of the three countries in a show of solidarity known as the Baltic Chain. In 1991, the people resisted a coup attempt by Russian hardliners, and the Republic of Estonia was formally established.

The needed level of change will require many approaches and incentives. I see it as a stool with three legs—true cost accounting, improved policies, and social pressure focused by education. Up to now, policies have been weak, education and social pressure modest at best, and true cost accounting absent.

This has led to a failure to respond, even though environmental groups, regulatory agencies, health departments, teachers, accountants, and finance agencies in the US and Europe have acknowledged the environmental and social problems we face. But "recognizing" these impacts and addressing them are two different things. Rules and regulations, market pollution trading (cap and trade), and subsidies of various kinds have done little, and often made things worse. True cost accounting will lead to action at a much lower cost.

The Final Step—True Cost Accounting with External Cost Recovery

Determining the true costs of how we live is a key step in making the leap to a more sustainable economy.[398] When companies and consumers begin to pay the true cost of energy and CCGs for transportation, it will become more attractive to make products domestically and buy locally rather than importing almost everything we use from distant countries. True cost accounting will also make it more economical to grow food organically and to buy it locally. Farmers will be able to make a better living. True cost accounting will help return local control of meat and knock out massive feedlots, improving rancher's prospects. Renewable energy is already the lowest-cost new supply of electricity in most of the world, but if we count true costs, it is even better, just one tenth the cost of natural gas and 2 percent of the true cost of coal.

External impact cost recovery will change behavior. Only four countries have been able to establish fees for CCGs that may begin to approach costs.[399] Sweden and Uruguay lead the way at almost $140 per ton of CO_2e. Finland and Sweden have had carbon taxes since 1990 and 1991. Income from the Swedish CCG fee goes into the general fund to reduce taxes. The majority of the Swiss proceeds are also reimbursed to the citizens. In September 2021, Swiss voters in Bern approved a canton constitutional amendment (by a vote of 63.9 percent to 36.1 percent) that makes being climate neutral by 2050 a legally binding obligation.[400]

There are more than sixty carbon pricing initiatives in force across the globe on various regional, national, and subnational levels, according to the World Bank. Together, these initiatives have been estimated to cover 21.5 percent of the global greenhouse gas emissions in 2021. For most countries, the fees for CCGs are far below the true costs. When I last checked, the fee in China was $4.60 per ton, the EU $49, UK $61, Canada $40, and the US $51. In 2021, a CO_2e tax was proposed that would require non-EU companies exporting to Europe to pay the same price for their carbon footprint as European companies. The goal is to impose a duty on imports from countries with low climate and environmental standards to assume the climate change gas impact burden.[401] This will also discourage companies in developed countries from transferring even more manufacturing to areas with few or no controls. This border fee would help level the playing field for companies that do not want to race to the bottom. A levy on EU imports of $30 per metric ton of CO_2 emissions would reduce the profit for foreign producers by about 20 percent if the price for crude oil remains in the range of $30 to $40 per barrel. If the price of oil continues to rise ($100+ in May 2022), as seems likely, and the carbon levy is set closer to Sweden's, it will be a game-changer.

External cost recovery fees make the most sense and can extend far beyond CCGs. The success of the Global Reporting Initiative is encouraging. The 2020 KPMG Survey of Sustainability Reporting found that almost all of world's largest companies (the G250) now report on their sustainability performance. GRI reporting has evolved over the years with extensive input from stakeholders. We just need to extend the scope of these reports to include true costs.

Impact fees can be set even when the science is unclear and when the impacts are global and far-reaching. Because we do not fully understand the complex interactions and long-term effects, it is likely the estimates will rarely or never be below true cost. True costs for different emissions and impacts have been developed for some materials and activities (Appendix 2), but more needs to be done. Extending true cost considerations throughout the economy is essential. Climate change is not the only critical crisis we face. Habitat destruction, depletion of groundwater and other resources, extinction of a wide range of species, and many other external costs have been ignored. California is making an effort to ensure groundwater use is sustainable.

The environmental costs are staggering, but in the short term, they are often outweighed by social costs. The healthcare market in the US is an inequitable financial mess. There have been signs of movement. California is trying (as of 2022) to move to universal healthcare. The Swiss model, discussed in Chapter 7, may make the most sense. Particular emphasis must be placed on righting the wrongs that cause such severe disparities in the health of non-white people and those with limited resources.

Nongovernmental organizations and individual researchers have also explored true costs for transportation, food, agriculture, and many other sectors of the economy. Consultants and companies are starting to emerge that can help companies calculate the true costs of materials, buildings, products, services, and operations. The challenge is folding external costs into standard bookkeeping, mergers, acquisitions and financing. CPAs, chartered and registered accountants, financial advisors, and bankers will need to understand and use these methods and data. We also need to develop and train True Cost Accountants. Environmental and social impacts are often well described in annual reports, but the external costs are not calculated. This is starting to change, and I am confident that true costs will increasingly appear in financial reports, audits, and financial disclosures.

CCG emissions have received the most attention, and their measurement offers lessons for more inclusive reports. The EPA and others use three levels of responsibility for CCG emissions. Scope 1 covers direct emissions from owned or controlled sources. Scope 2 covers indirect emissions from the generation of purchased electricity, steam, heating, and cooling consumed by the reporting company. Scope 3 includes all other indirect emissions that occur in a company's value chain.

Few companies look beyond Scopes 1 and 2, but responsibility should be expanded to other factors. These range from energy use for employee commuting and business travel, to water use, impacts on human health, and ecosystem integrity. Impacts are often talked about as "upstream" as the products or services are being made and coming to the company, and "downstream" after the product leaves the facility or the service is completed. Many of these issues are discussed in GRI reports, but financial costs must be estimated.

Here is a climate change gas example from Proctor and Gamble's 2018 sustainability report.[402] They have done a decent job of Scopes 1 and 2, and were courageous enough to explore Scope 3.

	Million Tons CO_2e
Scopes 1 and 2	4.1
Scope 3	
Use of sold product	199.1
Purchased goods and services upstream transport & distribution	16.4
End of life treatment of sold product	13.3
Waste generation in operations	9.0
Downstream transport & distribution	5.4
Fuel and energy activities	0.5
Capital goods	0.3
Business travel	0.15
Employee commuting	0.12
Total	248.4

Not included in P&G's estimates were processing of sold product, upstream leased assets, downstream leased assets, franchises, and perhaps most important, investments. It is clear why Scope 3 is so important. In this case, Scopes 1 and 2 represent less than 2 percent of P&G's total CCG impact. We should also fold in more upstream and downstream impacts, end of product life, and related issues. Responsibility for paying the external costs after sale might be split with the consumer and retailer. Employee commuting miles and miles of business travel should definitely be included. If your company accepts responsibility for your commuting CCG, you might consider taking it off your home CCG account to avoid double counting.

If we price the CCG cost impacts for Scopes 1 and 2 for P&G calculated emissions, the CCG fee would be $200 million at $51 per ton of CO_2e, the current CCG cost in the US. If we used the Swiss Re (a reinsurance firm with 15,000 employees) CCG internal cost of $100 per ton, P&G would owe $400 million. Certainly affordable, at just about 4 percent of P&G's typical net profit of $10 billion a year. If Scope 3 is included and we use the Swedish impact fee of $137.50 per ton, the cost would rise to $34 billion—more than the company's net profit.

In the fight against climate change, companies can use carbon pricing as a tool to improve operations and decision-making. Some companies are already taking steps to include their own external costs in accounting. Swiss Re is the one of the first multinational companies to set a true cost for their carbon emissions (including business travel). Starting in January 2021, the company raised their internal carbon impact recovery fee from $8 per ton of CO_2e to $100, and set it to rise further to $250 by 2030. This money will be used to reduce corporate impacts and external costs.

All corporations, government organizations, communities, and families should consider following suit. Corporations can start by reporting to the CDP (the carbon disclosure NGO). CDP is a not-for-profit charity that runs the global disclosure system for investors, companies, cities, states, and regions to manage their environmental impacts. More than 2,500 corporations have reported to CDP. Many use (or expect to soon adopt) an internal CCG fee to cut emissions from their operations. These companies, with a combined market capitalization of $27 trillion, include 226 of the 500 largest global companies as measured by the FTSE Global All Cap Index. CDP also reports there are 680+ investors with over $130 trillion in assets and 200+ large purchasers with over $5.5 trillion in procurement spend who are requesting thousands of companies to disclose their environmental data through CDP.[403] Governments should also start external cost accounting for their climate change gas emissions and other environmental and social impacts.

An internal fee of $100 per ton of CO_2e might be split, with half used within the company and half distributed to NGOs, schools, and communities around the world to reduce climate change emissions and repair damage from climate change. Funding could be used to improve true cost accounting, resource sustainability, and innovation. Priority could be given to efforts in the developing countries that contribute the least to the problems but are already experiencing the worst effects.

True cost accounting for accountants

As sustainability reporting has increased, the international accounting groups have become more involved. A big step was taken in 2011 when the nonprofit Sustainability Accounting Standards Board (SASB) was founded to help accountants, businesses, and investors develop a common language for financial impacts of sustainability. SASB Standards are now available for seventy-seven industries. These help companies identify the environmental, social, and governance (ESG) issues that are most likely to be relevant to their company.

The International Federation of Accountants (IFAC) highlights climate change as an urgent, global issue.[101] They acknowledge that the transition to a low-carbon society cannot be achieved by business as usual. Climate action will require relevant policy initiatives and incentives, consistent and well-considered regulation, robust climate risk assessment, responsive business practices, and high-quality disclosures that advance climate action and adaptation. More complete accounting will be the responsibility that IFAC's 180 member organizations and their 3.5 million professional accountant members have in driving climate change mitigation, adaptation, and reporting. Climate action is a good starting point, but the impacts need to be costed and the scope must still be expanded to other issues with large external costs.

In June 2021, the International Integrated Reporting Council (IIRC) and the Sustainability Accounting Standards Board (SASB) merged to form the Value Reporting Foundation. In August 2022, the IFRS Foundation assumed responsibility for SASB Standards. The IFRS Foundation's International Sustainability Standards Board (ISSB) is committed to building on the industry-based SASB Standards and adopting SASB's industry-based approach to standards development. The goal is to make reporting easier and more effective by improving communication between accountants, companies, and investors. They have developed several options to help organizations integrate SASB standards into their activities. Asset managers and asset owners; banks; data, analytics, and research firms; and corporate reporting software companies can license SASB frameworks and data.

SASB is working with XBRL (the nonprofit international standard for digital business reporting), used in more than fifty countries, to make reporting easier, stronger, and more transparent. Millions of XBRL documents are created every year, replacing paper-based reports with more useful and accurate digital versions. XBRL US has published a guide (available on their website) to help preparers create XBRL financial statements. The American Institute of Certified Public Accountants (AICPA) was involved in developing the rules and guidance for using XBRL technology for financial reporting. SASB plans to fully support XBRL to make digital reporting easier. In 2020, SASB announced an agreement with PwC (formerly Price Waterhouse Coopers) to support the development of the SASB XBRL system.

What Next?

In 2013, the UK coalition government implemented mandatory carbon reporting that required all UK companies listed on the Main Market of the London Stock Exchange (around 1,100 of the UK's largest listed companies) to report their energy use, greenhouse gas emissions, and at least one energy intensity metric every year. The report must include a narrative description of measures taken to improve the businesses' energy efficiency in that year. This has created a demand for advisors and experts in CCGs and sustainability. If a company needs further advice, private sector organizations active in CCG reporting can help. These include Carbon Footprint, Carbon Smart, Carbon Trust, Ricardo-AEA, CDP partners, Waste Resources Action Programme (WRAP), Greenstone, Ecometrica, Anthesis Group, IEMA, Verco, Loreus, and WS Group.

Other multinational financial advisory firms and management consultants are also moving into this arena and expanding to true cost considerations. True Price (trueprice.org) has done more than sixty true pricing projects for companies ranging from small and mid-size enterprises (SMEs) to multinationals and for a variety of products. True Price is based on the work of the Impact Institute. Other active firms include Forum for the Future (UK), Deloitte (Amsterdam), Soil & More Impacts GmbH (Hamburg), CE Delft (Netherlands), S&P Global, Töpfer, Müller, and Gaßner GmbH (Berlin). These companies may be able to provide assistance with true cost accounting. There are also a growing number of university programs related to sustainability and some are considering cost more clearly.

The consideration of ecological issues is particularly weak, but essential.[405] It simply won't work if we continue to say it may be important but we have no information and no cost estimate. Water issues are likely to be critical in many areas and will get worse year after year. Health and well-being, equity, and community integrity and vitality are also important and undervalued. The current impacts and costs from the misuse of pesticides and antibiotics, air and water pollution, nutrient pollution impacts on aquatic and terrestrial ecosystems, and potential extinction of many species are all important. Chapters 5-12 should give you other ideas of what needs work in your company, town, or region.

Improving consideration of true costs will help the American Institute of Certified Public Accounts (AICPA) and NGOs support the Security and Exchange Commission's effort to require more detailed climate-related disclosures.[406] CCG emission reports for larger firms will be subject to assurance with certified audits. Filings are likely to require assessments of climate-related risks and the actual or likely material impacts of climate change on the registrant's business, strategy, and outlook. Climate-or CCG related trends, targets and goals may be described. The next step is monetizing the impacts, folding in true costs, and balancing the books.

What You Can Do!

True cost accounting affects what we do and how we live. But we don't manage what we don't measure and monitor.

1 Calculate your carbon,[407] water, food, and waste footprints. Determine the external cost you should pay at $100 per ton of CO_2e.

Put half of this in an account to pay for upgrades to your home, work space, and transportation that will reduce your footprint. Invest the other half in NGOs working for true cost accounting here and abroad. If you are unable to modify where you live and work, consider giving half the fee to an American true cost NGO, and half to an international NGO.

2 Set an example with your food purchases, garden, transportation, rainwater harvesting, and recycling. Calculate your carbon footprint and offset your emissions. It is not always easy to evaluate the offerings. Many of the programs that offer carbon offsets have been found to be weak or flawed.[408] If you do the work yourself, you can be more confident. You may choose to plant trees at home or in your town. Or you may help less-wealthy communities and schools around the world upgrade and improve their gardens, water supply, and energy systems.

There are many options, but make sure they are real savings. Tree-planting is a long-term proposition, and there are already many offerings. Some are sound, others are fraudulent. Consider 8 Billion Trees, the Nature Conservancy, Trees for the Future, and American Forests. Trees for the Future works in developing countries and gets much done with limited resources.

3 Encourage your local high school and college to start teaching courses and workshops on TCA. Students are capable of great work if given the chance and good mentoring.[409] Many schools and colleges already have sustainability related courses and clubs. Even a modest financial investment can yield remarkable results.[410]

The Vital Signs project for evaluating buildings at UC Berkeley helped provide needed information on building performance.[411] Every state and many cities could use a similar program. The Center for the Built Environment at UC Berkeley has done very important surveys of building occupants for more than 20 years. This information has been used to improve the comfort and performance of hundreds of buildings.[412]

Students can also help develop new strategies to heal damaged ecosystems. My field research on ecological restoration was made possible by a mix of volunteer and paid students. They often added new insights and contributed to the project's success. More companies could offer paid internships like Patagonia has done for their employees. This enables them to work for an NGO or community that could benefit from an energetic, web-savvy youth.

Support for TCA can provide important life lessons. The goal is to develop a culture of sustainability across geographic, demographic, and social sectors. This will not be easy and will take education from kindergarten to advanced degree programs including technical training—from city councils to governors, farms to forests, bishops to imams, and presidents to chancellors. Reach out to women's groups; they have done excellent work in improving resource management and building toward a sustainable future.[413] Women often manage the family money and many of the household resources, from gardens to goats. Examples can be found around the world, in Zimbabwe (irrigation[414]), Nepal (reforestation[415]), Kenya (mangrove replanting[416]), and India (water[417]).

4 Don't put it off. Support true cost reporting where you live and work. Starting with CCG from fossil fuel use may be easiest as almost everyone has heard of it. Encourage your companies, organizations, and schools to adopt true cost accounting. Try a simple project like Deloitte's True Price coffee bar. Look for savings and new market potential with more sustainable solutions. Get to work fixing uncomfortable, ill-lit, and under ventilated schools and offices. The productivity gains will surprise everyone.

5 Recommend a community or state TCA reporting competition modeled after the Defense Advanced Research Projects Agency contests. Develop foundation and corporate support for a significant prize, perhaps $100,000 for the best app, educational materials, or applied program.

6 Contact your legislative representatives at the city, state, and federal level and tell them you want true cost accounting to keep

the planet safe for their children and future generations. Write an email or letter in support of True Cost Accounting to your congressperson, governor, mayor, and any other politicians who purport to represent your interests. To have an impact, the letter should: **Be specific.** Focus your letter on one issue or legislative proposal for true cost accounting. I would suggest a short letter or email stressing the importance of true cost accounting for a sustainable future. This could recommend adding true cost accounting to the rules and regulations of the US Securities and Exchange Commission.

Be short and polite. Be calm, cool, collected and kind. Explain how this issue has or will affect you, your family, your community, and the world. Use personal examples.

Cite facts, and use your email or letter to deliver expert research that they may not have seen. Cite credible reports from reliable sources (look for edu, gov). Link to carefully selected media that matters.

Be easy to read without typos or grammatical errors, and with a solution or two to the problems you address. Consider a webpage, blog, or other social media. Be sure to include your name and address in your letter—particularly if you are contacting your politician. Invest some time in identifying the best person or organization to contact. If you can get a professional organization's newsletter or newspaper to mention your ideas, you can reach hundreds of important people at once. E-mail newsletter editors are often more open to interesting ideas and new perspectives than print editors.

7 Contact the accounting organizations in your area and ask them to support true cost accounting. Write to your bank president and/or the CEO or CFO of a company you patronize and ask for their support for true cost accounting. The TCA contest may have some appeal. Encourage companies to do internal carbon impact fee allocation—half to corporate improvements and half to NGOs in developing countries that are working toward true cost accounting for equity and social justice.

8 Talk with your children and grandchildren. What kind of world do they want? Take responsibility for your actions and make changes to reduce your impact and external cost. Younger people offer hope with their protests and educational efforts, but the older, more conservative people of power must also be engaged for effective change.

True Cost Accounting and a Sustainable Economy

Building a sustainability culture means integrating sustainability into everyday decisions for every family, company, and country. True cost accounting helps, but is just a tool, not the ultimate solution. Strategies for making sustainability part of daily activities must be developed and refined. Wendell Berry articulates a clear vision of a sustainable way of living.[418] Ruth DeFries provides a very good overview of lessons from history and nature about reducing the risk of catastrophe.[419] Mark Carney, former governor of the Bank of England (2008–2013), offers an insightful look at values for a sustainable future.[420]

We can learn a great deal from traditional societies that have managed their resources more effectively. They often had no choice if they wished to survive. Chinese society throughout thousands of years offers examples of remarkable success in innovation and efficiency in food production, but also terrible failures. Primitive" societies developed sophisticated resource management strategies in many cases.[421] They often promoted sustainable behavior with emotionally powerful cultural symbols and activities. Festivals, fairs, shrines, feasts, and other events can play a role in engaging and educating people. The salmon festivals found in Yurok and many other American First Nations are an excellent example. Japan has particularly strong local cultural traditions that are often shaped by resource use and conservation.

Never under estimate what students can do. The survival of the endangered red-crowned crane (*Grus japonensis*) in Hokkaido, Japan, was almost entirely due to the efforts of the Akan Middle School Crane Club (founded in 1957). The student club captivated the nation with their evocative narratives about nature and wildlife. Students started to sprinkle corn next to a playground every morning in winter to supplement the food supply for cranes, a ritual that continues to this day. Several local farmers also helped. They succeeded in mobilizing public support because they elicited empathy, motivated people to care, and galvanized people to act. In turn, national recognition in the form of prestigious awards, media coverage, donations, and visits from overseas experts empowered children and helped reinforce the belief that they possessed the power to effect change and make a difference. The population had dropped to twenty-five birds but now is at about 1,800. Now, ecotourism and the cranes draw tourists: in 2017, Hokkaido welcomed 56.1 million Japanese tourists and almost three million foreigners. Hundreds of thousands of visitors travel to see and photograph the magnificent cranes, which have also become a symbol for Japan Airlines. The economic benefits from the actions of the Akan school children have been truly remarkable.

The Nordic nations have made some progress in developing a sustainability culture. The Norwegian philosopher Arne Naess (1912-2009) articulated the need for a deep ecology.[422] Most students in Norway now receive a sustainability-infused education that begins in preschool. In many preschools, the children are outside for the majority of every day. Outdoor schooling—*uteskole*—continues up the grades and moves students out of the classroom and into the local environment. This gives pupils the opportunity to use their bodies and senses as they continue to learn in the real world, not in a stuffy classroom. Rain or shine, snow or cold, the classes still go out. Outdoor schooling allows room for academic activities, communication, social interaction, experience, spontaneity, play, curiosity, and fantasy. Students develop a love and sense of responsibility for the natural world. Norway's strong cultural ties to nature and the Norwegian value of *friluftsliv*, "open-air living," contribute to health and a feeling of joy in the interaction with nature.

The Scandinavian countries also have a history of policies to improve environmental quality and promote sustainable living, including impact fees for CCGs (as well as for other environmental problems) and financial incentives for recycling. Norway leads the world with a 97 percent recovery rate for plastic bottle waste. This is handled by Infinitim, a company founded in 1999. More than 90 percent are returned clean enough to be turned back into bottles and used again.

The ultimate challenge is developing a culture of health and sustainability to replace a culture of consumption and destruction. These new attitudes are growing in America with organic foods, school gardens, farm-to-table dining, climate activism, solar cars, and solar electric systems becoming mainstream. But much more is needed, and true cost accounting can drive the change.

Seeking balance

Many different strategies will be needed to help cultures around the world develop and adopt true cost accounting. True cost accounting is essential because it focuses attention on something almost everyone relates to: money. Balancing the books is an essential step for families, companies and countries. Adding true costs can change behavior without intrusive and cumbersome regulations, rules and enforcement.

It will not be easy because it confronts our historic neglect of social and environmental cost. The biggest challenge is likely to be in the richest countries that do the most damage. Those who are the biggest polluters are too often the most resistant to change, and they often use the riches gained by ignoring true costs to defeat efforts to change.

Financial rewards for winning environmentally focused competitions can be effective. The Water Cup competitions in India are an excellent example. The Water Cup is a competition between different villages to see who can do the most work for watershed management and water conservation. It is an initiative of the Paani Foundation, a not-for-profit company that works toward creating a drought-free Maharashtra. Participation is based on self-selection. A four-day Training Camp trains villagers in the science of watershed management. Villages are at liberty to mobilize funds, machinery, and materials. Thousands of workers, with just hand tools in some cases, completed some remarkable projects. The village that did the most work in rainwater harvesting, water conservation, and soil protection won $76,000, and honor. Second place was $45,000 and third was $30,000. The top village from each subdistrict also won a cash prize of $15,000.

A sustainability research project agency like the Defense Advanced Research Projects Agency (DARPA) would be very helpful. DARPA has proven the value of competition as it explicitly reaches for transformational change instead of incremental advances in its work with academic, corporate, and governmental partners. The contests they held for autonomous vehicles were pivotal for improving self-driving technology. The first, second, and third places in the 2007 Urban Autonomous Driving Challenge received $2 million, $1 million, and $500,000, respectively. A series of similar but true cost/sustainability focussed challenges funded at the same level would be very helpful.

The Association for the Advancement of Sustainability in Higher Education (AASHE) could be encouraged to add TCA to their work. They already provide guidance and support for sustainability reporting as well as curriculum guides and use competition to increase engagement. The twelve winners of their 2021 Sustainability Awards in December were chosen from fifty-four finalists out of 900 applicants. Similar projects can be done in grades 2-12. True cost can be an integrating theme for math, science, biology, and social studies.

Make true cost accounting and sustainability fun for all and create a role for everyone. Take some of the work and research outside into the community. Get together with local scientists, accountants, and businesses. Perhaps a TCA blitz would be effective?[423] External cost estimates and true cost accounting can be done for classrooms, campuses, buildings, local small businesses, and communities.

Every newscast and newspaper now seems to include at least one climate change catastrophe. Climate change is not coming—it is here. These stories make it clear that we must start now; better late than never.

Action nurtures hope. Change can be engaging and joyful instead of distressing. True costs can help provide the pressure needed to make change.

We have no choice. We have to get 'er done!

MATERIAL FLOW ANALYSIS AND LIFE CYCLE COST

M aterial flow analysis includes product flow accounting, material balance, and total material flow accounting, while substance flow analysis is narrowly focussed on a specific item, element or chemical.[424] As you have seen in the book, information about material flows is available for some topics, but less known

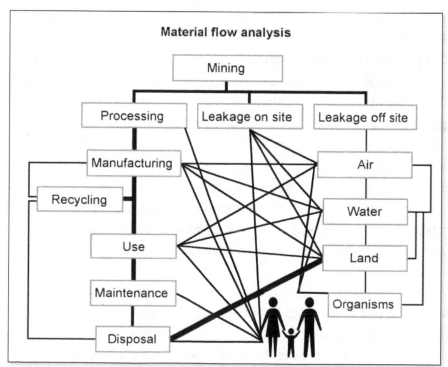

Material Flow Analysis and Life Cycle Cost.

about others. You can become a material flow detective and determine where materials come from, how they are processed, used, and where they go. How do they leak into the environment or break down? Do they accumulate in the environment or in people? How much is unaccounted for or missing?

You can track these flows over the lifetime of a product, building, farm, or community. The goal is developing a material balance, with everything accounted for. Analyzing the structure and processes of material and substance flows provides insights into their impacts on society, the economy, the resource base, and the environment.[425]

Initial studies suggest that industrial products typically carry nonrenewable ecological footprints that average thirty times their own weight,[426] which means consumers derive value from less than 5 percent of the nonrenewable natural material used to make a typical product. The ecofootprint for a personal computer may reach 200 pounds per pound of product. The catalytic converter on a car weighs about 8 pounds but has a footprint of three tons of nonrenewable resources. This is a staggering 750 pounds per pound of desired product.

Tracking the flow of high value or high risk materials is important. The rapidly increasing value of the precious metals in catalytic converters (platinum, palladium, rhodium, and gold) has led to a growing rash of thefts of converters by thieves who strip them from cars in a matter of minutes and then can sell them for $50-$250 for recycling or resale. The car's owner may have to pay $2,000-$4,000 for a replacement. Pollution control with an end-of-pipe catalytic converter solution leads to environmental damage, pollution, and crime. ID numbers will need to be added to converters, and scrap buyers will need to be vetted and charged when buying stolen converters.

The development of material flow information feeds into the assessment of Life Cycle Cost. A life cycle analysis will help develop a more accurate picture of the flows and impacts over time. Life cycle analysis is a well developed field with many resources (see list at the end this section) and a journal, *The International Journal of*

Life Cycle Assessment. A good Life Cycle Cost Assessment (LCCA) will try to imagine and consider every impact a product has during its lifetime and what these cost. This will include resource depletion, air pollution, water pollution, land degradation, release of toxics, ecosystem damage, global warming, health, and other social costs. Transportation costs are often significant.

A detailed life cycle analysis may require considerable research, even for something as simple as a bar of soap.

The Life Cycle of a Bar of Soap

A typical bar of soap may seem quite small and insignificant, but it can have quite a few impacts.

Soap Ingredients

- Tallow derived from animal fat with impacts from grazing, farm operations, corn and soybean production and processing, CCGs from shipping, meat packing, rendering, etc.
- Lye, typically made by the electrochemical treatment of salt with impacts from production of sodium hydroxide and the use of electricity.
- Perfumes and scents, with impacts from refining, chemicals from petroleum, and other sources, health impacts, air and water pollution, energy use, climate change gases, and regional pollution.
- Water, with impacts from sourcing, transportation, and contamination.

Packaging

- Paper and cardboard, which impact forests from logging operations and wood chipping, clay for paper, water, energy, and chemicals (chlorine).
- Plastic wrap, made from petroleum, energy, water, and additives.
- Paints and inks, containing petroleum, dyes, pigments, and oils.

Transportation

- Mining metal ores, processing, manufacturing, mainte-
  nance, and use of equipment, CCGs.
- Fuel use with CCG emissions.
- Energy for shipping materials around
- Consumer car CCG emissions for travel to and from the
  store.

Disposal

- Much of the soap ends up in the sewage water.
- Paper, plastic, and other wastes end up buried in a landfill.

The True Cost of Soap

Much of the soap we use is made using beef tallow. The true costs
of animal products studied appear to be about $1.10 per pound of
product.[427] A bar of the soap I use weighs 90 grams and costs 66¢.
The true cost would add about 20¢ for the tallow, perhaps another
10¢ for the other materials, paper wrapper, plastic wrapper, dyes,
and transport. So the true cost would add about half again of the
current price. If organic plant-based oils are used, the cost would be
less, but only if they come from a sustainable plant oil or oil palm
plantation. Many palm oils now come from oil palm plantations
that have replaced biodiverse tropical forests.

The environmental and social cost impacts are offset by health
benefits and improved longevity of clothes and other products, but
the goal should always be to minimize all costs and increase benefits from use. Nontoxic soaps should be the norm. Antimicrobial
soap has been heavily promoted, but is risky. Triclosan, a synthetic
biocide used in antimicrobial hand soap, is now found throughout
the environment, including in human urine, blood, and mothers'
breast milk.

Balancing

After assembling as much information as possible on flows, next try
to "balance the books." Sewage, landfill, and air and water pollution are often key concerns for materials with human health risks or

risks of ecotoxicity. How much is ending up in humans? In aquatic ecosystems?

Research on material flows can highlight areas where more study is needed. Uncertainty is inherent in many material balances because the information quality and quantity is often very poor. Estimates, therefore, should be given as ranges (with probability and statistics for the most harmful substances). This is a good area for students to study and report on.

Denmark has done some very good work on material flow analysis.[428] The balance sheet for lead found in the solid waste in Denmark in 1994 is illustrative.[429] The difference between high and low estimates suggest how much more environmental detective work is needed.

LEAD IN DENMARK'S SOLID WASTE STREAM ESTIMATE, METRIC TONS PER YEAR

	low	high
TV tubes	450	750
Fishing weights (sinkers)	230	300
Ammunition	10	15
Shredder fluff (from car recycling)	200	1000
Pigments (paint, plastic)	150	250
Electronics solder	90	150
Flashing and lead sheets (roofing)	50	200
Crystal glass	50	100
Stabilizer in PVC plastic	30	100
Ceramic glazing	25	150
Solder	120	210
Curtains, wine bottle foil, etc.	10	100
Batteries	<100	—
Sewage sludge	3	—

Material Impact Analysis

The next step is to estimate a material's potential for harmful effects to humans. Have the effects been studied? What types of exposure are there? Is there industry data on health effects for people who have had high exposures? Are the typical blood levels known? Are state, regional, or national data available? Has another company or country done a comparable analysis that can be used as a starting point? Has there been litigation over rules and regulations? Are there class action lawsuits underway?

What are the ecosystem impacts? How ecotoxic is the material? Some materials that are relatively harmless to humans, such as nitrogen, phosphorus, zinc, and copper, can be very damaging to ecosystem structure and function. Is the material biomagnified? We can estimate the current costs and long-term risks of disease and death for each impact.

Interactions between chemicals or compounds may also be very harmful and may increase damage far beyond that of each chemical or compound by itself. Much less effort has been made to understand these risks to health and ecosystems because this type of research is complex and takes time. Funding has been scarce, in part, because it might lead to conclusions about liability and the need for new regulations that would require industries to change their manufacturing processes and operations.

Harmful materials in the food chain may increase by a multiple of 10-20 or more in concentration from biomagnification. Seemingly low levels released into the environment may reach toxic levels in higher-level consumers such as humans (see: the Inuit), large fish, seals, birds, and so forth. What are the risks and costs of contamination? What are the potential costs of cleanup?

And finally, what are long term risks and true costs?[430] Are there any risks that have resulted in a crisis that appears to demand immediate attention? If the price of the product increases, will use decline? Are there substitutes, or is demand inelastic? How significant are the risks? Where would we expect to find the most serious impacts? What priority should be given to a pollutant or product? What are the benefits and costs?

Recommendations to Reduce the True Cost

The final discussion may focus on just one or a few critical factors. This typically will include human health factors first, and perhaps one or two significant environmental issues. If possible a more comprehensive material analysis should be done.

Prepare a clear and compelling description of what needs to be done to reduce the true cost. Estimated cost in Appendix 2 may help. What can be done to prevent human and environmental impacts during the life cycle of a product? What might it cost? Is the first priority to compile better data on material flows? Are there obvious leaks that should be plugged immediately? What are the trends? Are impacts going to get better or worse? Are new rules and regulations needed? What financial incentives or subsidies exist that make the impacts worse?

Material flow analysis in developing countries is also essential. International assistance and support for local agencies and NGOs will help. Users in the developed countries should be tasked with improving material flow studies where materials are mined, refined, or processed. Information may be required for imports crossing borders.

Factor 10 Improvement

Our goal is to live as well or better with only a tenth of the impact. End-of-life management for automobiles in the Netherlands shows what can be done if life cycle and material studies are done. In 2018, the country managed to reuse almost 98.5 percent (by weight) of end-of-life vehicles. The RDW (*Rijksdienst voor het Wegverkeer*) oversees the operations of Auto Recycling Netherlands (ARN), the organization that collects and recycles the wastes from the automotive sector. ARN receives a recycling fee of just $40 for each new vehicle purchased and a recycling premium ranging from $6 to $200 for purchased batteries (depending on their weight).

By comparison, in California, the auto recycling system is weak, and over 360,000 end-of-life vehicles go unaccounted for each year. The underground economy of unlicensed auto dismantlers costs legitimate licensed business owners over $1.5 billion a year in potential lost earnings, and costs the government (and ultimately taxpayers) over $100 million in uncollected taxes. Hazardous and harmful wastes from vehicles are spread across the state, where they cause ecosystem damage and adversely affect people's health. Abandoned cars are often dumped, causing problems in a variety of areas ranging from sparsely inhabited tribal lands, to rural areas, the suburbs, and even urban streets. Unlicensed auto dismantlers are less than careful in handling and disposing of hazardous materials (lithium, mercury, lead), refrigerants, and fluids (oil, gas, antifreeze). They leave messes around the state. Piles of vehicles in both legal and illegal dismantling yards often catch fire and burn, generating hazardous smoke.

We can recover 95 percent of materials that are not hazardous, and we can aim to recover 99 percent of those that are. The technology for recycling or reusing most materials is understood but is not done because it costs more than landfilling or dumping. When true costs are counted, most materials will be conserved, and external social and environmental costs will be minimized.

Life Cycle Cost Resources

Most of these resources do not include true or comprehensive costs but can be helpful in life cycle analysis and full cost (conventional accounting) determination. This, in turn, helps make true costing (and minimizing environmental and social impacts) possible.

- Adell, D., Seebach, M., Möller, M., & Tepper, P. (2011). *LCC-CO$_2$ tool user guide*. Procura. Intelligent Energy Europe. The SMART SPP consortium, c/o ICLEI – Local Governments for Sustainability.
- Archer, D., Kite, E., & Lusk, G. (2020). The ultimate cost of carbon. Climatic Change, 162, 2069–2086.
- Bainbridge, D. A., & Bainbridge, R. W. (2010, August 26). Seven sins of building design and construction. *Triple Pundit*. https://www.academia.edu/3809870/2010_seven_sins_of_building_design_and_construction

- Bainbridge, D. A. (2001). *Ecocomposites*. https://buildwellsource. org/materials/210-ecocomposites-david-bainbridge/file
- Biggs, J. E. (2000, April 14). What to do with old computers? *Los Angeles Times*, p. B2.
- Campanelli, M., Berglund, J., & Rachuri, S. (2011). Integration of life cycle inventories incorporating manufacturing unit processes. *Proceedings of ASME 2011 international design engineering technical conference & computers and information in engineering conference IDETC/CIE 2011*. Washington, DC.
- Costanza, R., Cumberland, J., Daly, H., Goodland, R., & Norgaard, R. (1997). *An introduction to ecological economics*. St. Lucie Press.
- Cucuzzella, C., & De Coninck, P. (2008, April 18-19). *The precautionary principle as a framework for sustainable design: Attempts to counter the rebound effects of production and consumption*. First International Conference on Economic De-growth for Ecological Sustainability and Social Equity, Paris.
- Curran, M. A. (1993). Broad-based environmental life cycle assessment. *Environmental Science and Technology, 27*(3), 430–436.
- Estevan, H., & Schaefer, B. (2017). *Life cycle costing state of the art*. ICLEI–Local Governments for Sustainability, European Secretariat.
- Fuller, S. (2008). *Life-cycle cost analysis*. National Institute of Standards and Technology. Washington, DC. (*This is helpful but about full cost—not true cost.*)
- Graedel, T. E., & Allenby, B. R. (1995). *Industrial ecology*. Prentice Hall.
- Giudice, F., La Rosa, G., & Risitano, A. (2006). *Product design for the environment: A life cycle approach*. CRC Press.
- Hapuwatte, B. M., & Jawahir, I. S. (2021). Closed-loop sustainable product design for circular economy. *Journal of Industrial Ecology, 25*, 1430–1446.
- Keoleian, G. A. (1994). Sustainable development by design: Review of life cycle design and related approaches. *Air and Waste, 44*, 645–668.

- Life Cycle Initiative. (2005). *Life cycle management—a bridge to more sustainable products training toolkit.* UN Environmental Program-SETAC.
- Luttropp, C., & Lagerstedt, J. (2006). EcoDesign and the ten golden rules: Generic advice for merging environmental aspects into product development. *Journal of Cleaner Production, 14*(15/16), 1396–1408.
- McDonough, W., Braungart, M. (2002). *Cradle to cradle: Remaking the way we make things.* North Point Press.
- Papanek, V. (2005). *Design for the real world* (2nd ed.). Academy Chicago Publishers.
- Papanek, V. (1995). *The green imperative: Natural design for the real world.* Thames and Hudson.
- Perera, O., Morton, B., & Perfrement, T. (2009). *Life cycle costing: A question of value.* International Institute for Sustainable Development.
- ISO. (2006). *Environmental management—life cycle assessment—principles and framework.* ISO 14040. International Organization for Standardization, Geneva.
- Ritthof, M., Rohn, H., & Liedtke, C. (2002). *Calculating MIPS.* Wuppertal Institute. WS27e.
- Socolow, R., Andrews, C., Berkhout, F., & Thomas, V. (Eds.). (1997). *Industrial ecology and global change.* Cambridge University Press.
- Spangenberg, J. H., Fuad-Luke, A., & Blincoe, K. (2010). Design for sustainability (DfS): The interface of sustainable production and consumption. *Journal of Cleaner Production, 18*(15), 1485–1493.
- Spangenberg, J. H., Hinterberger, F., Moll, S., & Schütz. H. (1999). Material flow analysis, TMR and the mips concept: A contribution to the development of indicators for measuring changes in consumption and production patterns. *International journal of sustainable development, 2*(4), 491 - 505.
- Turcksin, L., Macharis, C., Sergeant, N., & Van Mierlo, J. (2009). Life cycle cost analysis of alternative vehicles and fuels in Belgium. *World Electric Vehicle Journal, 3*, 255–270.

Journals

- Journal of Industrial Ecology, Journal of Cleaner Production, Ecological Economics
- The Cradle to Cradle Products Innovation Institute administers a certification program as a third-party nonprofit organization. Cradle to Cradle Certified® is more than a recognized mark of product quality—it is a process that leads companies to make better products, better companies, and better communities.

EXTERNAL COST ESTIMATES

E conomic valuation for social and environmental costs is challenging, but needed. Even a rough idea of true cost can make it possible to compare different management options. Try to develop an impact network to see how things are related and to develop a better estimate of health and environmental costs. When possible, include the range of true costs and the confidence level for the sources and details. Ideally, we would like to develop an understanding of financial, health, and environmental risks and resilience. It seems likely the environmental costs will often exceed health costs, but they are harder to determine.

External Cost Information

Health

- The full range of health impacts known, unknown, and uncertain

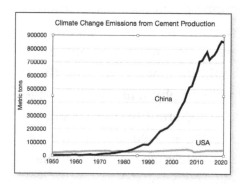

This large wood building is home of the Centre for Interactive Research on Sustainability at the University of British Columbia.

- Most important health impacts and costs
- Developmental brain injury and lifetime reduced earnings
- Health quality impacts, targets, and standards
- Health impacts—known impacts should not be ignored even if they are not easily monetized. A range of best-guess prices might be tested.
- Changes in social capital

Environment

- Environmental quality impacts, targets, and environmental standards
- Environmental impacts—best-guess costs
- Most important environmental impacts and costs—biodiversity, native species percentages
- Extinctions
- Decline in Natural Capital
- Decline in Nature's Services
- Impairment of use value

You may need to consider the value of a life. In the US, this varies according to different agencies. In 2021, the Department of Transportation's value of a life increased to $11.8 million. Many economists seem to feel $10 million is appropriate. A quality year of life is valued at between $50,000 and $129,000.

For more important true cost evaluations, it may be desirable to use sensitivity analyses to explore how dependent the results are on the economic assumptions. The final step is providing this information to stakeholders, managers, policy-makers, communities, and the public at large. Trends should be made clear—are things getting better or getting worse? Simple graphics, maps, and images can help. Results may be presented at different levels of detail and by types of damage. The valuation methods used to make the estimates should be described. It should be clear whether the estimates refer to damage reduction costs, reduction in health costs, the costs of unavoidable health risks, or environmental damage.

Here are the external cost estimates for a variety of common materials and compounds. These are from different years, varied assumptions, and different levels of analysis, but they are still instructive. Euros have been converted to US dollars. Conversions were not date-adjusted for inflation or variation in currency exchange. The EU and some of the impact reporting companies have large databases[431] that may be useful, with true cost calculations down to specific chemicals.

EXTERNAL COST ESTIMATES FOR A VARIETY OF COMMON MATERIALS AND COMPOUNDS

	$/ton
Climate Change Gases	
carbon dioxide or CO_2e	$50-150
carbon dioxide long-term cost	$10,000–$750,000[432]
carbon dioxide at 2.5% discount 2020	$83.60
carbon dioxide at 2.5% discount 2050	$127.60
carbon dioxide impact fee in Sweden 2021	$137.50
Suggested True Costs for Materials, Elements and Chemicals	
cement manufacturing (CO_2 0.59 tons per ton)	$59
steel (1.9 tons CO_2 per ton)	$190
methane (2.5% discount 2020)	$2,200
methane (2.5% discount 2050)	$4,180
aluminum (18 tons CO_2 per ton)	$1,800
coal	$9-$2,689
CFC12	$1 million
HFC 134A	$143,000
HFC152a	$12,400
arsenic (€10,351 kg no future discount rate)	$11.4 million
cadmium (added to soil from fertilizer €334 kg)	$368,000
cadmium (€20.9 kg related to cancer)	$19,000
cadmium (€236,691 kg related to other health)	$230 million
cobalt (€29,900 ton)	$32,960
chromium VI (€9,930 kg)	$11 million
chromium VI (€297,895 lung cancer)	$328 million
chromium primary (€140 kg health)	$154,000
composites (€5 kg for recycling some types)	$5,500

landfill waste (€19 kg)	$20,900
lead (€23,000 kg)	$25 million
lead (€41,920 kg no discount health)	$46 million
lead emission (€102 kg infant)	$11,200
lithium	*high but unknown*
mercury (€29,000 kg)	$32 million
mercury (€74,867 kg no discount health)	$83 million
nickel (est. €2,900 kg)	$3.2 million
PFAS (health only)	$564,000
phosphate PO	$4
particulate PM2.5	$199,630
particulate PM2.5 (€75,000)	$82,025
particulate matter ($110,000 mt)	$122,000
platinum	*high but unknown*
N manure	$246
Total N marine ecosystems	$4,450
N_2O (2.5% discount rate 2020)	$29,700
N_2O (2.5% discount rate 2050)	$96,800
NH_3 (all)	$82,514
NH_3 (€31,000)	$34,000
NH_3 (€9,482 health)	$10,452
NH_3 (€3,266 biodiversity)	$3,600
NO_x (all)	$31,941
NO_x (€5,591 health)	$6,163
NO_x (€903 biodiversity)	$995
NO_x (€328 crop damage)	$361
NO_x (€71 damage to buildings, infrastucture)	$78
NO_x (€,12,000)	$13,230
SO_2 (all)	$42,588
SO_2 (€6,070 health)	$6,691
SO_2 (€177 biodiversity)	$195
SO_2 (€259 damage to buildings, infrastucture)	$285
SO_2	$16,000
VOC	$7,453 ton
Dioxin (€338,500 kg)	$373 million

In Europe, the Registration, Evaluation, Authorization and Restriction of Chemicals (REACH) Regulation took effect in 2007. This

requires all chemicals manufactured in quantities greater than 1 ton a year to be registered, and those in quantities over 100 tons must be evaluated. In 2022, the European Commission released an updated Restrictions Roadmap for harmful substances to help identify and prioritize treatment and regulation of harmful chemicals. The goals are to ensure transparent (to stakeholders) and timely fulfillment of the strategy's commitments. The aim is to identify the most harmful substances: carcinogenic, mutagenic, and reprotoxic substances; persistent, bioaccumulative, and toxic substances; very persistent and very bioaccumulative substances; endocrine disruptors; immuno-toxicants; neuro-toxicants; respiratory sensitizers; and specific target organ toxicity substances.

This got off to a good start, but funding and staffing have been inadequate. In 2018, there were 65,000 files registered on 16,000 substances. The intended reviews were weak, and in many cases the information was substandard. Over half the files evaluated were incomplete, and they were not being updated as required. The impacts and risks have not been monetized.

The US EPA maintains a wide range of material on chemical safety and reports global warming potential of 198 substances out of the tens of thousands in use.[433] Detailed information can be hard to find and is limited. Data on health and ecosystem risks are limited. True costs are missing.

These weaknesses highlight the need for more research to develop a better understanding of the risks and costs of even commonly used chemicals and substances. As we improve our understanding, we can improve our true cost estimates. It seems every new study that is done adds to the realization that critical costs are being underestimated or ignored altogether. The long-term health impacts are a special concern. Lowered lifetime IQ with exposure to heavy metals as an infant or child is a good example. This is now valued as a loss of up to $70 million per ton of mercury.

This work provides an excellent opportunity to put the energy and skill of students in high schools and universities to work. With modest funding and mentorship, students can help monitor the environment and well-being of the community. Student workers played an important role in UCSD's exemplary COVID wastewater monitoring. Every morning, a team of students and staff in matching T-shirts would deploy across campus in golf carts to collect sewage samples from 126 collection robots set up to monitor 350 buildings.[434] They were able to identify infections even before people realized they were sick.

Resources

- BioIntelligence Services & O₂France. (2003). Study on external environmental effects related to the life cycle of products and services. *Directorate General Environment. Directorate A: Sustainable Development Policy*. European Commission. Paris.
- de Bruyn, S., Bijleveld, M., de Graaff, L., Schep, E., Schroten, A., Vergeer, R., & Ahdour, S. (2018). *Environmental prices handbook (EU28 version)*. CE Delft.
- de Bruyn, S. (2020). *Further explanation of methods used for monetizing impacts from air pollution*. CE Delft.
- Munk, M., Sørensen, M., Carlsson Feng, M., von Bahr, J., Marcelia Sletten, T., Kiiski, J., & Krarup, S. (2016). *Inventory of valuation literature on chemicals*. Swedish Chemicals Agency, Ministry of Environment and Food of Denmark, Norwegian Environment Agency, Finnish Safety and Chemicals Agency. Nordic Working Paper. Nordic Council of Ministers.
- Papai, S., de Bruyn, S., Juijn, D., & de Vries, J. (2021). *The value of human toxicity. An explorative research for use in environmental prices*. CE Delft.
- Smith, M., Moerenhout, J., Thuring, M., et al. (2020). *External costs: Energy costs, taxes and the impact of government interventions on investments: Final report*. European Commission, Directorate-General for Energy, Publications Office.
- Streimikiene, D., & Alisauskaite, I. (2016). Comparative assessment of external costs and pollution taxes in Baltic States, Czech Republic and Slovakia. *Ekonomie a Management, 19*(4), 4–18.
- Trueprice.org. (2021). *Monetisation factors for true pricing* (version 2.0.3).

NOTES

1 Bainbridge, D. A. (1985). Ecological education: Time for a new approach. *Bulletin of the Ecological Society of America, 66*(4), 461–462.
2 Costanza, R. (2020). Valuing natural capital and ecosystem services towards the goals of efficiency, fairness and sustainability. *Ecosystem Services, 43*(1-7), 01096.
3 Daily, G. (1997). *Nature's services: Societal dependence on natural ecosystems.* Island Press.
4 And remarkably, the maintenance manual is available online.
5 The Task Force on Climate-Related Financial Disclosures was established in 2015 by the International Financial Stability Board.
6 The International Sustainability Standards Board (ISSB), the International Financial Reporting Standards Foundation (IFRS), the International Accounting Standards Board (IASB), the Financial Stability Board, the Value Reporting Foundation (VRF), the International Organization of Securities Commissions (IOSCO), and the World Economic Forum.
7 Archer, D., Kite, E., & Lusk, G. (2020). The ultimate cost of carbon. *Climate Change, 162,* 2069–2086.
8 "Illth" is a term coined by John Ruskin to mean "the opposite of wealth." A useful term that can be applied to many aspects of management related to climate change.
9 Bell, J., Poushter, J., Fagan, M., & Huang, C. (2021, September 14). *In response to climate change, citizens in advanced economies are willing to alter how they live and work.* Pew Research Center Report.
10 Kachaner, N., Nielsen, J., Portafaix, A., & Rodzko, F. (2020). *The pandemic is heightening environmental awareness.* Boston Consulting Group.
11 (2021). Environmental sustainability becoming a business imperative. PWC.
12 Bainbridge, D. A. (1985). Ecological education: Time for a new approach. *Bulletin of the Ecological Society of America, 66*(4), 461–462.
13 Kenny, A. (2017). Ecosystem services in the New York City watershed. *Ecosystem Marketplace.*

14 Porris, I., Barton, D. N., Chacón-Cascante, A., & Miranda, M. (2013). *Learning from 20 years of payments for ecosystem services in Costa Rica.* International Institute for Environment and Development.

15 Bent, D. L. (2006). Towards a monetised triple bottom line for an alcohol producer: Using stakeholder dialogue to negotiate a 'licence to operate' by constructing an account of social performance. In S. Schaltegger, M. Bennett, & R. Burritt (Eds.), *Sustainability Accounting and Reporting* (61–82). Springer.

16 Taplin, J. (2008). *Windfall: Putting a value on the social and environmental importance of orchards.* Forum for the Future/Bulmer Foundation.

17 Patel, K. (2022, June 2). How humid air, intensified by climate change, is melting Greenland ice. *Washington Post.*

18 Horton, B. P., Kopp, R. E., Garner, A. J., Hay, C. C., Khan, N. S., Roy, K., & Shaw, T. A. (2018). Mapping sea-level change in time, space, and probability. *Annual Review of Environment and Resources, 43*(1), 481–521.

19 Siegert, M., Alley, R. B., Rignot, E., Englander, J., & Corell, R. (2020). Twenty-first century sea-level rise could exceed IPCC projections for strong-warming futures. *One Earth, 3,* 691–703.

20 Hanley, S. (2019, Sept 13). 15 to 20 foot sea level rise possible sooner rather than later. *Cleantechnica.*

21 Jevrejeva, S., Jackson, L., Grinsted, A., Lincke, D., & Marzeion, B. (2018). Flood damage costs under the sea level rise with warming of 1.5 °C and 2 °C. *Environmental Research Letters, 13*(7), 074014.

22 Goodell, J. (2017). *The water will come: Rising seas, sinking cities, and the remaking of the civilized world.* Little Brown.

23 Meyers, E. (2022, December 4). Labor depeartment finds compromise in ESG investment rule. San Diego Union Tribune. p. C4.

24 (2021). *Monetization factors for true pricing, version 2.0.3.* True Price, Amsterdam. *See also* True cost accounting. Sustainability Impact Metrics, EcoCostValue *and* S&P TruCost.

25 Reuters. (2022, August 17). Pharmacy operators CVS, Walmart and Walgreens ordered to pay $650.6 million to Ohio counties in opioid case. It will be appealed.

26 Trinomics. (2020). *Final report external costs.* European Commission.

27 IPCC. (2005). *IPCC special report on carbon dioxide capture and storage.* Working Group III of the Intergovernmental Panel on Climate Change. Cambridge University Press.

28 Moyle, P. B., & Randall, P. J. (1998). Evaluating the biotic integrity of watersheds in the Sierra Nevada, California. *Conservation Biology, 12,* 1318–1326.

29 US CO2e emissions in 2020 were 5,200 million metric tons × $137.50 ton = $715 billion. By comparison, USAID's budget is $60 billion a year.

30 Ritch, W. A., & Begay, M. (2002). Smoke and mirrors: How Massachusetts diverted millions in tobacco tax revenues. *Journal of Epidemiology & Community Health, 56*, 522–528.

31 The Storm Drainage Citizen's Oversight Committee consists of three members. The committee is tasked with ensuring that storm drain fees (approved by Burlingame residents in May 2009) are used only for the city's storm drain program.

32 World Bank. (2022). Carbon pricing dashboard. https://carbonpricingdashboard.worldbank.org/

33 Ministry of Finance. (2021). *Sweden's carbon tax*. Government Offices of Sweden.

34 Murray, B., & Rivers, N. (2015). *British Columbia's revenue-neutral carbon tax: A review of the latest 'grand experiment' in environmental policy*. NI WP 15-04. Duke University.

35 Pedersen, A. B. (2016). *Pesticide tax in Denmark*. Aarhus University, IEAP.

36 Boehm, R. (2020). *Reviving the dead zone: Solutions to benefit both Gulf Coast fishers and Midwest farmers*. Union of Concerned Scientists.

37 Backus, G. B. C. (2017). Manure management: An overview and assessment of policy instruments in the Netherlands. *World Bank Regional Agricultural Pollution Study*.

38 Stokstad, E. (2019). Nitrogen crisis threatens Dutch environment and economy. *Science, 366*(6470), 1180–1181.

39 Taylor, C. A., & Heal, G. (2021). *Algal blooms and the social cost of fertilizer* [working paper]. CEEP, Columbia University.

40 Burkhart, K., Bernhardt, C., Pelton, T., Schaeffer, E., & Phillips, A. (2018). *Water pollution from slaughterhouses*. Environmental Integrity Project.

41 Water Planning Division. (1983). *Results of the nationwide urban runoff program*. EPA.

42 Kumar, P., & White, A. (2018). *Stormwater utility survey*. Black and Veatch Management Consulting.

43 Bainbridge, D. A., Corbett, J., & Hofacre, J. (1979). *Village homes' solar house design*. Rodale Press.

44 Lancaster, B. (2006). *Rainwater harvesting for drylands*. Rainsource Press.

45 McCallum, W. (2018). *How to give up plastic*. Penguin Books.

46 Eriksen, M., Thiel, M., & Lebreton, L. (2016). Nature of plastic marine pollution in the subtropical gyres. In H. Takada & H. Karapanagioti (Eds.), *Hazardous chemicals associated with plastics in the marine environment. The handbook of environmental chemistry* (vol. 78, pp. 135–162). Springer.

47 Major, K. (2022, June 30). Plastic waste and climate change—what's the connection? *World Wildlife Fund Newsletter*.

48 Conti, G. O., Ferrante, M., Banni, M., et al. (2020). Micro- and nano-plastics in edible fruit and vegetables. The first diet risks assessment for the general population. *Environmental Research, 187,* 109677.

49 Science Action and Advocacy Network. (2019). Effectiveness of plastic regulation around the world. *ScAAN.net.*

50 Fleurbaey, M., & Zuber, S. (2013). Climate policies deserve a negative discount rate. *Chicago Journal of International Law, 13*(2), Article 14.

51 In the *Organic Farmer's Business Handbook*, Richard Wiswall lays out full cost issues for an organic farm very effectively; it may help others explore their business function and economics.

52 Renzetti, S., & Kushner, S. (2004). Full cost accounting for water supply and sewage treatment: Concepts and case application. *Canadian Water Resources Journal, 29*(1), 13–22.

53 Donley, N. (2019). The USA lags behind other agricultural nations in banning harmful pesticides. *Environmental Health, 18,* 44.

54 Gill, L. (2022, June). CR investigation finds dangerous salmonella bacteria in nearly one-third of ground chicken samples tested. *Consumer Reports.*

55 Burke, D. (2019, March 30). Sweden has figured out how to keep food free of salmonella. Why can't Canada? *CBC News.*

56 de Bruyn, S., Bijleveld, M., de Graaff, L., et al. (2018). *Environmental prices handbook EU28 version.* CE Delft.

57 Better understanding increased cost to 105.7 billion in 2008: a 51 percent increase in ten years.

58 European Commission, Directorate-General for Research and Innovation. (2009). *ExternE: Externalities of energy* (vol. 2, Methodology).

59 Wang, S., & Ge, M. (2019). Everything you need to know about the fastest-growing source of global emissions: Transport. *World Resources Institute.*

60 Proctor and Gamble. (2019). *Environmental sustainability report* (p. 74).

61 Becker, U. J., Becker, T., & Gerlach, J. (2012). *The true cost of automobility: External cost of cars.* Technische Universitat, Dresden.

62 Lemp, J. D., & Kockelman, K. M. (2008). Quantifying the external costs of vehicle use: Evidence from America's top-selling light-duty models. *Transportation Research Part D: Transport and Environment, 13*(8), 491–504.

63 Buehler, R., & Pucher, J. (2021). The growing gap in pedestrian and cyclist fatality rates between the United States and the United Kingdom, Germany, Denmark, and the Netherlands, 1990–2018. *Transport Reviews, 41*(1), 48–72.

64 Buehler, R., & Pucher, J. (2011). Sustainable transport in Freiburg: Lessons from Germany's environmental capital. *International Journal of Sustainable Transportation, 5,* 43–70.

65 Holland, M., & Watkiss, P. (2002). Estimates of the marginal external costs of air pollution in Europe. *BeTa benefits table database*. NetCen for the European Commission.

66 Trinomics. (2020). *Final report external costs*. European Commission.

67 Gonzalez, S. (2020, April 23). Your life is worth $10 million. *All Things Considered*. NPR.

68 Lowder, S. K., Skoet, J., & Raney, T. (2016). The number, size and distribution of farms, smallholder farms and family farms worldwide. *World Development, 87*, 16–29.

69 Murata, M., Batchelor, C. H., Lovel, C. J., et al. (1995). *Development of small-scale irrigation using limited groundwater resources, 4th interim report, November*. IH Report ODA 95/5.

70 Lovich, J., & Bainbridge, D. A. (1999). Anthropogenic degradation of the Southern California desert ecosystem and prospects for natural recovery and restoration. *Environmental Management, 24*(3), 309–326.

71 Gemmill-Herren, B., Baker, L. E., & Daniels, P. A. (2021). *True cost accounting for food*. Routledge. *see also* Scholte, M., et al. (2021). *True cost of food: Measuring what matters to transform the US food system*. Rockefeller Foundation; *and* Riemer, O., van Leerzen, S., von Wolfersdorf, J., Wollesen, G., et al. (2022, March). *True cost accounting agrifood handbook. True cost/TMG/soil and more* [whitepaper].

72 Carlson, S., & Leith-Jennings, B. (2018, January 17). *SNAP is linked with improved nutritional outcomes and lower health care costs*. Center on Budget and Policy Priorities.

73 Anderson, M. L., Gallagher, J., & Ramirez-Ritchie, E. (2017, May 3). How the quality of school lunch affects students' academic performance. *Brown Center Chalkboard*. Brookings Institution.

74 Warnert, J. E. (2014, September 17). Farmers market prices compare well with the supermarket produce aisle. *Food Blog*. University of California DANR.

75 The supplemental nutrition program (SNAP), colloquially known as "food stamps," allows consumers with income less than the net eligibility standard (based on the federal poverty level) to use these debit-like cards anywhere the benefits are accepted.

76 Drabova, L., Alvarez-Rivera, G., Suchanova, M., et al. (2019). Food fraud in oregano: Pesticide residues as adulteration markers. *Food Chemistry, 276*, 726–734.

77 Harley, K. G., Parra, K. L., Camacho, J., et al. (2019). Determinants of pesticide concentrations in silicone wristbands worn by Latina adolescent girls in a California farmworker community: The COSECHA youth participatory action study. *Science of the Total Environment, 20*(652), 1022–1029.

78 Editors. (2022). Why superbugs are in your meat. *Consumer Reports, 87*(8), 36–38.

79 Benbrook, C. M., & Baker, B. P. (2014). Perspective on dietary risk assessment of pesticide residues in organic food. *Sustainability, 6*(6), 3552–3570.

80 Organic Trade Association. (2021, May 25). US organic sales soar to new high of nearly $62 billion in 2020.

81 Subak, S. (1999). Global environmental costs of beef production. *Ecological Economics, 30*(1), 79–91.

82 Energy Star Program. (nd.). *What is energy use intensity?* EPA.

83 Data from a variety of sources, including: Stylianou, N., Guibourg, C., & Briggs, H. (2019, August 9). Climate change food calculator: What's your diet's carbon footprint? *BBC News.*

84 Pimentel, D., Zuniga, R., & Morrison, D. (2005). Update on the environmental and economic costs associated with alien-invasive species in the United States. *Ecological Economics, 52*(3), 273–288; *see also* Crystal-Ornelas R., Hudgins, E. J., Cuthbert, R. N., et al. (2021). Economic costs of biological invasions within North America. *NeoBiota, 67*, 485–510.

85 Corey, P. (2021, November 1). Proposed methane fee would mark major development in US climate policy. *S&P Global.*

86 Quinton, A. (2019). *Cows and climate change.* UC Davis Media Release.

87 Uri, N. D. (2001). Agriculture and the environment—the problem of soil erosion. *Journal of Sustainable Agriculture, 16*(4), 71–91.

88 Odgaard, A. J. (1984). *Bank erosion contribution to stream sediment load.* Iowa Institute of Hydraulic Research. IIHR#280.

89 Pimentel, D. (2006). Soil erosion: A food and environmental threat. *Environment, Development and Sustainability, 8*, 119–137.

90 NOAA. (2021). *Larger than average Gulf of Mexico dead zone* [media release].

91 Boehm, R. (2020). *Reviving the dead zone—solutions to benefit both Gulf Coast fishers and Midwest farmers.* Union of Concerned Scientists.

92 Bainbridge, D. A. (1983). Farm accounts 1982: A very bad year. *Acres USA, 13*, 9.

93 EPA. (2022). *Inventory of US greenhouse gas emissions and sinks: 1990-2020.*

94 Detailed source notes and assumptions at Bainbridge, D. A. (2020). *True cost of American agriculture.* Case Studies. truecostalways.com.

95 Philpott, T. (2008, February 8). A reflection on the lasting legacy of 1970s USDA Secretary Earl Butz. *Grist.*

96 Schnitkey, G. (2022). *Revenue and costs for Illinois grain crops, actual for 2015 through 2021, projected 2022.* University of Illinois.

97 Harris, L. 2022. What are food miles? *Connect4Climate.* https://www.connect4climate.org/initiative/what-are-food-miles

98 Cassman, K. G., & Grassini, P. (2020). A global perspective on sustainable intensification research. *Nature Sustainability, 3*, 262–268.

99 Bandel, T., Köpper, J., Mervelskemper, L., Bonnet, C., & Sheepens, A. (2021). The business of TCA. In *True cost accounting for food* (pp. 209–220). Routledge.

100 Langley, J. A., Heady, E. O., & Olson, K. D. (1982). Macro implications of a complete transformation of US agricultural production to organic farming practices. *CARD Working Papers, 4.*

101 Hernandez, S. (2022, October17). Beverly Hills billionaires give UC Davis $50 million to build agricultural research hub. *Los Angeles Times.*

102 Rappeport, A. (2022, February 21). Black farmers fear foreclosure as debt relief remains frozen. *New York Times.*

103 Census of Agriculture. (2017). Farmland Information Center/NRCS.

104 Chase, C., Delate, K., & Johanns, A. (2011). *Organic crop production enterprise budgets. July,* Iowa State University.

105 Bison would be even better, but can be more challenging to manage on a small farm.

106 Zwilling, B. (2022). Cost to produce corn and soybeans in Illinois—2021. *farmdoc daily, (12),* 52, Department of Agricultural and Consumer Economics, University of Illinois at Urbana-Champaign.

107 Mitchell, S., & Bainbridge, D. A. (1991). *Sustainable agriculture: A guide to information.* University of California, Division of Agriculture and Natural Resources, Publication 3349.

108 Shepard, M. (2013). *Restoration agriculture.* Acres USA.

109 Sustainable Food Trust. https://sustainablefoodtrust.org/our-work/true-cost-accounting/

110 Olmstead, G. (2018, October 1). Wendell Berry's right kind of farming. *New York Times* [opinion].

111 Victory Garden at the National Museum of American History. https://gardens.si.edu/gardens/victory-garden/

112 Dilawar, I., & Mang, F. (2022, August 31). Deadly floods inundate farms in Pakistan, flushing away crops. *Bloomberg.* Unprecedented climate change intensified storms, killed 800,000 farm animals, and damaged or completely destroyed two million acres of crops and orchards. Pakistan produces less than half a percent of global CCGs.

113 Graham, L. T., Parkinson, T., & Schiavon, S. (2021). Lessons learned from 20 years of CBE's occupant surveys. *Buildings and Cities, 2*(1), 166–184.

114 In 1976, I worked on the passive solar design of a large office building for Sacramento, California. Computer modeling showed the design we developed would lead to a 90 percent reduction in energy use for heating, cooling, and ventilation. Our plan was rejected because the temperature would fluctuate a bit. We monitored existing office buildings with conventional heating and cooling and showed the

variations in temperature and discomfort were much worse—but it was to no avail.

115 Jungclaus, M., Esau, R., Olgyay, V., & Rempher, A. (2021). *Reducing embodied carbon in buildings: Low-cost, high-value opportunities*. Rocky Mountain Institute.

116 Hannon, B. M., Stein, R. G., Segal, B., Serber, D., & Stein, C. (1976). *Energy use for building construction*. Energy Research Group, University of Illinois; *and* A-1 Embodied Energy Coefficients at https://www.wgtn. ac.nz/architecture/centres/cbpr/resources/pdfs/ee-coefficients.pdf

117 Magwood, C. (2019). Opportunities for CO_2 capture and storage in building materials. http://dx.doi.org/10.13140/RG.2.2.32171.39208.

118   Brojan, L. Petric, A. & Clouston, P. L. (2013). A comparative study of brick and straw bale wall systems from environmental, economic and energy perspectives. *Journal of Engineering and Applied Science*. 8(11), 920–926.

119 Allen, G. (2009, October 27). Toxic Chinese drywall creates a housing disaster. *NPR Morning Edition*.

120 CPSC. (2011). *Repairing aluminum wiring*. US Consumer Product Safety Commission Publication 516.

121 Kernan, P. (2002). *Old to new design guide salvaged materials in new construction*. Greater Vancouver Regional District Policy & Planning Department.

122 Elliot, K., Locatelli, E., & Xu, C. (2020). The business case for deconstruction. *Unbuilders*. Vancouver Economic Commission, Sustainable Building Leadership.

123 Wilson, E. K. (2019, April 30). Benzene found in the water supply of fire-ravaged Paradise, California. *Chemical and Engineering News*.

124 Lewis, S. (2018, July 19). Cleaning up: Inside the wildfire debris removal job that cost taxpayers $1.3 Billion. *KQED*.

125 Sims, B. (2017). Hurricane trash pile, removal costs could reach staggering levels. *Environment, Reuters. See also* Hurricane Katrina report. *World Vision*.

126 Bainbridge, D. A., & Haggard, K. (2011). *Passive solar architecture*. Chelsea Green.

127 Starr, D. (2021). The air investigator. *Science, 373*(6555), 612–614.

128 EPA. (1991). Indoor air facts number 4: Sick building syndrome. *R&D MD56*.

129 Fisk, W. J., & Rosenfeld, A. H. (1997). Estimates of productivity and health from better indoor environments. *Indoor Air, 7*, 158–172.

130 Huizenga, C., Abbaszadeh, S., Zagreus, L., & Arens, E. A. (2006). Air quality and thermal comfort in office buildings: Results of a large indoor environmental quality survey. *Proceedings of Healthy Buildings, Lisbon, 3*, 393–397.

131 Lang-Yona, N., Levin, Y., Dannemiller, K. C., Yarde, O., Peccia, J., & Rudich, L. (2013). Changes in atmospheric CO_2 influence the allergenicity of *Aspergillus fumigatus*. *Global Change Biology, 19,* 2381–2388.

132 Cutts, E. (2022, July 25). Why are heat waves becoming so common in Europe? *Voice of America.*

133 Coi, G., & Weise, Z. (2022, August 3). Excess deaths surged as heat wave hit Europe. *Politico.*

134 Zhao, Q., Guo, Y., & Ye, T., et al. (2021). Global, regional, and national burden of mortality associated with non-optimal ambient temperatures from 2000 to 2019: A three-stage modelling study. *Lancet Planet Health.* 5(7), e415–25.

135 Rachal, M. (2021, October 19). How one of the hottest US cities is finally restructuring its heat response. Smart Cities Dive. https://www.smartcitiesdive.com/news/phoenix-heat-mitigation-response-office-david-hondula/608366/

136 Leopold, L. (1968). Hydrology for urban land planning. *USGS Circular 554.*

137 Blakemore, E. (2015, September 30). Climate change is turning 500-year floods into 24-year ones. *Smithsonian Magazine.*

138 Levenson, M., Hauser, C., & Berger, E. (2022, July 26). Flash floods swamp St. Louis Area, breaking a century-old rain record. *New York Times.*

139 Bainbridge, D. A., Corbett, J., & Hofacre, J. (1978). *Village homes' solar house designs.* Rodale.

140 (2018, October 24). Biological magnification: Definition, examples, and practice. *Biology Junction.*

141 Alava, J. J., & Gobas, A. P. C. (2012). Assessing biomagnification and trophic transport of persistent organic pollutants in the food chain of the Galapagos Sea Lion (*Zalophus wollebaeki*): Conservation and management implications. In *New approaches to the study of marine mammals* (chapter 4). InTech Publishing.

142 He, W. (2002). *Atmospheric corrosion and runoff processes on copper and zinc as roofing materials* [PhD dissertation]. Royal Institute of Technology, Stockholm.

143 Winters, N., & Graunke, L. K. (2014). *Roofing materials assessment: Investigation of toxic chemicals in roof runoff.* Washington Department of Ecology. #14-03-003.

144 American Peat Technology. Aitken, MN. americanpeattech.com

145 Paylar, B., Asnake, S., Sjöberg, V., et al. (2022). Influence of water hardness on zinc toxicity in *Daphnia magna. Journal of Applied Toxicology, 42*(9), 1510–1523.

146 McCall, M., & Rozmyn, L. (2014). *Investigation of toxic chemicals in roof runoff from constructed panels in 2013 and 2014.* Washington State University Stormwater Center.

147 Sirova, V. (2015). *Urban stormwater management: Treatment of heavy metals and polycyclic aromatic hydrocarbons with bioretention and permeable pavement technologies* [MS thesis]. Capstones. USF 247.

148 Allen, E. B., Rao, L. E., Steers, R. J., Bytnerowicz, A., & Fenn, M. E. (2009). Impacts of atmospheric nitrogen deposition on vegetation and soils at Joshua Tree National Park. In *The Mojave Desert: Ecosystem processes and sustainability* (pp. 78–100). University of Nevada Press.

149 Kalmykova, Y., Harder, R., Borgestedt, H., & Svanäng, I. (2012). Pathways and management of phosphorus in urban areas. *Journal of Industrial Ecology, 16*, 928–939.

150 Loss, S. R., Will, T., Loss, S. S., & Marra, P. P. (2014). Bird–building collisions in the United States: Estimates of annual mortality and species vulnerability. *The Condor, 116*(1), 8–23.

151 La Sorte, F. A., Horton, K. G., Johnston, A., Fink, D., & Auer, T. (2022). Seasonal association with light pollution trends for nocturnally migrating bird populations. *Ecosphere, 13*, e3994.

152 Mason, J. T., McClure, C. J. W., & Barber, J. R. (2016). Anthropogenic noise impairs owl hunting behavior. *Biological Conservation, 199*, 29–32.

153 Loss, S., Will, T., & Marra, P. (2013). The impact of free-ranging domestic cats on wildlife of the United States. *Nature Communications, 4*(1), 1–8.

154 Flegr, J. (2007). Effects of toxoplasma on human behavior. *Schizophrenia Bulletin, 33*(3), 757–760.

155 Martin, C. (2008). Condor's new neighbors. *Current Biology, 18*(11), R450-R451.

156 de Palma, A., Lindsey, R., Quinet, E., & Vickerman, R. (Eds.). (2013). *Handbook of transport economics*. Edward Elgar Publishing Ltd. *See also* Lemp, J. D., & Kockelman, K. M. (2008). Quantifying the external costs of vehicle use: Evidence from America's top-selling light-duty models. *Transportation Research Part D, 13*, 491–504.

157 Söffker, M., & Tyler, C. R. (2012). Endocrine disrupting chemicals and sexual behaviors in fish—a critical review on effects and possible consequences. *Critical Reviews in Toxicology, 42*(8), 653–668. *See also* Laurenson, J. P., Bloom, R. A., Page, S., & Sadrieh, N. (2014). Ethinyl estradiol and other human pharmaceutical estrogens in the aquatic environment: A review of recent risk assessment data. *AAPS Journal, 16*(2), 299–310.

158 Krikstan, C. (2012). Intersex fish widespread in Potomac River basin. *Chesapeake Bay Program*.

159 Van Maele-Fabry, G., Gamet-Payrastre, L., & Lison, D. (2019). Household exposure to pesticides and risk of leukemia in children and adolescents: Updated systematic review and meta-analysis. *International Journal of Hygiene and Environmental Health, 222*(1), 49–67.

160 Donley, N., Bullard, R. D., Economos, J., et al. (2022). Pesticides and environmental injustice in the USA: Root causes, current regulatory reinforcement and a path forward. *BMC Public Health, 22*, 708.

161 Donley, N. (2019). The USA lags behind other agricultural nations in banning harmful pesticides. *Environmental Health, 18*, 44.

162 Bainbridge, D. A., & Haggard, K. (2011). *Passive solar architecture.* Chelsea Green.

163 Congregation Beth David San Luis Obispo. Beller Design/Build. San Luis Obispo, CA.

164 Browning, W. (1992, June). NMB Bank headquarters. *Urban Land.*

165 Bainbridge, D. A. (1981). *The integral passive solar water heater book.* Passive Solar Institute.

166 NHERI.2022. Shake Table Testing of A Full-Scale Resilient 10-Story Mass-Timber Building, Newsletter. NHERITallwood.mines.edu.

167 Bainbridge, D. A., Steen, A., Steen, B., & Eisenberg, D. (1994). *The straw bale house.* Chelsea Green.

168 A full discussion of social capital and external costs and benefits across society will require another book.

169 Wezerek, G., & Chodocc, K. R. (2020, March 5). Women's unpaid labor worth 10.9 trillion. *New York Times.*

170 Body Mass Index from 25.0 to 30 is overweight; BMI 30.0 or higher is considered obese.

171 OECD. (2019). The heavy burden of obesity. The economics of prevention. *Health Policy Studies.* Paris.

172 Fleming, S. (2019). Japanese schoolchildren are some of the healthiest in the world. *World Economic Forum.*

173 National Health Expenditure Accounts. *Centers for Medicare and Medicaid Services.*

174 Leggat-Barr, K., Uchikoshi, F., & Goldman, N. (2021). COVID-19 risk factors and mortality among Native Americans. *Demographic Research, 45*(39), 1185–1219.

175 (2022, August). COVID-19. Navajo Department of Health.

176 O'Neil, S., Platt, I., Vohra, D., et al. (2021, November 12). The high costs of maternal morbidity show why we need greater investment in maternal health. *Commonwealth Fund, Issue Briefs.*

177 Garnett, M. F., Curtin, S. C., & Stone, D. M. (2022, March). Suicide mortality in the United States, 2000–2020. *NCHS Data Brief, 433.*

178 Moore, B. J., & Liang, L. (2020, December). Costs of emergency department visits in the United States, 2017. *Agency for Health Care Research and Quality, Statistical Brief #268.*

179 Grover, M. (2020, June). What a $400 emergency expense tells us about the economy. *Federal Reserve Bank of Minneapolis.*

180 Mishel, L., & Kandra, J. (2021, December 13). Wage inequality continued to increase in 2020. *Economic Policy Institute*.

181 De La Cruz, M.-V., Chen, Z., Ong, P. M., Hamilton, D., & Darity Jr., W. A. (2016). The color of wealth in Los Angeles. *Federal Reserve Bank of San Francisco*.

182 Bureau of Labor Statistics. Footwear Manufacturing.

183 Selyukh, A. (2019, June 19). Why the American shoe disappeared and why it's so hard to bring it back. *NPR Morning Edition*.

184 Liu, S. (2020). *Minimum wage level for garment workers in the world*. Department of Fashion & Apparel Studies, University of Delaware.

185 Numerous studies have shown that women have a harder time quitting, with some suggestion this is linked to hormones and differences in the brain.

186 Doctors, J., & Weiss, E. (2010, February). *Cutting lead poisoning and public costs*. Pew Center on the States.

187 Wright, J. P., Dietrich, K. N., Ris, M. D., et al. (2008). Association of prenatal and childhood blood lead concentrations with criminal arrests in early adulthood. *PLOS Medicine, 5*(5), 101.

188 Muennig, P. (2009). The social costs of childhood lead exposure in the post-lead regulation era. *Arch Pediatric and Adolescent Medicine, 163*(9), 844–849.

189 Antimicrobial Resistance Collaborators. (2022). Global burden of bacterial antimicrobial resistance in 2019: A systematic analysis. *Lancet, 399*(10325), 629–655.

190 Lillestolen, D. J. (2018). MRSA in the United States, Sweden, and Syria. *Montview Liberty University Journal of Student Research, 4*(1), Article 2.

191 Center for Veterinary Medicine. (2016). *Antimicrobials sold or distributed for use in food-producing animals*. USDA.

192 Smith, T. C., Gebreyes, W. A., Abley, M. J., et al. (2013). Methicillin-resistant *Staphylococcus aureus* in pigs and farm workers on conventional and antibiotic-free swine farms in the USA. *PLOS One, 8*(5), e63704.

193 Delaney, J. A., Schneider-Lindner, V., Brassard, P., & Suissa, S. (2008). Mortality after infection with methicillin-resistant *Staphylococcus aureus* (MRSA) diagnosed in the community. *BMC Medicine, 6*, 2.

194 Sharma, L. L., & Adhikari, R. (2021). What Bhutan got right about happiness—and what other countries can learn. *World Economic Forum*.

195 Helliwell, J. F., Layard, R., Sachs, J. D., et al. (2022). *World happiness report*.

196 Girvan, G., & Roy, A. (2020). *Switzerland: #1 in the 2020 World Index of Healthcare Innovation*. Foundation for Research on Equal Opportunity.

197 Eddy, N. (2019, February 19). Intel gives glimpse inside its Connected Care health plans that saved 17% per month. *Healthcare IT News*.

198 Wood, L., Tam, S., Macfarlane, R., Fordham, J., Campbell, M., & McKeown, D. (2011). *Healthy Toronto by design.* Toronto Public Health.

199 Putnam, R. D. (2000). *Bowling alone: The collapse and revival of American community.* Simon and Schuster.

200 Bainbridge, D. A., Corbett, J., & Hofacre, J. (1978). *Village Homes solar house designs.* Rodale Press.

201 Francis, M. (2002). Village Homes: A case study in community design. *Landscape Journal, 21*(1-02), 23–41.

202 Keoleian, G. A., Blanchard, S., & Reppe, P. (2001). Life-cycle energy, costs, and strategies for improving a single-family house. *Industrial Ecology, 4*(2), 135–156.

203 Primarily from Sovacool, B. K., Kim, J., & Yang, M. (2021). The hidden costs of energy and mobility: A global meta-analysis and research synthesis of electricity and transport externalities. *Energy Research & Social Science, 72*(9591), 101885; see also Karkour, S., Ichisugi, Y., Abeynayaka, A., & Itsubo, N. (2020). External-cost estimation of electricity generation in G20 countries: Case study using a global life-cycle impact-assessment method. *Sustainability, 12; and* Smith, M., Moerenhout, J., Thuring, M., et al. (2020). *External costs: Energy costs, taxes and the impact of government interventions on investments: Final report.* European Commission, Directorate-General for Energy, Publications Office.

204 Brenchley, W., & Warington, K. (1958). *The park grass plots at Rothamsted 1856-1949.* Rothamsted Experiment Station, Harpenden. England.

205 Wedin, D. A., & Tilman, D. (1996). Influence of nitrogen loading and species composition on the carbon balance of grasslands. *Science, 274,* 1720–1721.

206 Baron, J. (2001). *Scientists discover unexpected pollutant while monitoring fragile mountain habitats.* United States Geological Survey, Midcontinent Ecological Service Center, Fort Collins, CO.

207 Allen, E. B., Rao, L. E., Steers, R. J., Bytnerowitcz, A., & Fenn, M. E. (2009). Impacts of atmospheric nitrogen deposition on vegetation and soils in Joshua Tree National Park. In R. H. Webb et al. (Eds.), *The Mojave Desert: Ecosystem processes and sustainability* (pp. 78–100). University of Nevada Press.

208 Nguyen, T. (2022, March 4). Can a fire-ravaged forest of Joshua trees be restored? *Knowable Magazine.*

209 Pacyna, J. M., Sundseth, K., Pacyna, E. G., et al. (2010). An assessment of costs and benefits associated with mercury emission reductions from major anthropogenic sources. *Journal of the Air and Waste Management Association, 60*(3), 302–315.

210 Trasande, L., Landrigan, P. J., & Schechter, C. (2005). Public health and economic consequences of methyl mercury toxicity to the developing brain. *Environmental Health Perspectives, 113*(5), 590–596.

211 Conniff, R. (2016, November 23). Tuna's declining mercury contamination linked to US shift away from coal. *Scientific American.*

212 Li, R., Wu, H., Ding, J., Fu, W., Gan, L., & Li, Y. (2017). Mercury pollution in vegetables, grains and soils from areas surrounding coal-fired power plants. *Scientific Reports, 7*(46545), 1–8.

213 Bennett, R. S., French, J. B., Rossmann, R., & Haebler, R. J. (2008). Dietary toxicity and tissue accumulation of methylmercury in American kestrels. *Archives of Environmental Contamination and Toxicology, 56*(1), 149–156.

214 Muniz, I. P. (1984). The effects of acidification on Scandinavian freshwater fish fauna. *Philosophical transactions of the Royal Society of London. Series B, Biological Sciences, 305*(1124), 517–528.

215 Mollerstrom, H. (1987, December 6). Lime treatment a stunning cure for Sweden's Atran River, sick from acid rain. *Los Angeles Times.*

216 Climate Change Action Group. (2022). *Extreme weather events in the Arctic and beyond.* www.ccag.earth

217 Cordan, N. (2019). *5 Reasons the US needs free-flowing rivers.* Pew Trusts.

218 Greco, J. (2021, February/March). A shocking toll. *Wildlife Conservation.*

219 Delucchi, M., & McCubbin, D. (2010). External costs of transportation in the US. In *Handbook of transport economics* (pp. 341–368). Edward Elgar Publishing; see also *External costs of transportation.* European Environment Agency. Version 20-08-2001.

220 Nikolewski, N. (2022, October 27). Used batteries from electric vehicles get new purpose. *San Diego Union Tribune.* C1,C4.

221 Hinsdale, J. (2022, May 4). Cryptocurrency's dirty secret: Energy consumption. *State of the Planet.* Columbia Climate School.

222 "Hashrate" is a measure of the computational power per second used when mining.

223 Schmidt, J., & Powell, F. (2022, May 18). Why does Bitcoin use so much energy? *Forbes Advisor.*

224 Epstein, P. R., Buonocore, J. J., Eckerle, K., et al. (2011). Full cost accounting for the life cycle of coal. *Ecological Economics Reviews. Annals of the New York Academy of Science, 1219*, 73–98.

225 Bickel, P., & Friedrich, R. (2005). *ExternE methodology update.* Directorate General for Research, European Commission. Luxembourg. *See also* Rabl, A., & Spadaro, J. V. (2016). External costs of energy: How much is clean energy worth? *Journal of Solar Engineering, 138*(4).

226 Cohon, J., et al. (2010). *Hidden costs of energy: Unpriced consequences of energy production and use.* National Research Council, National Academies Press.

227 Haggard, K., Cooper, P., & Resnick, J. (2005). Natural conditioning of buildings. In *Alternative construction: Contemporary natural buildings* (chapter 3). Wiley.

228 Haggard, K., Niles, P., & Hay, H. (1976). Nocturnal cooling and solar heating with water ponds and movable insulation. *ASHRAE Transactions, 83*(1), 793–801.

229 Bainbridge, D. A., & Aljilani, R. (2013). Light shelves for daylighting. https://works.bepress.com/david_a_bainbridge/25/

230 Hammond, J. (2017, Spring). Multiple modes of energy capture create ZNE building. *Solar Today*, 26–31.

231 Oakley, G., Riffat, S. B., & Shao, L. (2000). Daylight performance of lightpipes. *Solar Energy, 69*(2), 89–98.

232 Matthews, A. (2020, December 10). The largest dam-removal in US history. *Future Planet.* BBC.

233 Taylor, A. (2022, October 14). Most Floridians got power back quickly after Ian. But for some the wait has just begun. *Washington Post.*

234 Gunia, A. (2022, September 2). China's extreme drought is pushing the country to rely even more on coal. *Time.*

235 Ward, L. (n.d.). 7 tips for an energy efficient home. *This Old House. See also* Home energy checklist. Federal Energy Management Program.

236 NREL. (2011). *Energy audit data collection form for commercial buildings.* Golden, CO.

237 Ciolkosz, D. (2010, June). Increasing energy efficiency in your cars and trucks. *Penn State Extension.*

238 Mileto, M., Connor, R., et al. (2021). *Valuing water.* UNESCO.

239 Coble, A., Barnard, A. H., Du, E., et al. (2020). Long-term hydrological response to forest harvest during seasonal low flow: Potential implications for current forest practices. *Science of the Total Environment, 730*, 138926.

240 California Department of Water Resources. (2022). *Producing and consuming power.* DWR.

241 An acre-foot is 325,851 gallons; MAF stands for million acre-feet.

242 Cohen, R., Nelson, B., & Wolff, G. (2004). Energy down the drain. *The hidden costs of California's water supply.* Natural Resources Defense Council.

243 Renzetti, S., & Kushner, J. (2004). Full cost accounting for water supply and sewage treatment: Concepts and case application. *Canadian Water Resources Journal, 29*(1), 13–22.

244 Laville, S. (2021, July 9). Southern Water fined record £90m for deliberately pouring sewage into sea. *The Guardian.*

245 Sawyer, K. O. (2018). The wonderful empire: How land, nuts and water made America's biggest farmer. *Water Footprint.* Grace Communications.

246 Lindt, J. (2020). Pistachio war spreads to Tulare County. *Sun Gazette.*

247 Simons, T. (2022, June 23). Saudi water deal threatening Phoenix water supply. *Arizona PBS.*

248 Odell, R., & James, I. (2019, December 11). These 7 industrial farm operations are draining Arizona's aquifers, and no one knows exactly how much they're taking. *Arizona Republic.*

249 Bainbridge, D. A. (2013). Fan Shengzhi: An agronomist of Ancient China. *Sustainable Agriculture Note.* https://works.bepress.com/david_a_bainbridge/35/

250 Kefa, C. C., Kipkorir, E., Kwonyike, J., Kubowon, P. C., & Ndambiri, H. K. (2013). Comparison of water use savings and crop yields for clay pot and furrow irrigation methods in Lake Bogoria, Kenya. *Journal of Natural Sciences Research, 3*(8), 34–39.

251 Jezdimirovic, J., Hanak, E., & Escriva-Bou, A. (2020, March 11). *A reality check on groundwater overdraft in the San Joaquin Valley* [blog]. Public Policy Institute of California.

252 Lees, M., Knight, R., & Smith, R. (2022). Development and application of a 1D compaction model to understand 65 years of subsidence in the San Joaquin Valley. *Water Resources Research, 58*(6), WR030310.

253 James, I. (2022, November 25) 'It's a disaster.' Drought dramatically shrinking California farmland. Times Standard Newspaper.

254 Ronayne, K. (2022, December 2). Drought-hit water agencies to get little help from the state. San Diego Union Tribune, page 1.

255 Scanlon, B., Faunt, C. C., Longuevergne, L., et al. (2012). Groundwater depletion and sustainability of irrigation in the US High Plains and Central Valley. *PNAS, 109*(24), 9320–9325.

256 ASCE. (2022). Investment gap 2020-2029. https://infrastructurereportcard.org/resources/investment-gap-2020-2029/.

257 Doctors, J., & Weiss, E. (2010, February). *Cutting lead poisoning and public costs.* Pew Center on the States, Issue Brief #14.

258 Neltner, T. (2020, February 20). *Every lead service line replaced yields an estimated $22,000 in reduced cardiovascular disease deaths.* Environmental Defense Fund.

259 Stackpoole, S. M., Shoda, M. E., Medalie, L., & Stone, W. W. (2021). Pesticides in US rivers: Regional differences in use, occurrence, and environmental toxicity, 2013 to 2017. *Science of the Total Environment, 787,* 147147.

260 (2022). *Sampling for pesticide residues in California Well Water.* California Department of Pesticide Regulation.

261 Community Water Center. (2013, December). *Water & health in the Valley: Nitrate contamination of drinking water and the health of San Joaquin Valley residents* (p. 2).

262 National Partnership, Sierra Club, NAPAWF, & Black Women's Reproductive Justice. (2020). Case Study. Nitrate contamination in San Joaquin Valley, California. In *Clean water and reproductive justice* (p. 10).

263 Cohn, J. P. (2001). Resurrecting the dammed: A look at Colorado River restoration. *Bioscience, 51*(12), 998.

264 Triedman, N. (2012). Case study: The Tamarisk. In *Environment and ecology of the Colorado River Basin* (pp. 89–107). Colorado College State of the Rockies Report Card.

265 Flessa, K. W. (2004). *Ecosystem services and the value of water in the Colorado River delta and estuary, USA and Mexico: Guidelines for mitigation and restoration.* International Seminar on Restoration of Damaged Lagoon Environments, Matsue, Japan. 79–86.

266 Ohlendorf, H. M., Santolo, G. M., Byron, E. R., & Eisert, M. A. (2020). Kesterson Reservoir: 30 years of selenium risk assessment and management. *Integrated Environmental Assessment and Management, 16*(2), 257–268.

267 Bainbridge, D. A. (1988). *The potential use of vegetation for selenium management at Kesterson Reservoir.* Dry Lands Research Institute, UC Riverside, Riverside, CA.

268 Bainbridge, D. A. (2007). *A guide for desert and dryland restoration.* Island Press.

269 Davis, T. (2020, September 25). Ancient aquifers are dropping as Tucson's suburbs pump groundwater. *Arizona Daily Star.*

270 Hanak, E., Gray, B., Lund, J., et al. (2014, March). *Paying for water in California.* Public Policy Institute.

271 In our work on solar energy and conservation codes in Davis, California, we had an invaluable partner in a well-known and well-liked retired professor. My effort to shrink road width was blocked as "too dangerous" until I found a European study that highlighted a reduction in accidents with narrower streets. Our clothesline ordinance was stalled until a gracious and very well-spoken grandmother testified in favor.

272 Fisk, P., & Vittori, G. (1996). *Texas guide to rainwater harvesting.* Center for Maximum Potential Building Systems, Texas Water Development Board.

273 Hafen, K. (2017). *To what extent might beaver dam building buffer water storage losses associated with a declining snowpack?* [MS thesis]. Utah State University. 6503. https://digitalcommons.usu.edu/etd/6503

274 Yarnell, S. M., Pope, K., Wolf, E. C., Burnett, R., & Wilson, K. (2020). *A demonstration of the carbon sequestration and biodiversity benefits of beaver and beaver dam analogue restoration techniques in Childs Meadow, Tehama County, California.* Center for Watershed Sciences Technical Report (CWS-2020-01), University of California, Davis.

ACCOUNTABILITY

275 Chua, J. (2015, September). Do you know the true cost of water? *Ecobusiness*; *See also* Bernick, L. (2013, April 29). The true cost of water. *GreenBiz.*

276 Bainbridge, D. A., & Haggard, K. (2011). *Passive solar architecture.* Chelsea Green.

277 watercalculator.org has an excellent calculator that includes the water used to grow the food you buy, to supply the energy you consume, and other uses. My water bill is for just 99 gallons per day, but my footprint is nearly 1,000 gallons.

278 Bainbridge, D. A. (2015). *Gardening with less water.* Storey Press.

279 Donohye, M. J., Macomber, P. S. H., Okimoto, D., & Lerner, D. T. (2017). Survey of rainwater catchment use and practices on Hawaii Island. *Journal of Contemporary Water Research and Education, 161,* 33–47.

280 Gelt, J. (2009). *Home use of graywater, rainwater conserves water.* Water Resources Research Center, University of Arizona. http://ag.arizona. edu/azwater/arroyo/071rain.html

281 Brown, A. (2022). *Just enough: Lessons from Japan for sustainable living, architecture, and design.* Stonebridge.

282 Morse, A., Bhatt, V., & Rybczynski, W. (1978). *Water conservation and the mist experience.* Minimum Cost Housing Group, School of Architecture, McGill University. A two-gallon solar shower is available from REI. I have used a smaller version for years while backpacking and it provides plenty of warm or hot water.

283 Schmidt-Bleek, F. (2000). *Bridging ecological, economic, and social dimensions with sustainability indicators: The factor 10/MIPS-concept.* Factor 10 Institute, Carnoules.

284 Impact Institute. (2019). *The true price of jeans.* Commissioned by ABN-AMRO, Amsterdam.

285 Le, Q.-A. V., Sekhon, S. S., Lee, L., Ko, J. H., & Min, J. (2016). *Daphnia* in water quality biomonitoring—"omic" approaches. *Toxicology and Environmental Health Sciences, 8,* 1–6.

286 *Product stewardship and extended producer responsibility* (EPR). CalRecycle.

287 OECD Ministry of the Environment. (2014, June 17-19). *The state of play on extended producer responsibility (EPR): Opportunities and challenges.* Global Forum on Environment: Promoting Sustainable Materials Management Through Extended Producer Responsibility (EPR), Tokyo.

288 Bünemann, A., Brinkmann, J., Löhle, S., & Bartnik, S. (2020). *How Germany's EPR system for packaging waste went from a single PRO to multiple PROs with a register.* Deutsche Gesellschaft für Internationale Zusammenarbeit (GIZ) GmbH PREVENT Waste Alliance. Bonn.

289 *The problem.* Product Stewardship Institute. Boston, MA.

290 Cassel, S. (2016). *Electronics EPR in the US.* Annex K. OECD.

291 Eurostat. *Waste statistics—electrical and electronic equipment.* EC-Europa.

292 PaintCare in California. (2021, June 30-July 1). Program highlights.

293 Harjula, T., Rapoza, B., Knight, W. A., & Boothroyd, G. (1996). Design for disassembly and the environment. *CIRP Annals, 45*(1), 109–114.

294 (2005, January). Design for disassembly guidelines. *Active Disassembly Research.* http://www.engen.org.au

295 Boyd, E. (2020). *Beginning with the end in mind.* Dell Technologies.

296 iFixit is an American e-commerce and how-to website that sells repair parts and publishes free wiki-like online repair guides for consumer electronics and gadgets.

297 (2022). *This is your right to repair.* repair.org.

298 Giulioni, C., Maurizi, V.,Castellani, D., et al. (2022). The environmental and occupational influence of pesticides on male fertility: A systematic review of human studies. *Andrology.* 10(7):1250-1271, *See also* Giulioni, C., Maurizi, V., Castellani, D., et al. (2020). Impact of environmental toxin exposure on male fertility potential. *Translational Andrology and Urology.* 9(6): 2797–2813.

299 Grandjean P., & Landrigan, P. J. (2014). Neurobehavioural effects of developmental toxicity. *Lancet Neurology, 13*, 330–338.

300 Cirillo, P. M., La Merrill, M. A., Krigbaum, N. Y., & Cohn, B. A. (2021). Grandmaternal perinatal serum DDT in relation to granddaughter early menarche and adult obesity: Three generations in the child health and development studies cohort. *Cancer Epidemiology Biomarkers & Prevention, 30*(8), 1480–1488. https://doi.org/10.1158/1055-9965.EPI-20-1456

301 Xia, R. (2020, October 25). L.A.'s coast was once a DDT dumping ground. *Los Angeles Times.*

302 Haynes, E. N., Chen, A., Ryan, P., Succop, P., Wright, J., & Dietrich, K. N. (2011). Exposure to airborne metals and particulate matter and risk for youth adjudicated for criminal activity. *Environmental Research, 111*(8), 1243–1248.

303 Gottesfeld, P. (2015). Time to ban lead in industrial paints and coatings. *Frontiers in Public Health, 3*, 144.

304 Aurisano, N., Huang, L., Milà i Canals, L., Jolliet, O., & Fantke, P. (2021). Chemicals of concern in plastic toys. *Environment International, 146*, 106194.

305 Roberts, J. A., & Langston, N. (2008). Toxic bodies/toxic environments: An interdisciplinary forum. *Environmental History, 13*(4), 629–635.

306 Gaylord, A., Osborne, G., Ghassabian, A., et al. (2020). Trends in neurodevelopmental disability burden due to early life chemical exposure in the USA from 2001 to 2016: A population-based disease burden and cost analysis. *Molecular and Cellular Endocrinology, 502*, 110666.

307 Congleton, J., Sharp, R., & Lunder, S. (2014). *No escape: Tests find toxic fire retardants in mothers—and even more in toddlers.* Environmental Working Group/Duke University.

308 McMahon, P. B., Tokranov, A. K., Bexfield, et al. (2022). Perfluoroalkyl and polyfluoroalkyl substances in groundwater used as a source of drinking water in the eastern United States. *Environmental Science & Technology, 56*(4), 2279–2288.

309 Eriksen M., Lebreton, L., Carson, H., et al. (2014). Plastic pollution in the world's oceans: More than 5 trillion plastic pieces weighing over 250,000 tons afloat at sea. *PLOS One, 9,* e111913.

310 Steffen, A. (2021, July 31). EU introduces an €800 per ton tax on plastic waste. *Intelligent Living.*

311 Tyree, C., & Morrison, D. (n.d.). *Plus plastic: Microplastics found in global bottled water.* Orb Media.

312 Rahman, A., Sarkar, A., Yadav, O. P., Achari, G., & Slobodnik, J. (2021). Potential human health risks due to environmental exposure to nano- and microplastics and knowledge gaps: A scoping review. *Science of the Total Environment, 757,* 143872.

313 Rosane, O. (2021, October 18). This year's e-waste to outweigh Great Wall of China. *Agenda Weekly.* World Economic Forum.

314 van Engelsdorp, D., Evans, J. D., Saegerman, C., et al. (2009). Colony collapse disorder: A descriptive study. *PLOS One, 4*(8), e6481.

315 Ma, M. (2022, February 24). Electric vehicle battery recycling is starting in California. *Protocol.*

316 Buhtada, G. (2022, February 28). Mapped: EV battery manufacturing capacity, by region. *Visual Capitalist.*

317 Kane, M. (2021, July 7). Most of EV battery cells and packs are produced domestically. *Inside EEVs.*

318 Zhou, Y., Gohlke, D., Rush, L., Kelly, J., & Dai, Q. (2021). *Lithium-ion battery supply chain for e-drive vehicles in the United States: 2010–2020* (figure 2.7). Argonne National Laboratory ANL/ESD-21/3.

319 Suh, S. (Ed.). (2009). *Handbook of input-output economics in industrial ecology.* Springer. *See also* The Industrial Ecology Bookshelf: Books Received. https://jie.yale.edu/books

320 Weisse, M., & Goldman, E. (2022). *Forest pulse: The latest on the world's forests.* World Resources Institute.

321 FAO & UNEP. (2020). *The state of the world's forests 2020: Forests, biodiversity and people.* Rome. *See also* Runyan, C., & D'Odorico, P. (2016). *Global deforestation.* Cambridge University Press.

322 Associated Press. (2022, August 7). Wildfire implicated in death of tens of thousands of fish, California tribe says. *The Guardian.*

323 Robbins, Z. J., Xu, C., Aukema, B. H., et al. (2022). Warming increased bark beetle-induced tree mortality by 30% during an extreme drought in California. *Global Change Biology, 28*, 509–523.

324 (2011). *Western bark beetle strategy for human safety, recovery and resiliency.* USFS.

325 Prestemon, J. P., Abt, K. L., Potter, K. M., & Koch, F. H. (2013). An economic assessment of mountain pine beetle timber salvage in the West. *Western Journal of Applied Forestry, 28*(4), 143–153.

326 *What is sudden oak death?* California Oak Mortality Task Force. *See also* Oregon State University Extension. (2009). *Stop the spread of sudden oak death.* EC 1608-E.

327 Sudden Oak Death Research. Pacific Southwest Research Station. USFS. Davis, CA.

328 Mina, M. (2020, July 28). Are ash trees doomed? *Forest Monitor.*

329 Grayson, K. (2021, August 27). The invasive emerald ash borer has destroyed millions of trees—scientists aim to control it with tiny parasitic wasps. *The Conversation.*

330 McCullough, D. G. (2013, January 23). Will we kiss our ash goodbye? *American Forests.*

331 And not only is the tree species lost, but 100 or 200 other species that coevolved with the tree will disappear as well.

332 Skene, J., & Vinyard, S. (2019, February). The issue with tissue. *NRDC, R,* 19-01-A.

333 Krieger, D. J. (2001). *The economic value of forest ecosystems services: A review.* Wilderness Society. Washington, DC.

334 Ray, C. C. (2012, December 3). Tree power. *New York Times.*

335 Domke, G. M., Oswalt, S. N., Walters, B. F., & Morin, R. S. (2020). Tree planting has the potential to increase carbon sequestration capacity of forests in the United States. *PNAS, 117*(40), 24649–24651.

336 (2022). *Enrich your soil, improve your profit potential with carbon by Indigo.* www.indigoag.com

337 Mitsch, W. J., Bernal, B., & Hernandez, M. E. (2015). Ecosystem services of wetlands. *International Journal of Biodiversity Science, Ecosystem Services & Management, 11*(1), 1–4.

338 Yao, R. T., Palmer, D. J., Payn, T. W., Strang, S., & Maunder, C. (2021). Assessing the broader value of planted forests to inform forest management decisions. *Forests, 12*(6), 662.

339 Turner, J. A., Dhakal, B., Yao, R., Barnard, T., & Maunder, C. (2011). Non-timber values from planted forests: Recreation in Whakarewarewa Forest. *NZ Journal of Forestry, 55*(4), 24–31.

340 Phillips, S., Stoner, J., Schmidt, J. P., & Davis, S. (2017, September). *Ecosystem services and southern wetland forests: Baseline value and future prospects.* KeyLog Economics LLC.

341 Taylor, M. (2018). *Improving California's forest and watershed management.* Legislative Analyst's Office. Sacramento.

342 A board foot is the unit of measure of a piece of lumber one foot square and one inch thick.

343 Non-timber products are referred to as Minor Products in many forest management reports even when their value exceeds the wood value.

344 Hammig, B., & Jones, C. (2013). Epidemiology of chain saw related injuries, US: 2009 through 2013. *Advances in Emergency Medicine*, Article ID 459697.

345 Klun, J., & Medved, M. (2007). Fatal accidents in forestry in some European countries. *Croatian Journal of Forest Engineering, 28*(1), 55–62.

346 Butler, B. J., Butler, S. M., Caputo, J., et al. (2020). *Family forest ownerships of the United States, 2018: Results from the USDA Forest Service, National Woodland Owner Survey.* USDA Forest Service Gen. Tech. Rep. NRS-199, Northern Research Station, Madison, WI. https://doi.org/10.2737/ NRS-GTR-199

347 Tallamy, D. W. (2021). *The nature of oaks.* Workman Publishing.

348 Wright, S. F. & Nichols, K. A. (2002, September). Glomalin: Hiding place for a third of the world's stored soil carbon. *USDA Ag Research Magazine.*

349 Albert, G., Gallegos, S. C., Alexandra Greig, K., et al. (2021). The conservation value of forests and tree plantations for beetle (*Coleoptera*) communities: A global meta-analysis. *Forest Ecology and Management, 491*, 119201.

350 Mudge, K., & Gabriel, S. (2014). *Farming the woods.* Chelsea Green.

351 *The advantages of horse logging. L'energie Cheval* (horse power). https:// www.energie-cheval.fr/en/menu-principal/energie-cheval/.

352 Bray, D. B., Duran, E., Hernández-Salas, J., et al. (2016). Back to the future: The persistence of horse skidding in large scale industrial community forests in Chihuahua, Mexico. *Forests, 7*(11), 283.

353 Ambjörnsson, E. L. (2021). *Gendered performances in Swedish forestry* [PhD dissertation]. Stockholm University.

354 (2004). *SLIMF Eligibility Criteria.* Forest Stewardship Council. FSC-STD-01-003.

355 (2022). *1.5 SFI Forest Management Standard Objectives.* Sustainable Forest Initiative.

356 Stavins, R. N., & Richards, K. R. (2005). *The cost of US forest-based carbon sequestration.* Pew Center on Global Climate Change.

357 Butler, B. J., Butler, S. M., Caputo, J., et al. (2021). *Family forest ownerships of the United States, 2018: Results from the USDA Forest Service, National Woodland Owner Survey.* General Technical Report NRS-199.

358 US forest landowners earn private sector support via ecosystem service markets. *Ecosystem Marketplace.*

359 Lewis, N. (2020, July 27). This country regrew its lost forest. Can the world learn from it? *CNN Travel*.

360 OAS Department of Sustainable Development. *National payment for environmental services programs*. http://www.oas.org/dsd/pes/programs. htm

361 (2020). *Payments for environmental services program, Costa Rica*. United Nations Climate Change.

362 Bastin J. F., Finegold, Y., Garcia, C., et al. (2019). The global tree restoration potential. *Science, 365*(6448), 76–79.

363 Von Hedemann, N., & Schultz, C. A. (2021, October 14). US family forest owners' forest management for climate adaptation: Perspectives from extension and outreach specialists. *Frontiers in Climatology*.

364 Clover, C. (2006). *The end of the line*. University of California Press.

365 Reimchen, T. E., Mathewson, D., Hocking, M. D., & Moran, J. (2002). Isotopic evidence for enrichment of salmon-derived nutrients in vegetation, soil, and insects in riparian zones in coastal British Columbia. *American Fisheries Society Symposium*, 1–12.

366 Kurlansky, M. (1997). *Cod*. Penguin Books.

367 Census of Marine Life. (2005, March 21). First ever estimate of cod fishery in 1850s reveals 96% decline on Scotian Shelf. *Science Daily*.

368 Cudmore, W. W. (2009). *The decline of Atlantic cod—a case study*. Chemekta Community College. Salem, OR.

369 (2022). *The collapse of the Grand Banks cod fishery*. britishseafishing.co.uk

370 Rose, A. (2011). *Who killed the Grand Banks? The untold story behind the decimation of one of the world's greatest natural resources*. John Wiley & Sons.

371 (2022). *Cod spawning areas: Research*. https://www.gov.scot/publications/cod-spawning-areas-research/

372 Frank, K. T., Petrie, B., Choi, J. S., & Leggett, W. C. (2005). Trophic cascades in a formerly cod-dominated ecosystem. *Science, 308*(5728), 1621–1623.

373 Cleary, R. R. (2021). *29 years of northern cod moratorium have cost NL at least $26 billion*. Seaward Enterprises Association: Newfoundland and Labrador.

374 Smellie, S. (2021, April 19). After almost 3 decades, cod are still not back off Newfoundland. Scientists worry it may never happen. *CBC, the Canadian Press*.

375 Holm, P., & Rånes, S. A. (1996, June 5-8). *The individual vessel quota system in the Norwegian Arctic coastal cod fishery*. Sixth Annual Conference of the International Association for the Study of Common Property. Berkeley, CA.

376 Allen, B. et al. (2005). History and socio-economics of the fishery. In *Abalone Recovery and Management Plan*. 3.1–3.10. California Department of Fish and Game. Sacramento.

377 Barnett, C. (2021). *The sound of the sea: Sea shells and the fate of the oceans.* Norton.

378 Kurlansky, M. (2007). *The big oyster: A history on the half-shell.* Random House.

379 Shivaram, D. A. (2021, July 9).Heat wave killed an estimated 1 billion sea creatures, and scientists fear even worse. *National Public Radio*.

380 Mehaffey, K. C. (2021, July 9). Decline of five Pacific salmon species could signal tipping point for ocean. *California Energy Markets*.

381 Quinn, T. P., Helfield, J. M., Austin, C. S., Hovel, R. A. & Bunn, A. G. (2018). A multidecade experiment shows that fertilization by salmon carcasses enhanced tree growth in the riparian zone. *Ecology, 99*(11), 2433–2441.

382 Post, A. (2008, November). Why fish need trees and trees need fish. *Alaska Fish and Wildlife News*.

383 McGuirk, R. (2022, May 11). Majority of Great Barrier Reef coral studied in 2022 was bleached, Australian scientists say. *PBS News Hour*.

384 Cullinane, T., Huber, C., Skrabis, K., & Sidon, J. (2016). *Estimating the economic impacts of ecosystem restoration—methods and case studies.* US Geological Survey Open-File Report 2016–1016.

385 Graner, F. (2021, December 16). So, how is the Elwha River salmon recovery doing? *The Orcasonian*.

386 Moorhead, K., Storz, R., & Pinisetty, D. (2019). *Evaluation of the feasibility and costs of installing tier 4 engines and retrofit exhaust after-treatment on in-use commercial harbor craft.* Maritime Academy, California State University.

387 Bighui, M. A. (2017). *Use and environmental impact of antifouling paints in the Baltic Sea* [PhD dissertation]. Stockholm University.

388 EPA. (2019, February 19). *US settles with Trident Seafoods corporation to reduce ozone-depleting emissions* [news release].

389 Holmyard, N. (2019, September 30). The sticky problem of sea lice—and what's being done to stop them. *Sea Food Source*.

390 Martini, R. (2019, February 28). Many government subsidies lead to overfishing. *OECD*.

391 Gilbert, R. (2022, May 27). *Most long-distance fishing in foreign waters dominated by only a few governments.* Pew Trusts.

392 Pusceddu, A., Bianchelli, S., Martín, J., et al. (2014). Chronic and intensive bottom trawling impairs deep-sea biodiversity and ecosystem functioning. *Proceedings of the National Academy of Sciences*, 201405454.

393 Sala, E., Mayorga, J., Bradley, D., et al. (2021). Protecting the global ocean for biodiversity, food and climate. *Nature, 592*, 397–402.

394 VanSomeren, L. (2021, July 26). Indigenous tribes are leading the way to restore river ecosystems. *GreenBiz*.

395 Perroni, E. (n.d.). 16 organizations promoting sustainable fishing practices. *Food Tank*. See also *Trout unlimited*. Environmental Defense Fund & Save Our Wild Salmon.

396 Oleson, K. (2011) TEEB case: Taking an Ecosystem Service Perspective in Velondriake Locally Managed Marine Area. Available at: TEEBweb.org. *and see also* BlueVentures.org

397 Baker, P. (2011). *Remembering cod*. Pew Environment Group.

398 True Price. (2019, June). A roadmap for true pricing. True Price Foundation. Amsterdam.

399 World Bank. (2022). *State and trends of carbon pricing 2022*. World Bank. Washington, DC.

400 (2021, September 26). Climate protection enshrined in cantonal constitution. *SwissinfoCH*.

401 VoxEU. (2022, April 22). Designing an effective border carbon adjustment mechanism.

402 P&G. (2019). *2018 greenhouse gas emissions*. Proctor and Gamble Citizenship Report.

403 CDP. (2022). *Benefits of disclosure*. Carbon Disclosure Project.

404 International Federation of Accountants. (2022). *Climate Action*. New York.

405 Druckenmiller, H. (2022, July). Accounting for ecosystem service values in climate policy. *Nature Climate Change, 12*, 596–597.

406 SEC. (2022). *Enhancement and standardization of climate-related disclosures*. US Securities and Exchange Commission, Fact Sheet 33-11042.

407 Many carbon calculators can be found online, try: https://www.carbonfootprint.com/calculator.aspx/ *see also* Cool Climate calculator (US), WWF footprint (UK).

408 *Carbon offset guide*. GHG Management Institute & Stockholm Environment Institute.

409 City News Service. (2021, August 12). UCSD wastewater screening detected 85% of COVID-19 cases early, study finds.

410 I was fortunate to work as team leader on two projects like this in San Diego. The County Environmental Development Agency funded and guided two important projects: Protecting the Coastal Lagoons in 1970 and Mapping County Environmental Resources using professional USGS standards in 1971.

411 Kwok, A. G., Benton, C. C., & Burke, B. (1998). Taking a building's vital signs. *Architectural Science Association Conference Proceedings* (pp. 269–274).

412 Graham, L. T., Parkinson, T., & Schiavon, S. (2021). Lessons learned from 20 years of CBE's occupant surveys. *Buildings and Cities, 2*(1), 166–184.

413 IUCN. (2020, January). Gender and the environment: What are the barriers to gender equality in sustainable ecosystem management?

414 Bainbridge, D. A. (2015). *Gardening with less water*. Storey Press.

415 Wagle, R. (2019). Want to protect forests? Engage more women, says Nepal's joint-secretary for forests. *Who We Are*. World Bank.

416 Solberg, D., & Souther, M. (2022). The mangrove mothers. *Nature Conservancy, fall*, 40–47.

417 AFP Agency. (2022, June 30). India's women water warriors transform parched lands. *Economic Times*.

418 Berry, W. (2019). Conservation and local economy. In *Wendell Berry Essays 1993-2017*. (pp. 3-14). The Library of America.

419 DeVries, R. (2021). *What Would Nature Do? A Guide for Our Uncertain Times*. Columbia University Press.

420 Carney, M. 2021. *Values: Building a Better World for All*. Hachettte.

421 Gowdy, J. M. (Ed.) . (1997). *Limited wants, unlimited means*. Island Press.

422 Naess, A., Drengson, A., & Devall, B. (2010). *The ecology of wisdom: Writings by Arne Naess*. Counterpoint Press.

423 A BioBlitz brings together volunteer scientists with families, students, teachers, and other members of the community to get an overall count of the plants, animals, fungi, and other organisms that live in a place. Hundreds of BioBlitzes have been conducted all over the world. The first BioBlitz was sponsored by the National Park Service.

424 Bringezu, S. & Moriguchi, Y. (2019 [2003]). Material flow analysis. Chapter 6. In P. Bartelmus. & E. K.Seifert.. (Eds.). *Green Accounting*. Taylor and Francis. 149-166. *See also* Moriguchi, Y. (2007). Material flow indicators to measure progress toward a sound material-cycle society. *Journal of Material Cycles and Waste Management*. 9(2), 112–120; Brunner, P. H., & Rechberger, H. (2017). Handbook of material flow analysis for environmental, resource, and waste engineers (2nd ed.). CRC Press; and Brunner, P. H., & Rechberger, H. (2004). Practical handbook of material flow analysis. Lewis Publishers, CRC Press.

425 Huang, C-L., Vause, J., Ma, H.-W. & Yu, C.P. (2012). Using material/ substance flow analysis to support sustainable development assessment: A literature review and outlook. *Resources, Conservation and Recycling*. 68, 104–116.

426 Schmidt-Bleek, F. (1999). *The factor 10/MIPS-concept: Bridging ecological, economic, and social dimensions with sustainability indicators*. United Nations University, Zero Emission Forum.

427 Pieper, M., Michalke, A., & Gaugler, T. (2020). Calculation of external climate costs for food highlights inadequate pricing of animal products. *Nature Communications, 11*, 6117.

428 Hansen, E. (2008). Experience with the use of substance flow analysis in Denmark. *Journal of Industrial Ecology, 6*(3-4), 201–219.

429 Hansen, E., & Lassen, C. (1996). *Substance flow analysis for lead* [original in Danish]. Environmental Project No. 327, Danish EPA, Copenhagen.

430 Archer, D., Kite, E., & Lusk, G. (2020). The ultimate cost of carbon. *Climatic Change, 162*, 2069–2086. *See also* EPA. (2022). 40 CFR 98 global warming potentials. Substance Registry Services.

431 Cradle to Cradle, GIST Impact, Sensefolio, Arabesque, CDP, ESG-Book, Workiva, SustainableHQ, Green Guard, Bees On-line, Declare, the Pharos Project, the Quartz Project, CEDelft, Wuppertal Institute, and Impact Cubed. A comprehensive review of data bases and options to improve integration/interoperability of data sets would be useful. See for example: S. Ramesohl J. Sebestyén, H. Berg. 2022. Data Ecosystems for the Sustainability Transformation. A study commissioned by Huawei Technologies Deutschland GmbH. Wuppertal Institute.

432 Archer, D., Kite, E., & Lusk, G. (2020). The ultimate cost of carbon. *Climatic Change, 162*, 2069–2086.

433 Global Warming Potentials- 40 CFR 98: Global Warming Potentials. EPA Substance Registry Services.

434 City News Service. (2021, August 12). UCSD wastewater screening detected 85% of COVID-19 cases early, study finds.

Image Credits

1. Andrew McCall, Direct Relief/DB/NOAA: 2. NOAA/DB: 3. DB: 4. Deloitte, Amsterdam: 5. DB: 6. DB/Jonathan Hammond-Indigo Architecture: 7. DB/ RAGBRAI: 8. US Nat'l Archives/Google Earth/DB: 9. DB/ UN: 10. Ted Dave/ Adbusters/web: 11. DB/Roger Ottmar, USDA Forest Service: 12. H.W. Elliott/ DB: 13. Paani Foundation, Wellness Almanac/ Spaceaero2/DB: A1. DB: A2. DB/Centre for Interactive Research on Sustainability University of British Columbia.

SUGGESTED SOUNDTRACK

Jack Gladstone, "Fossil Fuel Sinner"
Jack Gladstone, "Conspicuous Consumption"
Joni Mitchell, "Big Yellow Taxi"
Stan Rogers, "The Idiot"
Stan Rogers, "The White Collar Holler"
Stan Rogers, "The Field Behind the Plow"

ACKNOWLEDGEMENTS

With special thanks to my wife, Laurie, for editorial assistance and wisdom. My editors at Red to Black Editing Company made a big difference in readability and form, thanks to Bill, Christopher and Judy. Sutton Wemple edited earlier work that also helped shape this book. Kippy Flur helped me set up my web page at **TrueCostAlways.com**.

My friends, students and staff at UC Davis, UC Riverside, San Diego State University and United States International University (later renamed Alliant International University) have provided inspiration, support, hard work in often difficult conditions, and added insight from around the world. Nancy Mancilla at ISOS Group brought me in to the GRI reporting world. Tod Neubauer, Ken Haggard, Polly Cooper, Phil Niles, Marshall Hunt, and Jon Hammond shaped my understanding of passive solar design and helped guide my research. Jerry Hatfield, Miguel Altieri, Steve Mitchell, Gene Anderson, Arturo Gomez Pompa, Scott Murray, Gary Nabhan, Florence Shipek, M. Kat Anderson, and Wes Jarrell added agricultural and ethnobotanical background. Ross Virginia, Edie Allen, Mike Allen, Ray Franson, and Ellen Bauder helped with support and thoughtful discussions about my restoration projects and research. Matts Myhrman, Bill and Athena Steen, Pliny Fisk III, Gail Vittori, Mike Evans and David Eisenberg were good companions on the straw bale trail. Linda Swanson, Al Zolynas, and Deans Ali Abu-Rahma and Ramona Kunard helped me develop my teaching and research skills at USIU.

ABOUT THE AUTHOR

I grew up in the West, spending my formative years in the dry lands east of the North Cascades. I completed my BA in Earth Sciences at UC San Diego and MS in Ecology at UC Davis. My research on passive solar heating and cooling in the 1970s led to the Passive Solar Pioneer Award from the American Solar Energy Society in 2004. I started research on desert and dryland restoration in the 1980s and completed many projects for a range of clients including national parks, state parks, BLM, US Forest Service, California Department of Transportation, the Department of Defense and many others. My research included super-efficient irrigation, container production, planting strategies, and soil management.

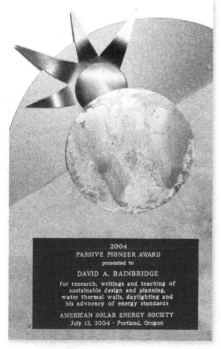

As a hobby I worked on the development of straw bale building systems from 1983–2004, and am known as one of the "godfathers" of straw bale building. In 1995 I returned to academia and retired in 2010 after fifteen years as Associate Professor of Sustainable Management in the College of Business at Alliant International University. I taught classes on management for the triple bottom line, ethics, resource management and ecological economics. I won awards for teaching, research and community service.

Pioneering is the most fun and I hope to stay on the frontier in the years to come. My research focus has always been on sustainable resource management, restoration of ecosystems, and building sustainable communities. My wide range of interests and research projects have led to many insights that have been missed by a narrowly focussed specialist. Over my 50 year career I have written more than 300 articles and reports, 25 book chapters and 22 books. Many of these are now available on-line at www.sustainabilityleader.org.